ON HARLEY-DAVIDSON

1978-1983

Reprinted From
Cycle World Magazine

ISBN 1 869826 523

Published By
Brooklands Books with permission of Cycle World

Titles in this series

CYCLE WORLD ON BMW 1964-1973
CYCLE WORLD ON BMW 1974-1980
CYCLE WORLD ON BMW 1981-1986
CYCLE WORLD ON HARLEY-DAVIDSON 1962-1968
CYCLE WORLD ON HARLEY-DAVIDSON 1968-1978
CYCLE WORLD ON HARLEY-DAVIDSON 1978-1983
CYCLE WORLD ON HARLEY-DAVIDSON 1983-1987
CYCLE WORLD ON TRIUMPH 1962-1967
CYCLE WORLD ON TRIUMPH 1967-1972
CYCLE WORLD ON TRIUMPH 1972-1987

Titles in preparation will cover: BMW, BSA, Ducati, Kawasaki, Honda, Husqvarna, Norton, Suzuki, Triumph, Yamaha, etc.

Distributed By

Cycle World
1499 Monrovia Avenue
Newport Beach
California 92663 U.S.A.

Brooklands Book Distribution Ltd.
Holmerise, Seven Hills Road,
Cobham, Surrey KT11 1ES,
England

CYCLE WORLD

We are frequently asked for copies of out of print Road Tests and other articles that have appeared in Cycle World. To satisfy this need we are producing a series of books that will include, as nearly as possible, all the important information on one make or subject for a given period.

It is our hope that these collections of articles will give an overview that will be of value to historians, restorers and potential buyers, as well as to present owners of these interesting motorcycles.

Printed in Hong Kong

HARLEY DAVIDSON FLH80

by Henry N. Manney III

■ Harley-Davidson is not one of those factories that rushes headlong into innovation. The FLH 80 is clearly a derivative of the veteran 74 ohv which in its turn (1941 model year) was a derivative of the popular 61 ohv which dates back to 1936. At that the 61 was probably not a clean sheet job. There have of course been modifications great and small over the years, most of them admirable and directed towards endless miles of trouble-free motoring, so that the FLH of today sports such features as hydraulic tappets, a proper clutch, and a wear index that put other manufacturers in the shade. By concentrating on the traditional aspect of these bikes, however, Harley-Davidson has built itself a very specialized machine indeed, one which amounts to an open-air car for long-distance touring. As any traveller across the country can tell you, there is a hard core of Harley enthusiasts (we are discussing the FLH now) who adore going from Wichita to New Orleans via Denver on their big Dressers and having done it that way since early Thirties aren't about to change. To them a motorcycle is a Harley and that's that; having driven Harleys on long runs for more miles than I care to think about, I can understand the attraction and even agree.

Since we last had an Electra Glide test in 1973 seems to me, the year that FLHs first got the electric starter along with head-waggings and murmurs of dissent from Harley fanatics, it is just as well to dissect the FLH a bit and clear up some of the mystery for those who think motorcycles were invented in Hammamatsu. The engine of course is a V-Twin of 1340cc . . . 80 cu. in. that is . . . enlarged 60 thou bore and 0.282-in. stroke from the parent 74. Heads and crankcases are alloy but the cylinders themselves remain resolutely iron (cast slightly differently on the 80) for a variety of reasons ranging from habit through noise dampening (although the rest of the machinery is noisy enough) to a happy relationship with the rather special pistons. No real tricks in the heads, fitted with two pushrod operated valves each via hydraulic tappets (see expansion rates of iron plus alloy), no tricks in the Keihin carb barring a flappy butterfly to avoid running with the choke on (see Gov't), and no tricks in the gear-driven camshafts. The bottom end is moderately tricky as it isn't since the Gobron-Brillié that one sees a forked-rod setup running on one crankpin. That's right; one rod is forked at the bottom and the other one nestles in its arms, the whole business avoiding friction via three sets of "loose" rollers in a three-way split retainer. The mains also live on rollers, the right-side one being another come-apart deal while the drive side enjoys a beefier Timken item. Under prodding by the EPA, the 80's sparks are now looked after by electronic ignition if you please made for H-D by Presto-Lite; my experience with electronic ignition in cars shows it to be highly efficient and worth 5 hp anytime, but when it goes, it goes . . . no baling wire fixes. So a spare should live in the saddlebags even if it will probably never be used. More mundane electrics are furnished by an alternator well hidden (and gear driven) down on the left side plus a gigantic battery. The gears (3.00, 1.80, 1.23 and 1:1, from the 74) live in a separate gearbox God save the Mark which Harley people like as who wants to split cases that size to get at the gears, should the occasion arise? The beefy, to say the least, frame is from the 74 as is everything else fore and aft barring the "80" emblems and the Black Cherry paint job. All very trad including the pipes, a bit of a fraud with the left-hand one joining in by grace of a T junction on the right side. But Electra Glide owners like two pipes. In fact, the whole motorcycle is designed to please present Harley owners instead of postulating what they might like; a refreshing point of view in these days of unmodulated change that pays dividends in their traditionally strong Midwestern and Eastern markets.

The 80's arrival at the office produced the same sort of effect as the Golem's arrival at a synagogue . . . Yecch . . . Why do they make motorcycles like that? . . . Sheesh what a monster . . . plus anguished screams from Vucci on being appointed to do the acceleration/braking tests. A few careful questions, though, revealed that none of those professing dislike had themselves ever owned (or in most cases even ridden) a Harley. They were instead repeating opinions obtained secondhand, which is to say of no value. Such people don't understand Harleys. I will admit that the not inconsiderable mass plus the ballet-second-position riding attitude plus a pronounced tendency to spin in at walking pace gives it all the grace of a double-jointed Greyhound Bus in low-speed traffic conditions but the Harley isn't made for that. At least it doesn't wag its head at speed and spit you off like a certain high-performance J*p*n*se make either. However, begone the mystical Harley starting drill (child's play to anyone with a big Single) as one now turns the ign switch, pulls out the choke, opens the throttle a crack, pushes the starter button and the big Twin starts. A bit of noise but quite tame. In California weather anyway the choke can be pushed home after a few seconds, the clutch pulled home (surprisingly light) and low gear selected with Harley's own rocker pedal. It makes quite a clank, in fact all the gears make a clank like someone living under the tank with a hammer but a bit of playing with the throttle, admirable clutch, and slack-taking-up with the gearshift may reward the rider with an almost noiseless change once in a while. Gives you something to do.

I don't understand, in these days of the Gov't shoving its unwanted nose into motorcycling in the holy name of Safety, how Harley gets away with some of its controls. The bike has footboards, all very well and good for long rides, but operation of either that damnable rocker shift or the high-mounted rear brake pedal requires disengagement of the relevant foot from underneath, a time-consuming move backwards, and then raising said foot up to do its job. This sort of toe-dancing tends to use up valuable avoidance time and while the disc brakes are pretty good, the similarity to one of those supertankers taking three miles to stop is all too plain. Consequently the pilot tends to ride neck-a-stretch watching for brakelights a quarter mile further up than he usually would. Perhaps Harley designed it like that. Furthermore the speedo and attendant idiot lights live on the tank practically in the rider's lap and inspecting them takes the eye off the road. As if that weren't enough, the cheapo winki winkis, one to each grip, operate only as long as they are depressed which sometimes means an awkward stretch with the fingers when they would rather be holding the clutch in, for instance, or the front brake.

The clutch, as I said, is sweet and getting under way is an easy matter of adding on a small amount of power from the surprisingly quick throttle providing you are already pointed in the direction desired. FLH 80s are quite heavy and it boggles the mind what would ensue if you dropped it off the stand (which locks on, by the way) let alone allow the very heavy steering and low-speed oversteer to take hold. $300 worth of chrome for a start not to mention a flat leg. Plus a hernia. So it is chugga>

chugga Bong Chugga chugga Bong etc; actually the rider gets used to the FLH quickly in traffic as with its low center of gravity and fat tires it tends to hold an upright stable posture while gliding to a halt. Riders with short legs are going to have a terrible time, even though the riding position seems to be designed for someone 5'3" and measuring 30" across the pelvis, as the 5-gal. "Fat Bob" tank, exceptional engine width, and protruding footboards mean that I am, at 6 ft., standing on tippy toes at rest. The Harley seat is a marvellous device on its sprung pillar, concealing underneath an equally marvellous linkage that provides an extra set-up for what used to be called buddy riding (more's the pity that the whole gemilla is held on with two hose clamps) but it does perch the occupant way up in the air.

Details. Millions of contented riders have driven Harleys across the country and that is the sort of thing that Harley does best. Briskly massaging the gearbox to get out of town and on the highway produces useful acceleration a la traffic cop but the bike appears to go just as well with moderate throttle and a drop into top gear as soon as practicable, say 40 mph. Then the giant bore and giant stroke and all that lovely torque take over to produce a most satisfying waffling beat from the big Twin that wafts the outfit effortlessly down the highway, doing seemingly about 800 rpm. There is a little vibration under normal operation but no particular vibration period appears, up the range till you get to 75 approx. although the engine smooths out marvellously in the region of 60–70 which by happenstance used to be the speed limit before the Gov't used Arabs as an excuse to shut us down. Designed as it is for carrying a couple plus baggage across long distances, the FLH 80 pays no particular interest in mountain grades or otherwise and for that matter, is just as stable (i.e. like a rock) on mountain bends as it is on a dead straight road so long as too great an angle of lean is not employed. Bumpy bends can set up a gentle wallowing, probably encouraged by the pillar-sprung seat and the drooped bars, but like those old trainer biplanes the Harley can undoubtedly fly itself, given the chance. I don't care much for the riding position, sitting with legs spread apart and bent over to hold those bars, but you might like it. Comfort-

A Surprisingly Tolerant Viewpoint

Can a Desert Rider Find Happiness on a Dresser? Let me say right away that I have changed my thoughts on 1. Fairings, 2. Floorboards, 3. Pegs on the crash bars, 4. Duckbill visors for the street, 5. Touring, and 6. Harleys. And realize at the onset that although I've been riding since 1953, my longest trips have always been in the dirt. Barstow to Vegas was a pleasant afternoon and 200-mile pre-runs in Baja were nothing to write home about but when Henry Manney suggested I ride the test Harley to Point Conception well . . . it was enough to cause a very restless night before the trip. You know the feeling, waking up an hour before the alarm goes off.

Of course a 360-mile day is nothing for a serious touring rider but I'd spent too much time at traffic lights looking over at those dresser Harleys and wondering how the hell do they ride those things. Good Lord, my Husky feels too heavy when the Baja tank is topped off. I also wondered what kind of people ride those behemoths and how they feel perched up there above the cars.

Hitting the San Diego Freeway north at six a.m. would put us ahead of the Los Angeles rush and crush. Wrong. We soon found ourselves in bumper to bumper stop and go traffic—an ominous start to our first touring experience. The Harley was much easier to handle in this situation than I expected and I was even beginning to relax a bit when we turned on to the Santa Monica freeway and headed out to Coast Highway and the ocean.

Traffic was still a bit thick until we passed Malibu and it was about this time I stopped and made my first underwear adjustment. Nothing serious, just a little uncomfortable. Beyond Malibu the traffic on our side of the road virtually disappeared and we had both northbound lanes to ourselves. The sun was up and at our backs and the smell of chapparal was mixing with the salt spray off the ocean. If I'm going to be a touring rider I want it to be like this.

The Harley wound its way around the curves of Point Dume and up the coast so effortlessly that I almost felt it knew the way north. The bike becomes nearly weightless at speed and lane changing is no more than a thought. It seems like anything that touches the rider is insulated and as a result very little engine vibration is felt. Another stop for underwear adjustment and I begin wondering what's wrong. Are my Levis too tight? Wrong underwear for touring?

We stopped to fill up with gas and I figured the gas mileage to be 45.5 mpg—not bad considering a lot of that was stop and go. Another underwear adjustment. Is it the seat?

Out of Ventura and up the beach with little or no traffic and a seventy degree day. I'm beginning to really enjoy both the Harley and this touring.

The handlebar position feels so strange when you first sit on the bike but after an hour or so it seems just right as does the position of the floorboards. The position of the rear brake pedal seemed awkward at first but even that's natural after awhile. I did find myself moving my feet around

wise, in spite of the Neanderthal front forks and the rear shocks being at the front end of the swing arm to clear the saddlebags, the FLH 80's fat whitewall tires mounted on stylish alloy wheels smooth out the road in impressive fashion. Rain grooves and similar manifestations of the paver's art have little or no effect. A badly cut-up surface, however, reminds one that Harley has never heard of the theory of unsprung vs sprung weight, i.e., those ornamental chrome doodads on each end of the front axle which weigh almost 200 grams (abt 7 oz) each. In spite of a rather poor finish on the fiberglass, both fairing (which resonates a little at times) and saddlebags make life much much easier on the road and although we made one run of about 200 miles, a longer one would be quite interesting. The big Twin idled faultlessly, ran reliably, never got hot, cured its own sticky tappet and only used one of the four quarts from its filtered dry sumped tank, most of that I suspect courtesy the rear chain oiler. The bike is very handsome and well finished off, drawing admiring looks from not only other Harley riders but smiling gents in big cars who are just apt to say "I useter have one like that". With a Harley you are in another mode of life from "normal" motorcycling and, to be honest, a very pleasant and relaxed one. Vancouver, here we come! >

after a few hours and I kept wondering how a set of pegs mounted on the crash bars would have felt. Maybe those extra pegs aren't just for the laid-back look.

Near Carpenteria I caught something out of the corner of my eye and looked towards the ocean to see an open cockpit bi-wing airplane winging its way north at about the same speed as the Harley. We looked at each other for a moment and then at the same moment waved. An unspoken thought between us said, "The only way to travel."

We arrived near Point Conception before noon and after another underwear adjustment had lunch with a friend and hit the beach for a few hours. Shortly after starting back for the city at four o'clock, we ran into off-shore winds that were blowing 30 mph with, according to the truckers, gusts to 45 mph. After seeing several semis nearly go over we decided to stop for dinner. Pulling into the roadside restaurant by Gaviota, we found all manner of vehicles waiting out the wind. Campers, VW buses, semis and even a few other touring bikes. Why do the Gold Wing riders pretend they don't see Harleys?

After dinner and against the advice of several professionals, we headed south towards Santa Barbara. The Harley punched into those gusts without so much as a quiver and the only trouble I had was with my duckbill visor catching gusts that came in around the fairing. A heavy bike is an asset in these conditions.

Another gas stop and the mileage calculated at 51.47 mpg. Most of this was between 60 and 70 mph and part of it in very windy conditions.

It occurs to me about this time that I've ridden nearly 250 miles and not one close call with a rude or unattentive driver. Is it just getting away from the city or could it be the size of the bike? A friend whose car I followed part way south admitted later that the sight of the Harley in his rear view mirror was most imposing. That's a nice change, a bike looking imposing. I was also a little surprised to find that riders don't wave like they did in the Fifties. Only one rider waved—a Triumph near Oxnard. And, of course, the Outlaw type that pulled alongside near Los Angeles International Airport and carefully looked over the Harley from front to rear. Only after what seemed like five minutes did he look at me and then flashed a huge grin and a thumbs up signal before disappearing into the night.

Near Long Beach a Beemer pulled up with what looked like a 25-year-old crouched low over the bars at 65-70 mph. He slowed for a moment and then in perfect mime indicated he wanted my fairing. Yes, it was nice to have a fairing on the road.

A full moon was directly in front of us as we dropped the bike off at Henry's and I realized I'd just ridden 360 miles and was ready for several hours more. Except for the underwear problem, the Harley provided a smooth and enjoyable ride and I found myself thinking about a trip to San Francisco. I guess that's the real test of a touring bike—as you're putting it away after a long ride, you find yourself planning the next. *—Chuck Johnston*

"Please, Sirs," The Touring Riders Said, "Can We Have Some More Of the Same?"

HARLEY DAVIDSON FLH80

SPECIFICATIONS

List price	$4905
Engine	ohv V-Twin
Bore x stroke	88.8 x 108mm
Piston displacement	1338cc
Compression ratio	8:1
Carburetion	38mm Keihin
Air filtration	oiled foam
Ignition	pointless electronic
Claimed power	na
Claimed torque	na
Lubrication system	dry sump
Oil capacity	8.0 pt.
Fuel capacity	5.0 gal.
Recommended fuel	premium
Starting system	electric
Electric system	12v 225w alternator
Clutch	multi-disc, wet
Primary drive	duplex chain
Final drive	# 530 chain
Gear Ratios, overall:1	
4th	3.73
3rd	4.59
2nd	6.79
1st	11.19
Suspension, front	telescopic fork
Suspension, rear	swing arm
Tire, front	5.10-16
Tire, rear	5.10-16
Brake, front	9.7-in. disc
Brake, rear	9.9-in. disc
Total brake swept area	196 sq. in
Brake loading (160-lb. rider)	4.7 lb./sq. in.
Wheelbase	61.5 in.
Fork rake angle	30 deg.
Trail	5.75 in.
Handlebar width	33.0 in.
Seat height	29.9-31.4 in.
Seat width	14.4 in.
Footpeg height	8.0 in.
Ground clearance	4.7 in.
Curb weight (w/half-tank fuel)	752 lb.
Weight bias, front/rear, percent	43.8/56.2

PERFORMANCE

Engine speed @ 60 mph	3069 rpm
Power/weight ratio, (160-lb. rider)	na
Fuel consumption	49.0 mpg
Speedometer error:	
30 mph indicated, actually	27.4
40 mph indicated, actually	36.7
50 mph indicated, actually	46.5
60 mph indicated, actually	55.9
Braking distance	
from 30 mph	38.0 ft.
from 60 mph	156.5 ft.
Standing start	
¼-mile	15.15 sec. @ 84.19 mph
Speed after ½ mile	89 mph

ACCELERATION / ENGINE AND ROAD SPEEDS

RPM X 100: 40, 60, 80, 100, 120

MPH: 20, 40, 60, 80, 100, 120

117 MPH

95 MPH

64 MPH

39 MPH

SS 1/4

TIME IN SECONDS: 10, 20, 30, 40, 50, 60

FRONT FORKS

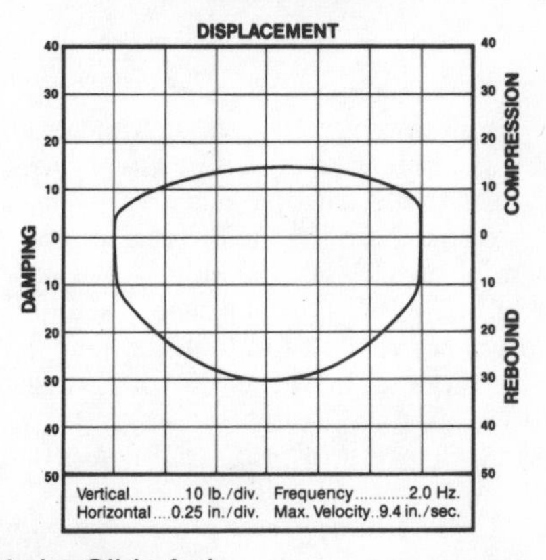

Hydra-Glide fork	
Fork travel	5.0 in.
Engagement	7.3 in.
Stanchion tube diameter	41 mm
Spring rate	50 lb./in.
Compression damping force	14 lb.
Rebound damping force	30 lb.
Static seal friction	36 lb.

Because of the size of the FLH, its front suspension yields a fairly soft ride. Static seal friction is unusually high, but effectively supplements the forks' relatively low damping rates. The fork springs, preloaded at nearly 80 lb., are not as stiff as one might expect, and allow utilization of the available travel with no bottoming or topping.

REAR SHOCKS

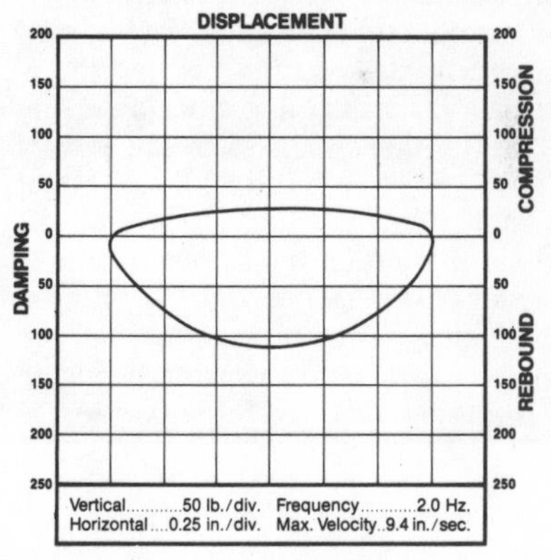

Gabriel shock, non-rebuildable	
Shock travel	2.7 in.
Wheel travel	4.1 in.
Spring rate	250 lb./in.
Compression damping force	25 lb.
Rebound damping force	110 lb.

For such a heavy machine, the stock shocks do an admirable job, at least for the solo rider. Adjusting the spring preload will compensate for most variations in laden weight, but the damping is not proportional to the scaled-up size of the machine. For additional control when the bike is heavily laden, a set of aftermarket shocks with extra firm damping would be advantageous.

Last of the Classic Flatheads

by Henry N. Manney III

Old racing bikes tend to stir different emotions in the eyes or minds of the beholder, even if he may never have seen that particular machine in action. Modern man, used to die-cast aluminum multi-cylinders, probably will react with indifference to a brakeless Cyclone board-tracker, remark Çor look at all those external pipes to the storied 120 deg. Twin Moto-Guzzi, turn his nose up at a classic camshaft Velocette as old-fashioned and simply not appreciate the difference between a GP Triumph and a newer Bonneville, not that there really is much externally.

A Harley KR, however, will always draw a crowd of silent onlookers in spite of being not all that special designwise, about as graceful as a safe and every inch a dinosaur. Why? The KR is very much a proper racing machine and demands respect, even as the sullen silver Auto-Union V-12 set men to musing what sort of person could manage to drive this device to its utmost?

Constant readers of Cycle World (advt) may remember our October issue in which we skipped fleetingly over Harley history and noted, in passing, that the flathead 45 cu.in.V-Twin WL made its appearance right after the Kaiser War and lasted, with the same bore and stroke (2.75 x 3.81 in.) up into the middle Fifties. That is to say the WL production flathead, which earned a swing arm chassis (and became the K series) in 1952, went on to an enlargement to 55 cu. in. three years later and in turn was given ohv (see XL) in 1957. For reasons known only to God, Harley and the AMA, in that order, the flathead formula was retained for racing and the flathead WR, a logical name, became the flathead racing KR, with rear suspension and in that form ran anyway through 1969 at least. Needless to say there was a certain amount of development, mostly empirical, over the 30-plus years to transform a mundane sidevalver into the King of the Dirt Tracks. An information handbook-cum-shop manual that Harley doled out to purchasers of its racing bikes is full of information garnered over 40 years of cut and try and is the stuff of which racing is made. The same empirical approach was rather less successful when a road-racing team was fielded as Harley seemed to forget the fastball that got it to the World Series and threw up a lot of cute junk. The party wasn't actually over, at least on dirt, but the flathead design had just about come to the end of the line.

The subject of our Salon is an ex-works bike that was ridden in 1969 (and possibly earlier) by Haaby and Reiman, the latter doing the honors at the rain-delayed 1969 Daytona. Departing from tradition with the lowboy springer frame designed by St. Louis Harley dealer Earl Widman and sporting an Airhart spot brake on the rear, the KR RR along with others on the team (barring one WR) had had the benefit of head rework plus domed pistons via a single-cylinder mockup in Harley's racing shop during the winter. Unfortunately the mods didn't turn out too well, carburetion being all over the lot, and Reiman was crafty enough to whip the cylinders, heads and probably pistons off his dirt-tracker and fit them at the last minute. Unfortunately for him the clutch went away (at least that's his story) and the KR retired. Due to our lack of back issues, I can't follow up how the bike did the rest of the year but in time it was sold to Buddy Stubbs in Texas (winner Novice 1966) who planned to go racing again and didn't, eventually selling it to celebrated restorer Steve Wright whose arm we twisted for this Salon. It says a lot for Mr. Wright that not only did he consent to trust his precious vehicle to the hands of our tester Mr. Eagan at Riverside Raceway but also furnished all sorts of useful background information.

Taken at face value, the AMA formula of that time (which meant 500cc ohv vs 750cc sidevalve) had worked out to be reasonably equitable. The English competition was getting a bit long in the tooth, while the Japanese menace was still casting shadows before itself in the form of 500cc Kaws or Suzukis plus a mixed lot of 250 and 350cc Yamahas. There wasn't all that much reason, therefore, for Harley to go to pieces (the fastest, Rayborn's, was 5 mph down on 1968's Daytona time and 6 mph down on DuHamel's best 350 Yamaha mark for this 1969 practice) except for those streaks of racing luck that afflict even the greatest from time to time. As it turned out, the monsoon came, washing out the event for a week and possibly giving Milwaukee a chance to get its act together as the classic Rayborn won at slightly over 100 mph, followed by Grant (Suz), Duff (Yam), Lawwill (HD), Gould (Yam) and Markel (HD). Haaby finished his KR 10th, Reiman dnf as related earlier, and I suppose only the HD factory knows which one of those two bikes is our Salon subject. I think Steve was told that eight only of these road racers were made and like most factory "specials" is a bit different from the norm, nothing unusual when apparently none of the Harley runners at Daytona '69 were absolutely identical. Judging by previous models, the most obvious differences were the spot rear brake, a separate Tillotson diaphragm carb for each cylinder and on some of the Harleys a megaphone exhaust system which, in the case of ours, has been reconstructed by Mr. Wright as the original had gone missing. Not showing is all the careful polishing work inside to make sure that all the oil speedily gets back to the lowest point, more detailing to make sure that said oil doesn't puddle there, endless hours of fudging about with roller bearings plus shafts fitting therein, days of lapping in the gears with a light abrasive followed by total disassembly and cleaning out. More hours delicately setting the oil pump and breather to operate just so, another day or two cutting the cam off its stub shaft, setting the timing exactly then welding it on another shaft, doing it again after picking the wrong cam, grinding away at the roller tappets reducing friction, chamfering the pistons, reinforcing the intake manifold, seating the valves just so, and

Photos by Henry N. Manney III

Harley's KR750, and Why You Shouldn't Change It When It Works

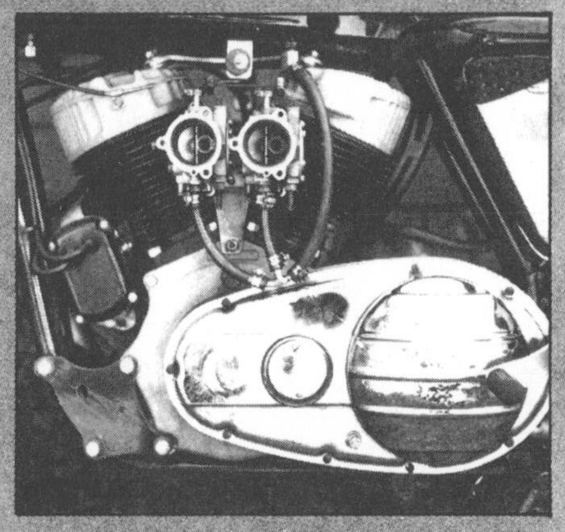

making sure that the head shape, with its funny steps and shelves, matches the latest factory manual. These factory documents are full of useful (i.e. empirical) information such as leaving x thou above the intake valve but y thou above the exhaust (the valves are anything but tulip, having almost a right angle between stem and head) but as Mr. Editor Girdler observed, tuners who really know their job don't need the factory bulletin. It breathes, however, a word from the past when it says Upon No Account remove the film of carbon from the piston crown or a loss of power will result. Flatheads are funny.

Assorted useful bits of information include a wheelbase of 54 in., 355 lb. dry weight approx., 18 in. wheels (3.00 front, 3.50 back although 3.50 f 3.25 b slicks are on it now), compression ratio probably around 6.5:1 with domed pistons fitted, four speeds (choice of 4 sets of gb ratios), horizontal magneto, head gasket via aluminum paint, clearance piston-cylinder head 0.035-0.040 in., ignition timing with Fairbanks-Morse magneto 38 deg. BTC on the front cylinder, oil pump turns ¼ engine speed, etc. Plugs I think were Champion N54R and there is a book on adjusting those Tillotsons. There were two camshaft sets listed for the KR and the KR-TT; tappets clearances for both are a lot less than those used for the XLR, which may explain why the ohv sounds like that. Don't say you never learned anything technical! The handbook is also a mine of information about how to set up end play in the transmission, rebuild the bottom end, shim the valves so they don't hit, and make you properly respectful of Dick O'Brien and his merry men not to mention all the privateers who rebuilt it in a dirt infield between races. And that's only the beginning, as the trick lads start with all the above and probably have a different arrangement for every race. Since 1920 you learn something.

So what's it like? Starting the KR is rather a dodgy proposition as the massive Tillotsons, bearing a reputation for being diabolical anyway, don't seem to have proper float bowls let alone a choke and thus require liberal applications of Easy Start plus a lot of pushing. Then it is dot carry dot dot carry dot carry erk which usually means a change of plugs although using the warmer N60R might obviate some of that. Anyway after a few tries in that vein, the venerable flathead decides to keep going (possibly the fuel lines looping down under the carbs have something to do with this) and with Steve up disappeared around the corner still going d.c., the other cylinder joining in at intervals.

Eventually they came back in full song, the staggered Harley beat bringing the mechanics of a nearby Can-Am car over on the run, and then I got to sit on it and go Woomph woomph while Steve bled the oil pump. Apparently Harley recommends that the oil be changed every time the bike is run (!) which means cleaning out the 5 qt. oil tank below the seat, draining the oil cooler under the tailfeathers, blowing out the lines and then bleeding the bleeding pump to get rid of any airlocks hiding inside. Anyway it was rather like sitting on a water heater, all fat and warm, going woomph up to three thou and actually I would have taken a tour around (on soft plugs) if anyone had asked as the CG is quite low and the whole business feels anything but flimsy. Of course the bars seem only an inch across, the grips are so big that the ends of your fingers scarcely touch and (although the tank and seat are adjustable fore and aft) the riding position jockey-style with knees up would be a little difficult, not to mention the R.H. shift being upside down and backwards. Perhaps it is just as well.

Considering the usual behavior of racing machinery, the KR really doesn't make much mechanical noise . . . perhaps after San Jose it would sound different . . . and it reminded me of those competition Ferrari V12 coupes that go diggadiggadigga in a fiendish fashion but every digga is under control, readily identifiable and doing something useful. Under way with Our Pat aboard it seemed to be turning easily enough, giving out its characteristic flat exhaust note and sounding way overgeared although in fact it had pretty short ratios, topping out before the end of the long straight. Mr. Eagan also reported that the bike was very steady and solid, barring the occasions when he grounded the bottom trumpet, yet was quite responsive to input from the handlebars. As one would expect, the engine was a bit of a shaker but not particularly cammy, even there was little response below 4 thou racing wise, especially after backing off for a corner. Cough cough hack hack and then "good power" would come in approximately at 4800, he would shift at 6 plus or minus, then carry on to 68 or thereabouts at which point it is producing near its 55 bhp. With new parts, the fast boys probably turn a bit over 7 which is pretty remarkable in terms of side valves and the elevated piston speed of 4500 ft./min. Clutch worked easily with light pressure, gearbox shifted nicely, rear brake retardation wasn't noticeable, front brake tended to tighten up on its own as it got the linings hot. The engine smoked a bit (figures of 1 gal. oil for 100 miles are casually tossed about) but conversely was well-mannered and quiet enough so that Eagan didn't even need his earplugs. Isn't that nice? A Gentleman's Racer. Style in every line. They don't make them like that no more. ■

BELL

HARLEY-DAVIDSON

ANYBODY CAN DRESS UP A HARLEY-DAVIDSON. NOT EVERYBODY CAN DO IT RIGHT.

[A Less Than Tolerant Viewpoint.]

Too many riders treat the purchase of a set of pipes or a sissy bar as though they were buying a star for the top of their Christmas tree. So long as it stays on, everything's fine.

Well, everything isn't so fine.

To most of you this won't be news, but you don't hang pipes on a Harley-Davidson® motorcycle. You fit them. Perfectly. So they become part *of* the machine.

The Sportster shown here illustrates our point. It's dressed with a chrome-finished sissy bar, padded backrest, flat black cast wheels, independent staggered dual exhaust pipes, chrome oil cooler and chrome point cover. And it's 100 per cent Harley-Davidson. Because every part on it is a perfectly tooled-to-fit genuine Harley-Davidson accessory.

What's more, every Harley-Davidson accessory—from coolers to highway pegs to touring seats—is available at any Harley-Davidson dealer. So when you dress your Harley-Davidson motorcycle, you can dress it right.

Look at it this way. You've already committed yourself to riding one of the finest motorcycles the world has ever known. A cycle built to such exact tolerances that the piston to cylinder wall fit on an FX 1200, for example, is between .001 and .002 *of an inch*—1/3 the thickness of a human hair!

That's what you paid for. That's what you got.

This is no time to start making compromises.

Harley-Davidson riders never compromise.

Harley Highlights

From Silent Gray Fellow To Throbbing Great Twin. A Success Story

by Henry N. Manney III

HARLEY-DAVIDSON is not a motorcycle; Harley-Davidson is a state of mind. Modern day motorcyclists with their grotesque motocrossers, tarted-up café racers, or complicated multis pretending to be transportation bikes simply have lost the point of the whole idea. Superannuated trail riders, adventurous secretaries with shiny new 125s, or your basic fireplug-shaped touring specialist see it more clearly. To find out why, we have to go back to the days when motorcycles were new and amazing and as exhilarating as that first shy kiss from the blonde little girl next door.

Consider an age when for transportation practically everyone walked or got on the train or the canal boat or resorted to horse and wagon. Americans, however, had settled the country and made it great by not being too stuffy to improvise; among the improvisations were teetery wheeled structures called bicycles (we ignore for the moment the question of who invented them first) that suddenly made it possible for a restive soul to leave Centreville behind and go out for a spin where the tram didn't run. Down to that little pool on the South Fork, out to where the barn burned down last week, off to visit your godmother Helend and all her pretty daughters. Helend always seemed to have fresh fruit pies cooling on the windowsill and the girls liked to sit on each side of you on the sofa and show slides on the bioscope. Another lemonade? they would ask with languishing glances and listen very carefully to the milder sort of gossip from town. My my wouldn't it be capital they sighed to whizz about like that brushing back an errant curl but no scorching!

Women being what they are, it was not long before special frames appeared on pedal cycles to accommodate the full serge outerskirt, three or four frilly petticoats, one or two flannel underskirts, voluminous bloomers (cf Amelia Bloomer) long stockings and high button-up shoes deemed necessary to keep from showing too much ankle. Corset, camisole, leg-of-mutton sleeved batiste shirtwaist and leghorn straw complete with ornamental hatpin did not keep even the more delicate ones from suddenly appearing where you were doing a little quiet fishing . . . well we saw you go by and we thought that you might be a little hungry (producing a sandwich) and with much fluttering of eyelashes it's awfully tiring don't you think may I just rest awhile I'll be as still as a mouse and then giving you one of those looks that fathers of daughters know very well. Gotcha.

Clearly something had to be done and quickly. Inventive souls with garden sheds had been regarding the new-fangled motors, already seen occasionally in horseless carriages, with some speculation as horseless carriages were expensive, unhandy, and difficult to hide in a ditch when they stopped running even if they had already put themselves there. All over the world, diabolical two-wheeled devices were brought forth with ill-tempered, oil-spewing little engines lashed on wherever the fertile mind of the inventor thought they might fit. In the front wheel, in the rear hub, on the back axle, on the front downtube, in the tank, or even in a little trailer towed behind. Mostly innocent of realistic brakes, clutch, suspension, throttle control or indeed any of the modern conveniences regarded as indispensable, these moto-cycles had not only the roadholding of a pig on ice but stopped with depressing frequency. After having traced the trouble, the rider then had either (a) to put the thing on its rear stand and pedal like sixty to make the engine fire (b) run and bump (c) push home (d) load it in the back of a convenient wagon. Clearly this was a pursuit for only the strongest and most athletic of men, let alone ribbon clerks and other assorted pooves. The ladies, encumbered with full serge skirt, three or four frilly petticoats ad lib. only pursed their lips and waited.

Mr. Harley and Mr. Davidson thought that there must be a better way. Calling in two other Davidsons who also owned the peculiar skills suitable for building motorcycles, they painstakingly constructed a flimsy, rather gutless De Dion-based Single in 1903 which obviously wasn't The Way either. Back to the old drawing board, the team produced a 3 hp, 25 cu.in. Single (3-5/16 × 4) with engine in the "Werner position" and beefed-up frame that was more like it; in fact, the new Harley-Davidson Company sold all its production run (3) of the Silent Gray Fellows in that first banner year. Slowly the factory found its feet and before long was turning out 50 or more in a year, their solid construction and relatively trouble-free running all too prominent in those days of any old rubbish being marketed. The Harleys and Davidsons did their homework well with such modern devices as alloy crankcase, loop frame and sophisticated belt tensioner (as a sort of a clutch) on those highboy pocket-valvers; some 100,000 miles later the first "production" example was still running. Other factories such as Indian, however, were progressing faster and the cry soon went up from dealers for Speed! More Speed! Harley replied in the classical fashion of those days by simply adding another cylinder to make a 53.68 cu. in, 45 deg. Twin (does that sound familiar?) which by the time America entered the Kaiser War had accumulated such refinements as a proper clutch, sheet metal primary chain case, mechanically operated intake valves, centre-post sprung saddle of immortal memory, the much-copied bottom link front forks (first on the Single), coil ignition as an option, chain drive ditto, kick starter, internal expanding rear brake, and three speed transmission, none of which were absolutely shattering advances engineeringwise but certainly made life easier for the rider. Actually the American factories, at least the larger ones, were quite conservative compared to designers on the other side of the Atlantic who had tried swing-arm suspension, disc brakes, foot change, a form of telescopic fork, pressure lubrication, overhead cams and even a Wankel-type engine very early on indeed! However, the needs of our motorcyclists were a bit different than those of England, say, with roads largely unimproved to put it mildly out of the cities, cheap gas, and much longer distances to cover without often any human habitation. The long-legged V Twins thus developed even became a cult in some foreign countries due to their lack of fuss. Some early issues of Pacific Motorcyclist (1913-14-15) lent to me by the Rev. Joe Parkhurst give the flavor of these early days in a way that any number of faked-up TV documentaries cannot. One issue speaks of a club run from LA to San Jose and back featuring "adobe" roads (very slippery when wet), drift sand, fords, and craters where the highway had just gone away, as happens occasionally in California's winter. Mileages were not high as a lot of time was spent nattering, trouble was usually confined to punctures or broken drive belts, and the worst panic (besides the support car falling off a cliff) came when everyone stopped for the night at Paso Robles to find out that it was a "dry" town. Yes, the ladies came too. Another issue speaks of a desert race from San Diego to Phoenix at a time when there simply weren't any roads . . . just cowtrails I suppose . . . over most of it. Indian was the big runner at this time with Thor, Excelsior, Yale, Cyclone, etc. close up and Harleys being regarded sort of like Plymouth Sixes in the Forties; reliable but not very exciting. Feature if you will struggling across the mountains and up through the blowsand dunes near Yuma on and off the deteriorated Old Plank Road, or through five miles of Mammoth Dry Wash before teetering along a railroad trestle across the Colorado, hoping the train wouldn't appear. All this on a single-speed Indian popper, looking like a corncob on a rock, with what amounts to no brakes and bicycle tyres. At least that's what the winner, Lorenzo Boido, rode.

Wars, whatever their negative feedback, tend to be looked upon by both politicians and industrialists as a source of graft as well as accelerated technical development. Aircraft engines, for example, went from agricultural flatheads through those odd rotaries to comparatively sophisticated ohv V8s before the Armistice rolled around. Harley of course had already shown its worth by furnishing big Twins (or even the 5-35 Single) as despatch mounts in the banana wars so practically all of the factory's production went to the AEF for service. In the bottomless mud of Flanders, anything that could break did break and the factory engineers filed all this information away, rejoicing meanwhile that the "colonial" roads of Middle America had forced them to build a solid motorcycle in the first place.

Given the strides in metallurgy and engine design, one might expect Harley to come out with something completely different and so they did in 1919, a fore and aft flat Twin drawing its inspiration from the Douglas (GB) which also had been a successful despatch machine. This new Twin of 37 cu.in. featured such niceties as enclosed chain final drive, full electrics and easy starting, obviously being pointed at the ladies' market (skirts were shorter, too!) but after a few years died an unlamented death. Many reasons have been advanced for this demise, among them the superior performance of the concurrent Indian Scout or the bother of setting up a separate production line (although I am sure many parts were interchangeable with those of the Twins or even the Singles that Harley kept trying in depression times) but looking back on my early days in motorcycling, the real reason was that no grown

The first Harley-Davidson, 1903. After 100,000 miles it's still in running condition.

"Red" Parkhurst aboard the racing version of an early (what else?) V-Twin.

man wanted to be seen on anything but a big V Twin. Even if it were khaki, as the factory must have had millions of gallons of o.d. paint left over. The W series 45 cu.in. sidevalve V Twin, developed for the AEF but too late for the war I think, appeared also in 1919 and showed the way things were going to go chez Harley, thus commencing the 45's long reign. Shortly afterward the 61 cu.in.Twin (inlet over exhaust valves) was joined by a bored and stroked 74 of the same configuration. On the face of it, a sidevalve engine seems less efficient than one with an ohv but on the older i over e design, the inlet valve lives in a little house of its own (sometimes the exhaust valve as well; see Daimler) supplying fuel through a tunnel. There are many reasons for this, including the frequent tendency for early valves to stick or break off, sketchy lubrication, ease of redesign from the earlier atmospheric inlet valve, poor fuel, ditto carburetors, and lack of research into combustion chamber behavior. The forced draft R & D into aircraft and racing car engines (this is well after when the twin-cam hemispherical Henri Peugeots

H-D's first Wrecking Crew, from left Muldwin Jones, Fred Ludlow, Ralph Hepburn, Jim Davis, Ray Weishart, Otto Walner and Walter Higley, at Dodge City, 1920.

On the boards, at speed. Riders nicknamed "Splinters" were not uncommon.

were running) apparently made no difference to Harley . . . or Indian for that matter . . . as H-D's next step in 1930 was to produce the 74 sidevalve (flathead) VL Twin, probably the best motorcycle Harley ever made. During my service in the Wah (under Stonewall Jackson? . . . Ed.) it was the accepted drill, on moving to a new base, to shop around for a used bike and as Indian owners used to guard theirs like gold, perforce the choice was from a selection of prewar VLs. Provided both wheels ran in the same direction and they started third kick, money changed hands and freedom was mine for $100 or so, the standard price for these old harvesters. I knew absolutely nothing about machinery at that time and don't recall even wondering what points, plugs, valves, pistons etc were, let alone actually touching any of those objects. The rider put gas in the gas tank, oil

When we Flew the flag. A '30s road racer, used only in Europe.

When Daytona Beach meant racing on a above the high tide line.

in the oil tank, and gave that little oil pump handle on top a shot or two during those hundred mile runs to civilization. Nothing ever went wrong or fell off and the VL uncomplainingly accepted any old drain oil or for that matter avgas filched out of B-29 tanks which really cleaned out the exhaust system wonderfully with a great display of sparks. When you were transferred, say, from Alamogordo to Florida with enough travel time, you went round it with an oil can lubricating anything that looked as if it moved and then took off, usually with some unfortunate on the back. I did that once in company with another GI; despite some hard starting due to a day-long rainstorm, the only trouble we had was a broken chain which a passing civilian rider fixed. We didn't know what a master link was. In those days all riders were in it together and even if you saw an Indian broken down, you stopped to see if some assistance could be offered. Not like today. There was very little traffic and no cops outside of the towns and no mass of ch*ck*nsh*t rules about riding sideways on the bike or even backwards if you felt like it. The post solo saddle was more comfortable, of course, for short runs but we felt that the ironing board "buddy" saddle (often with sheepskin cover) was better for long trips as the rider could move around a bit. With the peculiar muffled beat of those big flatheads and the tranquillizing rockinghorse gait typical of vintage machinery, it was sheer bliss to cover several hundred miles even across West Texas. The long bars, footboards, rigid frames, hand shift etc look awkward today but I don't recall being really uncomfortable. Of course I was younger then.

Generally speaking, basic motorcycle transportation for the lower orders (us) was furnished by 74 VLs which was always a bit of a surprise as I always understood that Indian production had been greater than Harley's and Indian shops appeared with great frequency. Harley dealerships in those days were havens of rest where you could have a cold Nehi, talk with the folks, and stand around listening to the incredible tales that you still hear at Harley shops. Opened-up-to-135-cu.-inches-do-a-hunnert-and-fifty-this-old-farmer-come-out-towing-a-trailer-I-laid-her-down-went-under-the-towbar-finished-up-in-a-big-pile-of-cow-flop-not-a-scratch-on-her and so forth. Visitors to Harley shops today will hear the same stories from the same sort of people and it is nice to know that some things haven't changed, even if you can't go stand around among the mechanics any more lest the service manager (!) complain. Occasionally, some rake-hell would appear on the remarkable, glittering, glamorous, and to our eyes fiendishly complicated 61 overhead (introduced in 1936)

A racing sidehack, powered by the 61 cu. in. V-Twin with overhead intake and sidevalve exhaust. Rider is Bill Minnick.

The legendary VL; side valves, 74 cu. in. an

s case 1959. The pits are to the right, just

Rayborn, in many minds the greatest all-round rider in racing history, throws his Harley ways.

which was, by Harley standards, all a brand new design with proper oil circulation at last (although they must have had it on the ohv Singles in '35 . . . see Petrali's Peashooter . . .), one cam working the staggered pushrods, four-speed transmission and a lot of other things taken for granted today. With a little tweaking the 61s would do an honest 100 mph and such was their reputation plus their dissonant, jangling mode of passing that they tended to attract the sort of kid who wore his cap backwards. NO nice girl would be seen on one. Naturally, the new owner's first move was to remove the muffler's innards, which gave the 61 a noise level like a Sherman tank with loose tracks, and I remember talking to a 61 owner whose bike had spent 30 days in a Georgia jail for buzzing the town. Anyway, Harley being what it is, the bore and stroke stayed the same as that on the original i over e 61 and I wouldn't be surprised if a lot of other bits were the same as well. According to Mr. Nielson of Harley's Engineering Dept. (yes, Virginia. . .) the V Twins have had roller bearing bottom ends and the forked rod setup since the first one and inasmuch as concrete Harley information is notoriously hard to come by except that vague stuff issued by the factory (I refer you to Hendry's book on Harley-Davidson if you can find one) we have to take it at that. At any rate, public acceptance of the 61 ohv was followed by the appearance, in 1937, of the 80 . . . an enlarged 74 flathead . . . while sundry modifications to bring the older models up to 61 mechanical specs such as aluminum heads, four speeds and superfat tyres were offered; mostly as options as the twin afflictions of cheap cars and the depression cut into motorcycle sales. Not until 1941 did the ohv 74, papa of today's Electra-Glide, make its appearance.

Racing has been an integral part of Harley history since 1914 or thereabouts, when in response to the successes of Indian et al the factory decided that racing was likely to pay dividends in both develop->

an an anvil.

Equally legendary, the 61 ohv. Note the twin fuel caps, the speedo on the tank and the ignition switch below it. If it works, don't change it.

ment and sales. Racing designer William Ottaway was hired away from arch-enemy Thor, crack riders like Otto Walker, Red Parkhurst, Ralph Hepburn, etc were put under contract to commence the "Wrecking Crew" and the hunt was on. A lot of the early running before the Kaiser War was on banked board tracks, high-speed devices made hurriedly out of God knows how many 2 by 4s laid on edge, and the perils of this sort of competition are illustrated not only by Mr. Beardsley's articles on the subject (see old issues CW) but also the graphic nickname of Glen "Splinters" Burke. Lapping at 100 mph on these unsanitary pistes with nailheads, rough joints, and sudden changes of camber where the banking came in (not to mention oil puked out by the total-loss engines) would be a bit alarming on a well-sprung, well-shod Harley today, let alone some weaving device with more engine than frame and bicycle tyres. The rough dirt tracks of the Midwest, storied Dodge City and the others, weren't much better what with their paralysing heat, potholes and dust. Covered with success, the factory "officially retired" their racing team in 1921 but the racing went on of course, the quick boys getting bikes, parts etc from the factory while everybody else raced for love and the hopes of making a few bucks to continue racing. It was a hard, hard life and only the hardest among them continued in this peculiarly American sport, its roots in pickup races between the pioneers' choice saddle horses. A lot of Harley's conservatism and love of status quo stem from these days as only the most solid construction, that tested by time, could hold the pace. Fast eight-valvers were sent out to act as rabbits while the slower, but more reliable pocket-valve twins were counted to finish after the "cracks" had blown up. For years the favored wear on dirt tracks was the rigid framed K series 45 cu inch v twins and it was just over ten years ago that the hoary flathead, dragged up to 60 hp by dint of relentless development by racing manager Dick O'Brien, gave way to an overhead valve setup. Some flatheads are still running on small, loose tracks where they are deemed to give a better bite.

Old issues of CW make fascinating reading and especially so in the case of the June 65 issue which has a nice story by Gordon Jennings (yes, he used to be Tech Ed here) on development of the 45 cu in flathead, especially in respect to competition at that time. I wish we had the space to reprint the whole article from a historical point of view as Harley, for reasons connected with the prevailing AMA racing formula, must have been the last people in the world doing development on flatheads. The article is too good to cut up with a précis but basically what is demonstrated is a combination of high-class empirical engineering by tuner Jerry Branch plus a lot of trick work on the heads and induction passages. As normal gasoline was used, the c.r. rarely rose above 6.5:1 which is laughable by proper racing standards but you must remember that the flathead (or sidevalve) engine is an obstinate device. What Harley was after was torque, mostly, (although the engines were safe up to 7600) for the shortish dirt tracks with long curves. A friend of mine was telling me about riding a WR for the first time on the half-mile after having blown up his Triumph or BSA or whatever it was; Harley's competition at this time was limited to 500 cc ohv or ohc by AMA ukase. Anyway the owner warned Gene (Curtis) not to do anything strange whereas Gene gave it a big handful in a corner and promptly fell on his ear. No, said the owner, just get on and ride it around; let the WR do the work. Gene tried it and said that he never had a smoother or less fatiguing ride in all his life . . . forty years of development on that old turkey took out all the labour.

Chauvinism, for which read Home Town Decision, is nothing unusual in any country, as the colored boxer who knocked out an Irishman on St Patrick's Day in Dublin and lost the match found out.

The 55 cu. in. KH, with suspension fore and valves notwithstanding.

Military service, in the form of the WD, an opposed Twin, side valve, with shaft drive.

Since the demise of Indian, it was more or less common gossip that Harley "owned" the AMA and there were a lot of peculiar rulings that came out of that august body. In retrospect, however, the 750 cc flathead vs 500 cc ohv or ohc worked out pretty well once Americans found out how to keep English production bikes (a Manx Norton is a production bike?) together and drag some horsepower out of them. Of course at that time postwar Daytona was the only really fast venue even with the beach course at first but there are those who say events like the San Jose Mile are faster, at least they feel faster. Harley managed to hold its own with some luck even up to the rule change which let everyone run 750s with ohv (see another CW article on head development for the ohv) but progress has passed it by on the increasingly popular road race circuits. On the dirt, of course, Harleys are practically unbeatable. The rot had set in by simple mathematics of piston area and overall weight even before the lighter two-strokes (especially Yamaha) really got going but who knows what wonders could have come about had not Harleys, baking every day to keep from baking for tomorrow, stuck with the flathead for so long? Nowadays the big Sportster can't even come close to cutting it in the Production bike event. And you don't run Sportsters or Electra Glides on the half mile.

Once Hitler was carbonisé and the Japanese (ho ho) were put where they couldn't do any more harm Harley commenced to look over the situation. Clearly the world market would change as already before the War the Europeans had shown that they could make fast, maneuverable, raceworthy bikes which could even be somewhat reliable. Indian was already on the skids

the superbike of the 50s, lack of overhead

from a bad case of long-time poor front-office management, bad luck, and assorted dirty tricks (see The Iron Redskin by H.V. Sucher) which could be regarded as either an advantage to traditional enemy Harley-Davidson or a disadvantage, depending on what point of view one took. At any rate, Indian fell into the trap of trying to make a bike which other people could make better with their 220 Single and 440 cc Twin continental-type machinery; promptly laying the biggest egg since Sinbad's roc. All this was not lost on Harley who contented themselves with ohv on the 74 which had barely got into production in 1941, hydraulic valve lifters as well, and then the telescopic Hydra Glide fork for a semblance of modernity. Anything that could roll, sold in those days but the market was further complicated by the masses (at first) of ex-WD 45s which promptly were painted in the most astounding colors by their new owners, all thoroughly sick of khaki. I had at that time one of the rare flat Twins, modelled on the little shaft-drive Zundapp I think, manufactured by Harley for the North African desert campaign and a nice bike it was too with foot shift, hand clutch, and oil bath air cleaner inside its cave. Unfortunately, I don't think it would have managed much sand as not only was it a bit cumbersome on rough going but also tended, as the fins were rather short and Harley had stuck to side valves, to get hot enough so that the cylinders in the region of the exhaust ports would get more than a little pinkish when driven hard. Another oddment, although HD Engineering claims it never existed, was an ex-WD 30.50 cu in (500 cc) model like the 45 cu incher scaled down. Hand shift, blackout lights, WD panniers, the lot. Little bitty cylinders. A first kick starter, great town bike, dead reliable. Has anyone heard of one like that?

The first English bikes started coming over and I remember standing with a bunch of other layabouts watching an early Ariel pogo gently about on its soft suspension going pop pop pop and muttering things like Nossir those light bikes don't hold the road, a comment still heard from old ladies of both sexes. However, the ease of control of the foot shift shafty Harley still stuck in my mind and clearly the Americans, after such a war, were ready for something new and different. Sales of British bikes took off, sales of sports cars like the bone-jarring MG TC followed suit and Harley brought forth, a little ahead of its time or a little behind it, a 125 cc two-stroke on "continental lines" (possibly made overseas) which got itself telescopic forks a few years later. In spite of the disadvantages marketwise of cheap gas, lack of mixer pumps (as in Europe) and absolutely no performance the little

Bart Markel (4) and Fred Nix, on team KR750s, at Daytona (the speedway, this time) in 1968.

The KR750, thanks to AMA rules allowing flathead engines more displacement, was a contemporary road race chassis with the ol' side valve 45.

two-strokes in various ramifications held on until after Harley made an arrangement with the Aermacchi plant in Italy to give itself a medium range of bikes, both two-stroke and four. The Aermacchi four-strokes weren't bad at all but nobody except the salesmen ever regarded them as Harleys. In any case, that little experiment has gone down the tube, the twin devils of labour troubles over there and a reluctance to put money into development probably being the answer.

More like it, to traditional Harley fans, were the new K series 45 cu.inchers in 1952 fitted with a lower frame which was sprung at both ends. A further bow towards the 20th Century came with the fitting of foot-shift-hand-clutch mechanisms although I think that you can still get the traditional setup on special order. Anyway, faced with a shrinking slice of the market and insistent calls for performance, the factory soon bumped (in 1955) the long-suffering 45 up to 55 cu. in. (which the KH racers didn't get to share) while two years later the venerable flathead design was finally flung out with the bathwater as the KH acquired ohv to become first the Sportster (XL) and then soon the racier XCLH . . . back to the magneto after thirty years. The Styling Dept (yes, Virginia. . .) has wrought some pretty unusual variations on the XCLH, pretty accurately aimed at what has been called the Café Racer Market but it *is* a bit bemusing to see a Mod Harley. The bigger Twins . . . well, not much bigger . . . have contented themselves with detail changes such as hydraulic brakes on the Hydraglide (1958), swing arm (1959) and then the Electra Glide with electric starting, and 12 volt system etc in 1966, a much appreciated move in most of our country as nobody really likes kicking over a big Twin on frosty mornings. Subsequent developments have been in the line of an alternator in place of the generator (although HD electrics have always been pretty good), hydraulic disc brakes and an insidious influx of Japanese parts into what used to be an All-American machine. The latest development (see test) is the ohv 80 which, though hardly modern (the crankpin has a 1941 part number) is a very comfortable touring mount and most Harley riders wouldn't have it any other way.

In 1969, for various reasons probably not a million miles from capital reserves, the family corporation of Harley-Davidson merged/was bought out by/taken over by/came under the control of (check one) American Machine and Foundry, better known as AMF. From the uproar ensuing, one would have thought that the Pope had turned up in a Gay Lib parade wearing beads (he *does* wear beads. . . Ed) and naturally enough there were a lot of complaints about handwork at the Milwaukee plant suffering as a result of a transfer to the new automated plant at York, Pa. You do hear a lot of comments about a basket under the engine to catch parts being an optional accessory and old Harley riders do wag their heads sagely and say Ar they ain't built like they useter be but then what is? Stories about Harley reliability or the lack of ("Harley-Davidson, made of tin. . .") are as much of America's folklore, especially to Indian owners, as Johnny Appleseed but motorcyclists have to talk about something standing around in the garage. Whether the prevailing abandonment of Harleys in favour of Japanese multis or Moto Guzzis by the motorcycle cops has anything to do with this merger either or whether just a question of price, I don't know.

Harley sources claim that they own between 40 and 50% of the "big bike" market, whatever that works out to overall. They also seem to be confident and hint of marvelous things to come in the future even if many of us, looking at some of the technologically advanced designs coming out of other countries feel a little apprehensive about the big Twin's survival. The sheer cost of tooling up or something completely new would be shattering for one thing at today's prices, plus the conservatism of HD itself and an unwillingness to copy anyone directly so that the 1980 Harley, say, could offer a decent three speed automatic perhaps, overhead cams to cut down reciprocating weight, shaft drive (remember the WD flat Twin?), an improved gearbox, suspension that suspends and possibly even fuel injection which even cheaper cars have now. Still it would unmistakably be a Harley. Rolling peaceably down a long oak-lined road on a Harley in the early evening is one of the most pleasurable experiences known to man. Wuffle wuffle clank clank clank. Smells of the country. A wave to another Harley rider. The big Twin sounding as if it would go on forever. This is the way Harleys began and how, we hope, they will continue. Happy Seventy-Fifth Birthday!

King of the Flattracks, the XR750, Jay Springsteen up.

HARLEY-DAVIDSON XLS-1000

I See By Your Outfit That You Are a Cowboy

CYCLE WORLD TEST

You don't have to
it Harley-Davidson
ith an iron barrel to
et their attention.
wo years or so ago,
arley introduced a
roduction chopper
ersion of the 74 Su-
er Glide and a pro-
uction cafe version
f the Sportster, it being Harley's habit to
ffer buyers what the owners already were
oing.

The Low Rider was an immediate suc-
ess. The XLCR wasn't.

Hint taken. For 1979, H-D's different
ersion of the Sportster is the XLS. It is to
e XL line what the Low Rider was to the
uper Glide; custom touches with me-
hanical changes and even a couple of
nprovements.

The mechanical changes have been seen before in other places. The XLS has extended forks, a change of steering head angle from 29.5° to 31° adding a bit more than one inch to the wheelbase and doing a chopper look to the front end. Rear wheel is 16-in., compared to the 18-in. wheels on the XLH and XLCH. All three of the models get the siamesed exhaust system first seen on the cafe Sportster and in a running change made late in 1978, the XL line gets the rear frame section patterned on that used on the XR750 racing bikes. This, with rear shocks to match, provides a little bit more suspension travel in the rear.

XLS handlebars are lower and have barely a hint of pullback or rise. They mount to 3.5-in. risers, though, which puts them just about half as high as the standard version bars.

The XLS seat is two-piece. Not stepped, but with a rider's portion steeply pitched and the passenger section a separate cushion, mounted on the rear frame and fender, for all the world like the pillions of 20 years ago. Behind the seat is a short sissy bar. Lashed to that is a small leather bag. A stash pouch, we're told, although of course nobody here knows what that means, nor would we admit it if we did. Highway pegs are standard equipment.

Then there are the normal Sportster bits, like the dual front and single rear discs, the grips only slightly larger than a human hand, oil tank beneath the seat, horn dangling on the left and air cleaner protruding from between the cylinders on the right. The engine is pretty nearly as it was last year and the year before, and before that on back if you figure the changes from 55 to 61 cu. in., from flathead to ohv and the

HARLEY DAVIDSON
EAGLE A/T

ike are merely updates.

What sets the XLS off most is the paint ınd trim. The bodywork gets black and leep metallic charcoal paint, the rear sprocket is chrome-plated and various other mechanical parts get chrome or a silver and crinkle-black finish. There's hand painted striping for the tanks, the H-D logo on the gas tank is gold. The subtle and different paint and polish works with the cast iron steering head, rough vs smooth, to produce a motorcycle the eye cannot resist. It's tough, it's attractive and there ain't nothing on the XLS doesn't ook like a motorcycle. To see the XLS is to know that all those people who've tried to add bodywork to bikes were wrong and deserved what they got. (Quick financial lisaster, in case you're too young to remember.)

There's a touch of the cowboy in all of us. Covering up a machine like this makes as much sense as putting a roof on a horse.

Which may be why the Sportster is what t is, no more and no less.

What Harley-Davidson set out to do with the Sportster, and the K and KH before it, was to build a sporting and high-performance motorcycle, in contrast only with the 74, which was the touring Harley and for all practical purposes was the only other big bike then on the market.

In 1962, this magazine's first year, we tested the Sportster of the day. Perfectly normal machine, with a fuel tank like the other bikes had and a two-person bench seat, hardly any suspension travel, kick start only. It was the fastest and quickest motorcycle we tested that year and we remarked about this in a calm way. There were, after all, few other contenders for the Superbike title because there were no other Superbikes. There was the Sportster, with optional solo seat, etc., with a small headlight because the big Harleys got the big lights, with a teardrop tank or a touring tank because the Sportster was sold to everybody who wanted a big powerful Twin and that's all there was.

Things changed, with larger motors from the other outfits, two-stroke Twins and Triples, the Honda Four and the Kawasaki Z-1, while the Sportster stayed much the same. No point in H-D invading the big bike market. H-D *was* the big bike market. The others invaded and innovated and the market grew beyond what Harley and Davidson ever dreamed possible.

And the Sportster found itself in a self-made gilded cage.

There never was a time the company could say, better do some radical revision. The guys who wanted Sportsters wanted By God Sportsters. A transverse Four might drive off the customers in hand with no assurance of luring the customers out there in the bush. And before you knew what to make of that, the others surveyed the riding public and discovered what>

Harley knew without asking, that is, what a motorcycle is supposed to look like. Round, as one of the other factories says it, as opposed to Square. Teardrop tanks, a flowing line curving across the top of the tank and down below the seat.

Those Customs and Specials and Limiteds aren't Harley copies, not directly. It's just that Harley *knows* its customers while the rivals *survey* them, so Harley got there first.

Another thing. These government regulations. The limits aren't based on exhaust noise, although that's what the public talks about. With ignition off, a chain-drive, air-cooled Twin makes more noise than does a shaft-drive, water-cooled Four. Making up some numbers, if the rest of the bike makes, say, 50 decibels and the limit is 80, you got 30 decibels for intake and exhaust. If the rest makes 40, you got 40, and that's why the Honda CX500 has a throaty exhaust note and the XLS has a big megaphone with an exit as big as your thumb, and an air cleaner the size of a breadbox.

No fear. None of the above really matters.

What matters is that despite the vintage engine and the limits imposed on it from within and without, York and Milwaukee have done good.

You have read here recently about how the technowhiz Multis are giving us fits on cold mornings. Gleaming labs, swarms of technicians and the confounded engines greet the dawn's early light like a schoolkid, that is, cough, moan, grumble and wake 'em up three times before they can stumble forward.

Pull the choke, turn the key and hit the button and three spins later the XLS engine is running and ready to go.

It will pull like a train off idle, and wind (well, relatively) easily. The only sign of any compromise with the mixtures and such is that when warm, on cruise and light throttle, 55 or 60 mph, every 10 miles or so the mighty Twin goes Bruuk! and then carries on as if nothing had happened. Normal, the Harley man tells us and no, he's not allowed to hint that perhaps raising the needle one notch would smooth out the glitch.

Punchline. The EPA has just finished doing some compliance testing, finding out which motorcycles meet the rules they're supposed to meet, and by how much. The winners, cleanest of the clean? The Harley V-Twins.

The compromises dictated by the conflict of Sportster buyers vs economics and the law appear first in ride and handling. The XLS is in effect a frame and suspension built around an engine. A large and heavy engine, while the machine must be relatively small and low. The Sportster is small for its weight, so to speak, with the mass concentrated in the center and without much room for wheel travel. The extended fork brings with it highway ease and low-speed awkwardness, aided and abetted by the bars and seat.

Cast steering head is a nice traditional touch.

Stanchion tubes are two inches longer and steering rake is increased by half a degree.

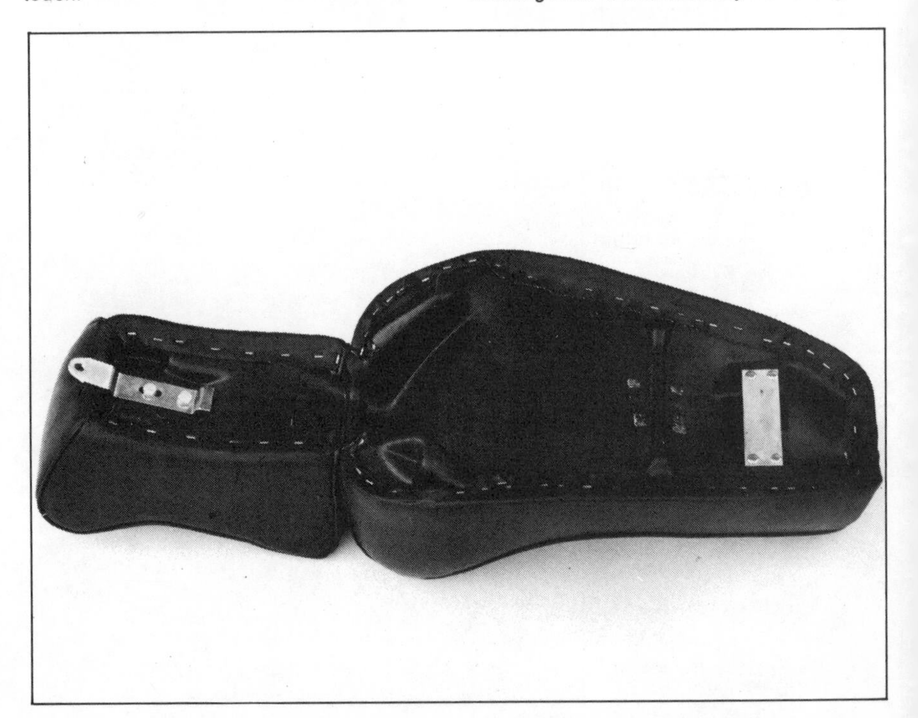

Main and pillion seats actually share a one-piece plastic base, which is secured by a frame tang in the front and a single bolt at the rear.

Despite the running changes over the years, as the factory has moved this and that and beefed here, trimmed there, the XLS frame remains just about as it was when rear suspension was introduced, that is, not obsolete but surely not the state of the art.

There is a certain suppleness to the frame and that means the practical cure is to supply a certain firmness for the suspension. Working with this, the low machine and consequent lack of wheel travel mean they dare not let the suspension move too much.

The ride is hard. More than firm. The forks can be seen and felt working up and down, the rear shocks can't. Our notes from the past, in particular the XLCR, indicated the stiffness was something new and it is. The first XLCR, one occupant only, had lower rate springs. When the model gained passenger space, the springs were stiffened, and when the CR's rear frame section became standard Sportster equipment, the stiff springs went with it. The XLS faithfully follows every bump in the road, large or small, for the hardest, most choppy ride we've had in years.

Handling is more a matter of control. The laid-back low seat doesn't match the forward-mount drag bars. The initial reaction is fine, as the rider assumes a modified racer crouch. But having the seat mounted aft, the pegs forward and the bars extra forward leans the rider off balance. The narrow bars reduce lean leverage. Low speed balance requires attention, fast work in the curves is never quite comfortable . . . the XLS tracks and steers well enough,

HARLEY-DAVIDSON XLS-1000

SPECIFICATIONS

List price	$3995
Engine	ohv V-Twin
Bore x stroke	81 x 96.8mm
Displacement	997cc
Compression ratio	9:1
Carburetion	(1) 38mm Keihin
Air filtration	oiled foam
Ignition	CDI
Claimed power	na
Claimed torque	na
Lubrication system	dry sump
Oil capacity	6 pt.
Fuel capacity	2.25 gal.
Recommended fuel	premium
Starter	electric
Alternator	12v 144w
Headlight	50/40w
Clutch	multi-disc wet
Primary drive	triple-row chain
Final drive	#530 chain
Gear ratios, overall:1	
4th	4.22
3rd	5.82
2nd	7.70
1st	10.63
Suspension, front	telescopic forks
travel	6.9 in.
Suspension, rear	swing arm
travel	3.75 in.
Tire, front	MJ90-19 Goodyear Eagle A/T
Tire, rear	MT90-16 Goodyear Eagle A/T
Brake, front	dual 10 in. disc
Brake, rear	11.5 in. disc
Total brake swept area	294.3 sq. in.
Brake loading (160-lb. rider)	2.4 lb./sq. in.
Wheelbase	59.6 in.
Fork rake angle	31°
Trail	4.9 in.
Handlebar width	27.5 in.
Seat height	31.5 in.
Seat width	9 in.
Footpeg height	12 in.
Ground clearance	6.8 in.
Test weight (w/half-tank fuel)	541 lb.
Weight bias, front/rear, percent	43.1/56.9
Gross vehicle weight rating	960 lb.
Load capacity	419 lb.

ACCELERATION

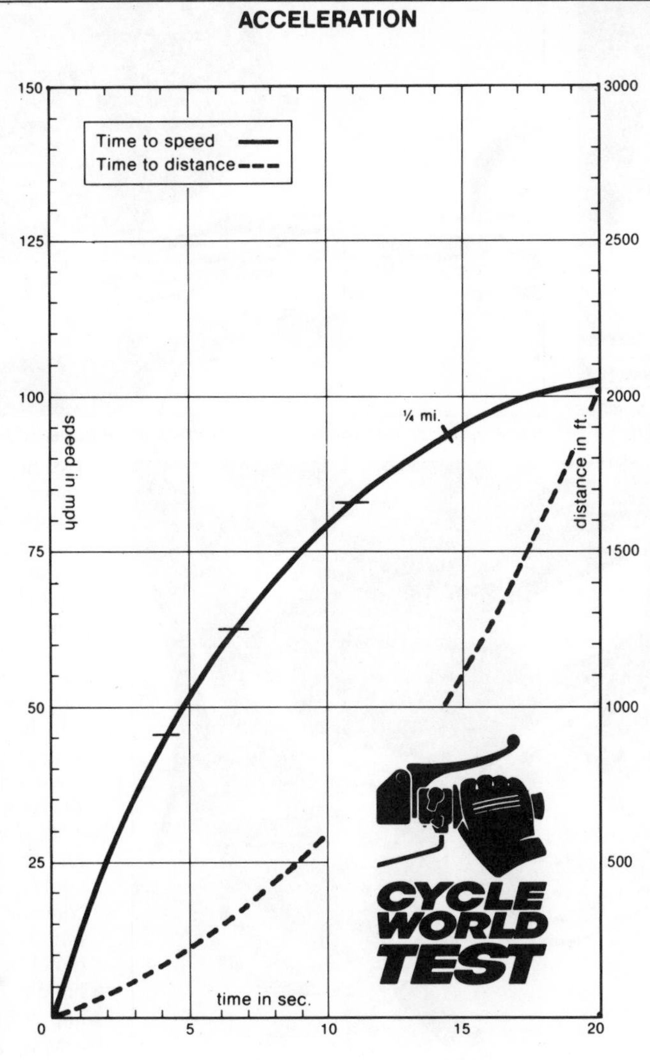

PERFORMANCE

Engine speed @ 60 mph	3260 rpm
Power/weight ratio (160-lb. rider)	na
Fuel consumption	52 mpg
Speedometer error:	
30 mph indicated	26 mph
60 mph indicated	54 mph
Braking distance	
from 30 mph	32 ft.
from 60 mph	144 ft.
Standing start	
¼-mile	13.98 sec. @ 92.78 mph
Speed after ½ mile	104 mph
Maximum speed in gears	
1st	45 mph
2nd	62 mph
3rd	82 mph
4th	114 mph
Acceleration	
0–30	2.23 sec.
0–40	3.25 sec.
0–50	4.61 sec.
0–60	5.97 sec.
0–70	7.93 sec.
0–80	9.98 sec.
0–90	12.64 sec.
0–100	17.86 sec.

Use of chrome, paint, shiny and matt finishes make the classic engine a work of art.

Made-in-Japan instruments are tastefully small but easily read.

Giant air cleaner quiets intake and gets in the way of the rider's leg when he uses the highway peg. Siamesed exhaust system is now standard on all Sportster models.

Rear suspension is reportedly reworked, feels stiff. Pillion isn't suited to long trips and the stash pouch lashed to the sissy bar drew curious comments.

As ever, horn dangles from between the cylinders and choke and ignition switch are semi-concealed between tank and horn.

wobbles just a bit, but never feels as if there's a Superbike racer hiding in there somewhere.

A more genuine shortcoming concerns the air cleaner and the highway pegs. This isn't Harley's fault. The law requires quiet and as mentioned when you have lots of mechanical noise, you cannot have intake or exhaust noise. A quiet intake means a big airbox and the XLS box is so big that it gets between the rider's right leg and the peg. All our riders, even the staff stork, commented on this. Too bad, as the pegs fit the Sportster image just fine.

Also normal is the Harley control system; clutch and brake pull Charles Atlas could learn from, turn signals that only come on when you keep your thumb on the button, key and choke tucked away on a panel below the tank. Shrug. If you can't handle that, you probably wouldn't be happy with a Harley anyway.

More to the point, the clutch and shift worked fine, the brakes stopped the bike within respectable distances and with good control. There is nothing wrong here. The XLS is different, is all.

What you get is an honest motorcycle. Numbers mean nothing when you muscle off the line, the legendary V-Twin making all those raw and romantic sounds as second gear comes at the torque peak and the flat bars strain your arms. The XLS is a reaffirmation of what motorcycling is, for motorcyclists who've always been motorcyclists.

The XLS is the cowboy's horse, built for and cherished by those of us who've always had a touch of cowboy.

Not even Harley-Davidson can explain this. The appeal is as strong and as established as it is difficult to define.

Case in point. Some of the people on the various motorcycle magazines are forming a motorcycle press association. One of the organizational meetings was held on a cold and rainy night. Only three guys rode to the meeting. Each was on a Harley.

Our man wasn't elected to the board of directors because he arrived on the XLS.

But it didn't hurt.

1980 Harley-Davidson FLT-80 Tour Glide

At Last Harley Redesigns Its Big Bike and the Results Are Hard to Fault

Harley-Davidson's new FLT-80 Tour Glide still looks like a Harley, with its 80 cu. in. V-Twin engine, 16-in. tires, low seat, and full accessories. But underneath the traditional Harley styling is an all-new motorcycle with as much original thinking behind it as any new motorcycle of 1980. Except for the engine, and even it has received numerous improvements, every part of the FLT is new.

All the new pieces wrapped around the traditional Twin bring Harley's touring machine much closer to the mainstream of motorcycling. The major new pieces include a frame with none of the cast junctions used on previous Harley frames, a rubber mounted engine to reduce vibration, five-speed transmission, fully-enclosed final drive chain, larger triple disc brakes, frame mounted fairing, instrument cluster mounted on the forks, rather than on the gas tank, and a front end geometry that has the fork tubes rearward of the steering head and angled differently than the steering head through the use of offset triple clamps.

The front end is the most novel piece of the motorcycle. With a steering head angle of 25° and the fork tubes mounted behind the steering head, there would normally be very little trail and a motorcycle would be unstable. But the Harley has the fork tubes offset 4° 15' from the steering head, yielding 5.88 in. of trail, slightly more than with the previous frame and steering. The changes make the big (725 lb. dry weight, claimed) motorcycle steer with gentle pressure and little body English. There's also excellent balance and stability so longtime Harley riders will be right at home despite the quick handling.

In order to retain sufficient steering lock,

Cut-away model shows rectangular backbone and engine mounting linkage.

FLT's exhaust system produces more power and is quieter than that of the older FLH model. Heel-and-toe shifter has separate adjustments for each end.

the new frame on the FLT places the steering head far enough forward so the forks can be turned tightly without bumping into the restyled gas tank. That's not all that's new with the frame. Ground clearance is 2 in. greater than on the previous FLH, which increases the allowable cornering angles up to 35° with the machine loaded. The new frame has a huge rectangular steel backbone, two downtubes, no centerpost and shocks positioned in conventional manner on the new swing arm for more rear wheel travel.

One of the most noticeable changes to the machine is in the rubber engine mounts. The power train is held by a rubber biscuit at the front of the engine and at the swing arm pivots on the frame. There are adjustable locating links at the front of the motor and at the top of the motor. In all, the system is similar to the Isolastic engine mounting used by Norton.

Changes to the motor include improved valve and valve seat materials for longer life, a new exhaust system that's quieter than previous exhausts and allows the engine to develop more power, the addition of a spin-on oil filter, and an electronic ignition with electronically-controlled ignition advance. The spin-on oil filter mounts behind the engine where it's easy to change and unobtrusive. The ignition, manufactured by Magnavox, uses Hall-effect magnetic triggering and incorporates a microprocessor to advance the ignition a maximum of 32° at 1600 rpm.

There's still a duplex primary chain connecting the engine to the dry multi-plate clutch, but there are rumors of a new belt primary drive now being developed. Gear ratios on the five-speed transmission are closer together than the ratios of the previous four-speed and the overall ratio in fifth is slightly higher than the previous top cog for a slightly lower engine speed on the highway. Engine and transmission cases are still separate so there's separate lubricant for each and it's also possible to remove the entire gear train (except for fifth gear) through transmission case inspection covers. The five-speed uses a drum shifter and roller bearings on all shafts.

It may be surprising to find a chain final drive on a new touring machine, but Harley-Davidson has its reasons for keeping the chain. The most important reason, of course, is that a shaft drive would cost more to design and build. A chain is a more efficient transmitter of power, and with the H-D motor positioned in the frame as it is, there would be two right angle drives reducing the efficiency of a shaft drive even more. Instead, Harley has come up with a full enclosure for the chain. The rear sprocket is encased in a two-piece aluminum cover that includes an oil level plug and oil filler cap. Connecting the aluminum cover and the transmission are rubber housings that protect the chain, keep the oil bath enclosed, and flex with the swing arm. Harley-Davidson claims a 16,000 to 20,000 mile chain life with the enclosure.

Stopping this new Harley should be less of an adventure than on previous big Harleys. There are double 10 in. discs in front and a single 12 in. disc at the rear that uses a double piston caliper. Total brake swept area is 352 sq. in., more than on any other big bike *CW* has tested recently. Harley-Davidson was the first motorcycle manufacturer to use metallic pads on the disc brakes for good wet weather braking performance. The hard pads meant more lever effort was needed, but the larger brake area of the new FLT reduces brake effort to normal levels, gives excellent brake power and should have the same wet weather braking ability Harleys have had for the past couple of years.

What gives the big H-D touring machines their distinctive appearance is the accessories, as much as anything else, and the FLT sports a whole bunch of new fiberglass and ancillary items. The fairing

Dual piston rear caliper operates on a 12-in. disc. Up front there are dual 10-in. discs.

Instrument cluster has speedometer/odometer, tach, voltmeter and warning lights positioned at steering head. Ignition switch includes integral fork lock. Fairing is frame mounted and includes locking storage bins.

is a frame mount design with dual round headlamps. There are locking covers over storage compartments on the fairing and room for gauges and a radio-speaker accessory package that fits at the base of the windshield. Saddlebags have the same profile as previous King of the Road accessories, but they're detachable and shaped differently so they can clear the rear-mounted battery that was moved from behind the engine. Volume of the bags is claimed at 1 cu. ft. each. The King Tour Pak rear box now hinges from the side so it can be opened with a passenger seated aboard the bike.

Even though there's no center post for Harley's traditional seat spring, there's still a sprung double seat available. The standard seat mounts directly to the frame for a lower seat height. The new 5 gal. gas tank is made in one piece and doesn't have the speedometer mounted in the middle any more. Now the gauges are mounted in an instrument cluster in front of the handlebars. Included are a speedometer, tachometer, voltmeter and idiot lights. The ignition switch mounted at the steering head includes an integral fork lock.

Floorboards, accompanied by a huge brake pedal and heel-and-toe shifter remain, but the floorboards are no longer spring-mounted to reduce vibration, as the rubber mounted engine takes care of that task. The heel-and-toe shifter now is made in two pieces so the heel and toe sections can be adjusted separately to suit the rider.

At a press introduction in Ruidoso, New Mexico, an FLT was available for brief rides, but a machine hasn't been available yet for thorough testing. A quick spin down a serpentine mountain road confirmed Harley's claims about the lighter and more agile handling. The FLT is a big bike, no doubt about it, but it doesn't feel as cumbersome as many of the other touring machines. The most immediately apparent change is in the new transmission that completely eliminates the labored clunk that used to accompany H-D shifting. The five-speed is a delightful addition to the motorcycle, as unnecessary as it would seem.

At idle the big 80 cu. in. V-Twin shakes the motorcycle as much as it did the FLH, but as soon as the bike begins to move the shaking is audible, but in no other way perceptible. The FLT honestly doesn't vibrate. Amazing.

Harley-Davidson isn't dropping the traditional FLH model touring machine with the introduction of the FLT. It remains, as the FLH-1200 and 80 Electra Glide and FLH-80 Classic along with the Sportster, Super Glide, Fat Bob, Roadster and Low Rider. The FLT should be available in dealers' showrooms by this time at a list price of $6013.

HARLEY-DAVIDSON FLT-80 TOUR GLIDE

No laughing out there, please. The Harley-Davidson FLT really does belong in this test. To begin with, it should win the Most Improved Motorcycle award. Surprised? We were.

This isn't the same Harley dresser we last tested. Fact is, there are only a few parts on this motorcycle that were used on Harley's older Electra Glide. Only the 80 cu. in. V-Twin engine is shared with other Harleys and even that has had enough new pieces added to change its performance remarkably. The frame, with its extended box-section backbone holding a steering head quite upright so the offset triple clamps can turn easily, is not just new for Harley, it is a novelty for any motorcycle. There's not even a center post for a seat spring and—better make sure Grandpa is sitting down—all the new frame and suspension pieces allow the graceful Hawg to lean waaaay over in the corners.

Underneath all the new pieces, there's enough Harley so the Faithful won't feel forgotten. Sitting on the low stepped seat, legs out in front with feet on the hinged floorboards, hands relaxed at the side while resting peacefully on the big handlebars, you know you're on a Harley. If the new ignition switch (including fork lock) hasn't been locked, no key is needed to turn it on and push the starter button and hear the big Twin rumble to life. At idle it even feels like a normal Harley, everything in motion, especially the engine. Then you heft the bike upright, fold back that wonderful locking sidestand (why can't they all have one like that?), pull hard on the clutch lever, rev it up to, say, 1000 rpm and chug away.

But the Tour Glide is as different from previous Harleys as a Harley is different from other motorcycles and the differences become apparent once the huge ship is underway. So what if it weighs 781 lb? Accepting that nearly half a ton of man and machine can't be hurried, piloting the FLT is delightful. Vibration fades away as the motorcycle picks up speed, the rubber engine mounts absorbing just the right energy so the engine doesn't flop around and the whole bike vibrates no more than a steamship. The new five speed transmission shifts much more smoothly and quickly than the previous four-speed, though downshifts still bring about a noticeable klunk. Unlike so many of the high strung multis, the big Twin has no driveability problems. It starts in the morning and it runs when it's hot and it never misses or coughs or lurches; the engine, instead, just does what the throttle grip tells it to do.

We won't go so far as to say it handles like a sport bike, though Harley-Davidson will. Instead, it handles like a big athlete, the kind who plays the game because he's big enough to do things smaller men can't, yet he's coordinated enough not to hurt himself. We never grounded anything on a corner. Harley-Davidson says the FLT has a lean angle of 35° loaded. That isn't in the league with a Honda 750F that has 45°, but it's on a par with the other big touring bikes.

Those six-ply Goodyears on both ends of the FLT would look at home on a Volkswagen, but on the Harley they take some getting used to. The profile is flat, so the bike wants to go straight and stay upright. Want to turn? Just push on the handlebars down by the knees. The bike turns. It doesn't take, nor respond to, body English. It doesn't even take much effort at the handlebars. With the offset triple clamps the FLT has a remarkably steep 25° steering head angle yet the trail is a longer-than-average 5.75 in. that makes for great straight-ahead stability. Harley-Davidson's not the first company to use offset triple clamps (several Italian road-racers have used the idea), but the FLT is the only modern motorcycle to try the idea and the results are very good. Combined with the throttle set screw, it's easy for a rider to cruise down the road with both hands off the bars, should one go in for that sort of thing.

Getting used to the handling isn't so easy. First time Harley riders aren't likely to lean the Tour Glide over much more than they would if riding on gravel. And the FLT doesn't flick from side to side as do lighter machines. But given patience and practice the Harley can go down a winding road as fast as most touring riders would ever want to go. It's surely fast enough to keep up with any group of touring riders.

Tires also limit braking ability. For the first time, a Harley-Davidson has enough brakes, triple discs with 352 sq. in. of swept area, to lock either end in hard braking. Brake lever pressure needed on the Harley is high. Not as much as the BMW, but more than that of the Japanese bikes. Harley has used brake pads with a high metallic content that work exceptionally well in the wet and these simply take more pressure to stop the bike. But they don't fade and they do work when it rains and if a rider gets used to the Harley brakes, they are fine. Besides, during the braking tests, the Harley was the only bike that kept going straight when the front tire was locked. Sure is stable.

Like BMW Harley-Davidson doesn't play by anybody else's rules so the Milwaukee gang is free to try things that may work better or worse. Things like the signal light switches. These are push buttons on the controls at each handgrip that trigger the blinkers when the button is held in. They're great for lane changes on the freeway and never stay on after the bike is through the corner, but they aren't as easy to use, in some situations, as the slide switches used on the other machines. Of course there's the locking sidestand that doesn't allow the bike to roll off and fall down. The instruments, a speedo, tach and warning lights, are mounted in front of the steering head in a large housing. They're large, accurate, readable and especially readable at night when they light up bright but not enough to be irritating.

Not all of the Harley's pieces are so good. No one liked the seat. No, it's not because the seat isn't sprung, it's just too confining, not allowing a rider to move around with its shape that holds a rider in only one spot, and that not a very good one.

All the other touring bikes have shaft drive. Not the Harley. Shafts are heavy and expensive and take away power and it's

hard to change final drive ratios with a shaft. But chains are messy and don't last as long and require maintenance. Harley's answer is a chain enclosure. Just like what European transportation bikes and tiny Japanese tiddlers used 20 years ago, only updated. The chain case is a full enclosure, that is, it contains an oil bath so the final drive chain is always lubricated and never covered with dirt or water. Harley figures the chain should last at least 20,000 miles and the adjustment interval is extended considerably. It's a good idea, it works and has anyone ever fixed a broken U-joint on a shaft drive bike with a master link?

Noise isn't a problem on the Harley. There isn't any. Noise is unwanted sound and the only sounds the FLT makes are joyous ones. In the sound meter test the Tour Glide had the lowest maximum first gear sound and readings comparable to the Yamaha XS1100 at cruising speeds. Only the BMW and Honda were any quieter and they were only slightly quieter at 60mph.

Unlike all the other bikes in the test, the Harley didn't have any optional equipment on it. Yep, this was a stripper. The floor boards and heel-and-toe shifter and fairing and saddlebags and top box and crash bars and rack and seat are all standard. Are there options? Is a bear Catholic? Certainly there are options, a whole page of them. There are radios and CBs and gas gauges and highway pegs and instruments and lots of chrome covers for all the non-chromed parts of the bike. Without options the Harley is as fully equipped as most any touring bike gets. With options it's a monument to Chromius, the Gaud of bad taste.

Rest assured the Tour Glide can handle the accessories. One wonders if it could handle without them. Designing a motorcycle knowing it's going to have a fairing and saddlebags and a top box means the engineer doesn't have to worry about weight distribution changes and variances in the center of pressure and all that technical stuff. Consequently the Harley is stable and the fairing doesn't hurt the motorcycle in any way.

Being designed to carry two people and a kitchen sink, at 1180 lb. the Harley has the highest gross vehicle weight rating of any of the motorcycles. Even minus its considerable heft it has a load capacity of 400 lb., second highest of the test. Loaded to the gills it loses less than any of the other bikes, due to the low center of gravity and high initial weight. The load becomes a smaller part of the total.

LOAD CAPACITY

	Capacity	GVWR
BMW R100T	308 lb.	881
Harley-Davidson FLT	400 lb.	1180
Honda GL1100	368 lb.	1105
Kawasaki KZ1000	362 lb.	1030
Suzuki GS850	354 lb.	1003
Yamaha XS1100	427 lb.	1090

The Harley deserves special mention for its two-up carrying capability. Back seat passengers generally rated the Harley the most comfortable of all the bikes. The seat was large and properly shaped. The backrest was positioned in exactly the right spot to lend support but didn't interfere with passenger comfort. With the controlled vibration and pleasantly restrained sound, the Harley was an enjoyable traveling machine.

That Most Improved Motorcycle isn't the only award the Tour Glide should get. In the voting the FLT was everybody's choice when asked what motorcycle they liked regardless of cost. That's especially shocking because there are several reformed Harley Haters around the office.

Only the Harley, when ridden down a straight highway, can make a rider smile. Nothing else feels or sounds quite like it, and when you ride a Harley, nothing needs explaining. It's all said. You feel good just looking at it. But that's not all.

Even on merit the Harley competes. It was one man's pick for the Sunday ride and another said it was second choice for the Sunday ride because it's so much fun to ride. Better yet, three people said they'd really like to take the Harley on the cross-country trip if they only had a little more confidence in its ability to get there without requiring any maintenance.

See, the big Harley doesn't have a reputation for being a maintenance free motorcycle and it does need a servicing every 1250 miles, according to the book, while some other bikes have a recommended service interval up to 7500 miles. Disregarding the concerns over service and reliability (only a balky trip odometer reset caused any problems during the test), the FLT would have been the top pick for the long haul. Amazing.

OWNER SURVEY HARLEY-DAVIDSON 74 and 80

How Do You Evaluate a State of Mind?

This is a Harley survey. So forget rationality. Forget acceleration times, weight, stopping distance, cornering clearance, vibration level, horsepower and all the other conventional means of comparing motorcycles. They don't apply. Using those criteria to judge a Harley would be missing the point–like judging a painting by whether it matches your wall paper.

Appraising a Harley-Davidson requires a different approach, one based on a gut-level reaction to the presence of the machine, the massive styling, the thundering exhaust note and, of course, the overall Harley image. As one rider told us, "Its a state of mind."

We can't measure a state of mind or put a value on it, but we can ask Harley riders what they think about their machines and whether the Harley image has substance. Eighty-six Harley-Davidson owners answered our questions, 81 with 1200-cc 74s and five with 1340cc 80s (We didn't ask for survey forms on the 80s, but when they came in, we decided to use them anyway because they are so similar to the 74s).

The models include five FLH (Electra-Glide) and FXS (Low Rider) 80s, eight FXS 74s, three Fat Bobs, 38 FLH and FLHS 74s, 25 FXE and FXEB Super Glides, two police models, a 1964 panhead (Current models are shovelheads.), six unspecified model 74s and three knuckleheads dating from 1932, 1939 and 1940. Seventy seven percent were bought new.

Even the older Harleys see regular use, but despite the Harley's reputation as a long-distance machine, touring isn't the most popular use. Pleasure riding (76 percent) comes first, then touring (66 percent), with commuting and transportation close behind (65 percent). In comparison, 76 percent of the BMWs and 90 percent of the Honda GL1000s are used for touring. Two of the Harleys are drag raced and one is used in parades with the Shriners.

Whatever the use, Harleys add up the miles at an average rate. The new bikes average 14,000 miles on the odo, with individual figures as high as 141,000 miles. The used bikes have covered an average of 16,500 miles, so overall, the Harleys average 14,600 miles, close to the GL1000, but way behind the BMWs (21,000 miles). Almost 1,200,000 miles have been covered by the bikes in this survey.

Some riders cover up to 36,000 miles per year, but the average is about 8500 miles per year, higher than some of the bikes we've surveyed, but lower than others. Fuel economy figures are excellent for such a large bike, ranging from 27 to 65 mpg, with an average of 45 mpg, a figure comparable to the smaller and lighter R75 and R80 BMWs.

If you think Harley riders ride hard, think again. According to our survey replies, Harley riders have the gentlest riding style we've seen, even gentler than the Honda GL1000 riders. Exactly half the Harley owners have an average riding style and 16 percent ride gentler than average. Thirty two percent ride moderately hard and only 2 percent ride very hard. According to one rider, "Riding comes natural, but don't venture into the supernatural (fast twisty-turnies)." Another said, "You cannot ride this bike to your limits, you must ride it to its limits."

The Harley-Davidson owners replying to our survey do less of their own mechanical work than the owners of any of the other bikes surveyed except the GL1000. Thirty percent always do their own work, 39 percent usually take care of repairs themselves, 26 percent sometimes do and 5 percent never work on their machines.

The owners are split on the subject of ease of maintenance. Half the owners say the Harley is very easy to work on and tell us, ". . . it can be kept running with baling wire and a Crescent wrench." Nine percent of the owners (the highest number so far on our surveys) hold the opposing viewpoint and call the maintenance difficult. "If you're not a wrench, don't buy a Harley." one told us. The remaining 41 percent say maintaining a Harley is of average difficulty.

For other than routine maintenance, one owner told us, ". . . a pat on the tank occasionally will keep it running for a long time." Twenty one percent of the owners would agree, telling us their bikes have needed no repairs. On the remaining bikes, brakes (12 percent) led the list of repairs, followed by the starter (9 percent), miscellaneous switches (8 percent) and valve problems (7 percent). Five percent each had to fix the alternator, the voltage regulator or repair cracks in the gas tank and 3 percent each needed reboring, complete overhauls or speedometer or carburetor repairs.

Maintenance problems on the Harleys (" . . . even a Sherman Tank has limitations.") include chain adjustment and brakes (1976–78 models) with 6 percent each, electrical problems (5 percent) and vibration and difficulty in setting the ignition timing or changing tires (3 percent each).

The most common hints are the usual ones to change the oil often and, " . . . show it some TLC and it will never let you down." Recommendations for which oil to use include Harley-Davidson oil, any oil except Harley oil, mixed with STP, Castrol 70w in summer and 50 in winter and Kendall Nitro 70. The owners also recommend turning off the chain oiler, using a spray chain lube and checking the chain for stretch every 1000 miles, frequently checking the engine mount bolts for tightness and using three cylinder base gaskets to allow it to use regular gasoline without pinging.

From what the owners tell us, parts availability is less of a problem with Harley-Davidson than with any of the bikes we've surveyed. Fifty six percent say parts are always available, 37 percent find them mostly available and 7 percent sometimes have trouble finding parts. The Harley is the only bike we've surveyed for which no riders always have trouble getting parts, and one rider (in Norway), reports being able to get the correct wheel bearings at his local tractor shop. Despite this, 10 percent of the Harleys have been idle while waiting for parts, a figure bettered by the BMWs (6 percent), but well ahead of the GL1000s (15 percent). The average wait was 18 days.

Are Harleys reliable? Depends on who you ask. A mechanic told us, "One guy came in on a 20 year old machine complaining about a rough idle, some engine noise and an oil leak he noticed while stopped at a stop sign. It had a broken rod, the rough edges of which were bludgeoned smooth, the bottom of the crankcases were broken out in pieces, the rear cylinder bottom was broken and the piston was still in the cylinder with half of the rod attached. This thing was still running! A little rough and noisy, like he said."

Unfortunately, every Harley isn't so determined to keep running. Twenty-two percent of the Harleys in this survey have broken down or stranded their owners. This is the highest figure we've encountered, almost double the previous high, the Honda GL1000s, of which 12 percent had stranded their owners. The most common breakdown reasons are the transmission, clutch cable, ignition wiring and contact points and the alternator.

Are Harley-Davidson dealers very good or very poor? Both, according to the owners. Harley dealers tied with Yamaha 750 and BMW dealers with 38 percent rated very good. On the minus side, 10 percent of the dealers were rated very poor, a new record in that category. Twenty percent got good ratings and 18 percent fair.

For bikes with such a high load capacity, the Harleys in our survey carry few accessories. Fairings and windshields are mounted on 27 percent (compared with 92 percent of the GL1000s), 22 percent have saddlebags, 19 percent have tour packs or trunks, 17 percent have sissybars, 16 percent have highway pegs, 15 percent have auxiliary lights and 14 percent have back->

rests. Rounding out the list of reasonably common accessories are luggage racks and radios (7 percent each), driving lights, center stands and floorboards (5 percent each), and crashbars, tool pouches and extra instruments (3 percent each).

Many riders told us how much they love or hate these products, but didn't identify them by brand name. The Radio Caddy, praised by two riders, is the only product mentioned by more than one rider.

On the list of best features, touring ability or ride comfort is first (42 percent), followed by torque (26 percent), styling ("People are always looking.") at 22 percent, sound (16 percent), fuel economy and being an unusual bike (14 percent each), load capacity ("Will haul a ton.") and reliability (12 percent each) and the low seat (10 percent).

Harley owners also like the weight and solid feel (9 percent), the high resale value, ease of maintenance and parts availability (8 percent each), the stability and the handling (6 percent each) and the solid construction, 5 gal. tank, horsepower and the smoothness (5 percent each).

For 31 percent of the owners, bad vibes are a worst feature, and some of the owners also disliked the brakes (10 percent), the noise (9 percent), the chain drive (8 percent), the ground clearance ("You can almost scrape bottom while going straight.") and the weight (6 percent each).

Six percent of the owners list the seat as a worst feature and comments range from "If I ever have to torture prisoners into divulging secrets, I will strap them on the back seat." to " . . . gives wife an orgasm shortly before her butt goes numb." Handling, performance, lack of a center stand, the shifting and the need for premium gasoline each bother 5 percent of the owners.

If they had their druthers, 17 percent of the owners would have a shaft or belt drive, 14 percent would have better brakes, 10 percent would get rid of the vibrations, 6 percent would change the seat, and 5 percent each would change the shocks, add an oil cooler, change the exhaust pipes or lower the compression ratio to use regular gasoline.

And now the $6400 question—would you buy another Harley-Davidson? Only 78 percent said yes, a figure 10 percent lower than the next lowest (Kawasaki at 88 percent). Those who say no to another Harley call it outdated, an antique and not competitive with the latest from Japan. The Harley fans reply with comments such as, "It ain't fast, but it sure is regular." "Fastest thing in the quarter mile—draggin' a plow" and "It's not the boulevardier that my conservatively chopped Sportster is, or the road racer my RD 400 is, or even (blasphemy) the great long distance runner my XS750 is, but it makes me feel good and forget all my troubles when I'm riding it and you can't ask for anything more."

Harley-Davidson Survey

Bought new	77%
Bought used	23%
Average mileage	14,600
Types of riding	
Commuting	65%
Touring	66%
Pleasure	76%
Riding style	
Very hard	2%
Moderately hard	32%
Average	50%
Gentle	16%
Miles per year	8500
Fuel economy	45 mpg
Serviced by owners	
Always	30%
Usually	39%
Sometimes	26%
Never	5%
Ease of maintenance	
Very easy	50%
Average	41%
Difficult	9%
Parts availability	
Always available	56%
Mostly available	37%
Sometimes hard to find	7%
Always hard to find	0%
Dealer rating	
Very good	38%
Good	28%
Fair	18%
Poor	6%
Very poor	10%
Ever broken down	22%
Had to wait for parts	10%
Average parts wait	18 days
Maintenance problems	
Chain adjustment	6%
Brakes	6%
Electrical problems	5%
Vibration	3%
Ignition timing	3%
Best features	
Touring ability	42%
Torque	26%
Styling	22%
Sound	16%
Fuel economy	14%
Worst features	
Vibration	31%
Brakes	10%
Noise	9%
Chain drive	8%
Ground clearance	6%
Buy another Harley-Davidson	78%

The Aluminum Steamroller

A Lean and Hungry Hawg

by Peter Egan

Harley Sportster engines are known for a lot of things. They are known for their spare, aggressive good looks, the deep, unrhythmic shuffle of the 45° V-Twin at idle, low-end grunt, and for inspiring admiration in those who like tradition and simplicity backed by years of refinement. They are famous for being as easy to repair as farm implements and providing all the power you will ever need on the highway. What they are not famous for is blowing away exotic, highly-tuned multicylinder Japanese superbikes on roadracing circuits.

So when a Harley race bike showed up for the AFM season opener at Ontario this spring we didn't get too excited. Roadracers and fans learn early in life to reserve judgement on motorcycles seen in the paddock. All too often the bike with expensive paint goes onto the track and wobbles into last place. The engine that shakes the earth with its shattering exhaust note during warmup sometimes blows up in the pit lane. Off-brand, oddball motorcycles that gladden your heart just because somebody was crazy enough to race them are often a disappointment. They end up on the trailer after first practice, while corner workers mop oil and the engine parts. Bikes are best judged after a race, when success or failure put them in perspective.

Case in point, that Sunday morning at Ontario. John Ulrich and I were waiting in the slow-moving tech line, sitting astride a couple of Oriental box stockers, when some kind of Harley-Davidson rolled into the line beside us. The bike was pushed by Vance Breese, a veteran roadracer from Redwood City, California.

At first glance the bike appeared to be an XLCR set up for Superstreet competition. The tank, at least was XLCR and the motorcycle was black. Then I noticed a pair of big Dell'Orto carb throats aimed out and rearward in threatening fashion. There was something different about the heads and cylinders, and the 2-into-1 exhaust system swept up and around the left side of the motor. The scale of the bike was wrong, too. It was all engine, like an old Vincent, with a short and compact frame. Mean and businesslike. Not the sort of Harley available in stores. I dismissed it as>

otos by Peter Egan, Steve Kimball, Patrick Behar and Brian Blades

The complete 166 lb. motorcycle engine. Sputhe aluminum barrels and heads make this a very light 100-hp-plus package.

Narrow engine with low cg contributes to nimble handling and exceptional ground clearance on Breese Harley.

Sputhe head next to stock Sportster item (left). Sputhe design offers low weight, increased finning, and lower valve angle for better flow from twin-carb setup. Intake ports are 36 mm.

another one of those noble experiments where a brand fanatic (usually British) trys an underdog assault on the usual lineup of Japanese hyperbikes. A campaign doomed, no doubt, to frustration and failure.

Right.

Two hours later the Harley was out on the track, challenging Pat Eagan's Moriwaki Kawasaki for second place in Open GP, turning short-course 1:43's and applying heavy pressure on a bike and rider that would finish fifth at Daytona two weeks later. In the Open Superstreet race later that afternoon, Eagan and Breese battled wheel to wheel the entire race, Eagan holding a slight edge until the last lap, when he took a wide line (i.e. straight off the track) in the last corner and Breese blasted his Harley across the finish line to victory. The crowd loved it.

No ordinary Harley, indeed. Breese was apparently riding something more than a breathed-on XLCR or an old Sportster with a sleek tank and clip-ons. After the race speculation filled the paddock. There were rumors of 1400cc barrels, and of funny fuel that evaporated before it hit the ground, burned smoldering holes in the pavement, or when touched caused the fingers to shrivel and fall off. The only thing anyone knew for sure was that the bike was very fast and had a lot of power. Obviously a motorcycle worth looking into.

Intrigued by the bike, we invited Breese and the man who designed and built the Harley's barrels and cylinder heads, Alan Sputhe, for a tear-down session and a day at Orange County Drag Strip.

"This is really just my street bike," Breese explained as he and Sputhe rolled the bike down a ramp from the back of a Datsun pickup. "I use it for riding on the weekends in northern California. I love to ride in the rain, which is good, because it's always raining up there. For that kind of riding I prefer light bikes, because I think heavy bikes like the Japanese multis are dangerous in the rain. Once you start to lose them, it's all over." Sputhe steadied the bike as Breese slid a center-lift under the frame. "So we built this as a street bike," he continued. "If we built a real race bike it would be a lot more radical than this."

Sputhe nodded his agreement. "The secret of the bike's performance is in the upper end. People think we're running fuel or real high compression, but we're not. The compression ratio is 9:1 and we use pump gas. The fuel rumors come from the smell of Castrol R in the exhaust. The bottom end is stock Sportster, from a '72 engine, with S&S rods, pistons and bearings. The barrels and heads are my own design."

Displacement?

"Twelve hundred and ninety cc's."

Sputhe and Breese checked tire pressures, tightened bolts and poured gas into the tank, while John Ulrich donned his leathers. Breese trotted the bike across the warm-up area, hopped onto the saddle, and the big Twin fired. There is no starter, kick or electric. He handed the bike over, with advice to go with a 6500 rpm redline and second gear out of the hole. First wouldn't stand up under a really hard drop of the clutch, and it wasn't needed anyway.

Ulrich made a couple of easy trial runs in the mid-elevens, then got down to business. A 10.95; 10.94, and then a 10.86 at 131.3 mph. He came in and parked the bike.

"This is the hardest bike to ride I've ever been on," he said, flexing his hands in front of his face, checking to see if they still worked. "The vibration pumps my hands up so much I can't tell if I'm really hanging on to the bars or if my hands are going to slide right off the grips. Also, it goes into a tank-slapper at the end of every run. It's scary."

Sputh and Breese looked at the bike and frowned. Tony Williams, their pipemaker from Williams Pipes who had come along to help with the drag strip tuning, got down on one knee and began to examine the bike. "It shouldn't be vibrating at all," Sputhe said. "It's balanced to smooth out as the revs climb toward redline."

"It shouldn't wobble, either," Breese added. "Even at Ontario it felt nice and stable on the banking." They checked the bike over and found a loose motor mount and a slight rear wheel misalignment. Breese backed one alignment bolt off two flats. Ulrich made another test run and reported the bike smoother and better handling. Not exactly a detuned Gold Wing, but improved.

Sputhe explained that the frame is an old Mert Lawwill dirt track frame which Breese bought for only $300 because it was bent in a crash. "We've straightened it—twice," he said. "But chrome-moly steel has sort of a memory."

Ulrich made another practice run and pulled in with an oil-soaked rear tire. The primary cover had loosened. "Sympathetic vibration," Sputhe said. "Harleys have a lot of it." Breese and Williams tightened the cover, ran a plug check and decided to lean out the Dell'Ortos. Williams added some discs to the Super Trapp muffler on the end of the pipes. The rear brake and tire were cleaned with solvent and Ulrich gave it another try.

The drag strip by mid-morning was becoming a dangerous place. The California Highway Patrol had set up a pursuit slalom course at the end of the strip and were careening in and out of orange pylons with Dodge Coronets. Ulrich had about half of the usual shutoff room, so every run ended in a cloud of brake dust and tire smoke as he hauled it down to a rapid stop. On the fourth run the throttle grip rotated on the bars and prevented the front brake lever from moving. Ulrich cleared the traps at

130 and ran straight through the cones, flying past speeding police cars, sliding the rear tire and downshifting. Unnerving, but a rare opportunity. I asked him if the police said anything and he said he didn't wait around to see.

When he came back there was more oil on the rear tire. The timing plug had fallen out on the strip. More sympathetic vibration. A replacement was borrowed from a full-dress FLT (hail interchangeability) being tested by another magazine, and a final jetting change was made. Tony Williams removed the muffler from the exhaust header. Breese discovered an oil leak into the clutch, which is a dry stock unit off an early Sportster, and replaced the plates and cover gasket.

Williams checked a barometer in the truck and pointed to some storm clouds over the Santa Ana Mountains. He said the air density, which had been dropping off all morning, was improving because of the nearby storm. A good time for a run.

Ulrich went out and turned two more times in the high tens. On the third try the Harley stopped the clocks at 10.554 seconds and 130.24 mph.

That made the Harley the quickest bike this magazine has ever tested. Quicker than the Yoshimura Suzuki GS1000 Superbike, which ran a 10.66 at a slightly faster 132.74 mph; faster and quicker than either the Yosh Z-1R (10.80 at 124.13) or the RC GS1000EC (10.73 at 128.57) we tested in our Taking it to the Tens report in November of 1978; and nearly a second quicker and 10 mph faster than the BAE/Magnum Turbo GS1000 we ran in January this year.

We set up our radar at the end of the strip (the cops had gone home or behind billboards or wherever it is they go) and the bike ran through the half-mile at 149 mph, still gaining speed as it ran out of drag strip. Another test record.

"It'll go faster than that on the top end," Breese said, "if it has more space. That's the trouble; its speed and acceleration really expand the room you need to play in. This bike can get you into deep trouble so fast . . ."

Sputhe suggested they regear the bike for a faster top end run, and possibly a faster quarter mile, but Ulrich said that was fast enough. The brakes wouldn't stop the bike in the short remaining runoff space if it went any faster. "This bike needs another disc on the front for racing," he said.

"This is just my street bike," Breese said. "If I built a race bike I'd probably put another disc on it." >

Hard launches without wheelies or rear tire pyrotechnics were made possible by good weight distribution and tractable low-end power.

Ulrich gets the good news from Vance Breese; a 10.554 at 130.24, quickest time ever through the quarter mile for Cycle World.

Sputhe shook his head. "Then you'd have to put decals on it."

Back to the shop for teardown.

Weight and measurement time. With a half tank of gas (2 gal.) the Harley tips the scales at 347 lb. Weight distribution is 48 percent on the front wheel and 52 on the rear. Rake and trail are 27° and 3.9 in. respectively. The wheelbase is 55.5 in. In other words, the bike is about half an inch longer than a 400 Hawk but weighs 51 lb. less. It also has more horsepower.

"There are two approaches to horsepower," Breese said. "There's the electric high-speed machinegun method, and then there's the big cannon. This is a big cannon. A big engine doesn't have to work so hard to produce power, and it's usually simpler and lighter."

The Harley has been on a rear wheel dyno only once, Sputhe said. The dyno had trouble with the Harley's irregular power pulses and allowed the rear tire to slip and smoke in the rollers. They came up with corrected figures of 108 bhp at 7000 rpm and just over 100 lb.-ft. of torque, peaking at 3800 rpm. Breese thinks actual horsepower may be closer to 120, according to his speed and gearing calculations, though he hesitates to make concrete claims because of the many imaginative and inconsistent ways horsepower is measured. Like Rolls-Royce, Breese and Sputhe could probably say the Harley's horsepower is "adequate".

The bike's 290cc of extra displacement over the stock Sportster is gained by a bore increase from 3.18 in. to 3.6 in. Stroke is stock, at 3.8 in. Sputhe says most speed tuners of Harley-Davidsons have increased power and displacement by lengthening stroke, but this limits rpm because of dangerous piston speed. The Harley needs better breathing and carburetion, he says, not a longer stroke. Enter the Sputhe heads and barrels.

The heads are cast from 356-T6 aluminum and have stellite valve seats shrunken in. Chambers are shaped into what Sputhe half-jokingly refers to as a "polyspherical bathtub chamber". The intake valves have stock Sportster head diameter, 1.9 in., but have longer shovelhead-style stems to allow a more laid-down valve angle for better flow through the ports. The exhaust valve, at 1.75 in., is 0.115 in. larger than stock. Valve springs are from Jerry Branch.

The barrels are of the same aluminum as the heads, with manganese iron liners. The aluminum is cast around the liners and then heat-treated to assure proper bonding and good heat transfer. Sputhe has spent considerable time experimenting with cooling fin shapes and numbers to arrive at the correct operating temperature for the Harley. He says the engine never has overheating problems; after the Ontario race the oil temp was 150° F.

The aluminum barrels and heads provide less weight and a lower cg for the bike, as well as more horsepower. A Sputhe head on our scales weighs 8.75 lb. versus 14.5 lb. for the stock part; the cylinder barrel 8.75 instead of 12.5 lb. Taken together, a weight saving of 19 lb. The entire engine, complete with carbs, weighs only 166 lb.

Four long studs of 4130 centerless-ground steel extend from the cases up through each cylinder and head, holding it all together. Threads are rolled on, rather than cut, for improved strength. Sputhe explains that strong studs are critical because a high performance Harley with stock base bolts can—and will—blow the

Photo by Patrick Behar

Vance Breese in Turn Four at Willow; the Harley's high lean angle is well suited to Breese' tucked-in riding style.

entire cylinder off the cases, endangering bystanders and causing the rider to lose his concentration.

Tapered pushrods, made of aluminum to match the coefficient of expansion in the cylinders and heads, ride on stock Harley roller tappets. Rocker boxes are also stock Sportster, with rocker arms lightly radiused to prevent cracking. The valve train is moved by Andrews DX drag racing cams. Jim Belland, who built the bottom end and did much of the advisory work on the project, reworked the cams. He cut and rewelded the cam gears to change the lobe centers from 105° to 101° for more bottom end power. Lift on all four cams is 0.560 in.

Crank and cases are stock '72 Sportster. Breese says the '72 is not the best foundation for a performance engine because the tach drive on that model creates a weak spot in the transmission case. He used the '72 because it was available in blown-up form for $500, and says a '73 through '76 would be more desirable. Those models have a stronger transmission case and will still accept the early dry clutch, which Breese says is stronger than the later wet clutch. Power arrives at the countershaft sprocket via a standard Harley C-type close ratio gearset.

Rods, pistons and bearings are off-the-shelf S&S parts. The oil pump is a competition unit from Mark Brelsford's old racebike, Goliath, which Breese bought and subsequently crashed in a big way at Sears Point when it threw a rod through the cases. Carbs are two Dell'Orto PHM 40's from a Moto Guzzi Le Mans. Accelerator pumps are blocked off "for better gas mileage." Breese and Sputhe made their own intake pipes. The exhaust system is a 2-into-1 Tony Williams design with 1.875 in. headpipes going into a 2 in. diameter collector. A muffler containing Super Trapp discs is detachable when top-end rather than mid-range is needed. Harley points and coil fire the plugs; ignition is total loss.

The bike itself is a fairly harmonious collection of odd bits and pieces Breese and friends had sitting around their garages. The wheels are Morris Mags, 3 in. front and 5 in. rear, from a '72 Harley roadracer. Forks and triple clamps are Ceriani roadrace with slider assemblies off the old Goliath (whose stanchion tubes were bent). Kosman discs are used front and rear, with a Brembo caliper at the rear and Grimeca caliper in front. S&W shocks with 90 lb. springs control the swing arm; 28 lb. springs are installed in the Cerianis. The frame is early Mert Lawwill dirt track, largely restraightened.

Breese uses different tires for varied purposes. Street riding on northern California's mountain roads he uses Dunlop Isle of Man racing rains, a 3.25/4.50-18 front and a 3.50/6.00-18 rear. Dunlop slicks of the same dimensions go on the bike for roadracing.

Vance Breese has had plenty of time to accumulate used racing parts. He has a long history of racing slightly offbeat motorcycles and doing quite well. Beginning with a Bultaco TSS in 1965, he has since raced such machines as a 305 Superhawk, a Norton Dominator 99, Manx, and 750 production racer; a Matchless 650, a Norvin and a Trident. He won the '75 AFM 500 GP championship on a BSA 500MX, the '76 500 GP title on an Eso, and in '77 placed second in Open Production points on a Guzzi Le Mans. He won the '79 sidecar title with a TZ750 engine in a homemade frame.

Breese once ran a motorcycle repair shop, but sold the business. "Working on other people's bikes made me not want to work on mine," he says. He now runs a carpet cleaning business and a telephone answering service and works on motorcycles as a hobby. The Harley idea came along when friend Jim Nezgoda urged him to take a test ride on Mark Brelsford's old Harley racer, Goliath. "I couldn't believe how nice it was," Breese says. "It felt like a 650 Triumph with 82 rear wheel horsepower. I knew then I had to have a Harley." He then bought Goliath from Nezgoda and raced it until he wrote the bike off at Sears Point by looping it at 125 mph. His current Harley is a descendent, in spirit and leftover parts, to the original Goliath.

"There's a real community of Harley high performance people," says Breese, "more than you'd think. Everyone is willing to help out when you've got a project going. The people at Belmont Harley-Davidson, for instance, helped us out with parts and gave us hours of free tuning help just because they liked the bike. Sportsters of San Jose did all kinds of plating for us . . . the list goes on and on."

Alan Sputhe is another member of that community, and says that he and Breese were bound to run into each other, even though they live a few hundred miles apart, because they were both Harley high performance men. Sputhe has a long background in manufacturing motorcycle parts. He worked for 10 years as a pattern and die-maker for Bob Corey at R&S Patterns before branching off into his own business and becoming Sputhe Engineering. His interest in the Harley engine comes from a respect for its basic concept.

"When Harley decided to build a motorcycle engine," he explains, "they went about it the same way airplane engine designers would. They figured out how much power a motorcycle needed to work properly, then built the slowest turning, lightest, most reliable engine they could to provide that power. Displacement didn't matter, as long as it was enough." To Sputhe there is nothing immoral about enough displacement, as long as the engine—and the motorcycle—are compact and light in weight. He views the usual displacement classes, 500, 750 and so on, as artificial divisions created by traditional roadracing classes; divisions which have little meaning where road bikes are concerned. He sees no reason why motorcycles of adequate displacement and power should have to be heavy and cumbersome, or wide. He shares with Breese a high regard for efficiency and simplicity. Their 166 lb. engine, with 108 hp and 35 mpg on the race track, is a fair measure of that regard.

The engine went back into the frame and out to Willow Springs Raceway for the season's first AFM roadrace on that desert circuit (the track has no willows and no apparent springs; a good track though, with clear desert air and a lot of sunshine).

During one of the morning practice sessions Breese fired up the Harley and told us to take it out for a few laps. Ulrich went first. He did a couple of respectably fast laps and came in. "It's really wobbling in the fast corners," he said.

"You can't hang off at all with this bike," Breese told him. "You have to hug the

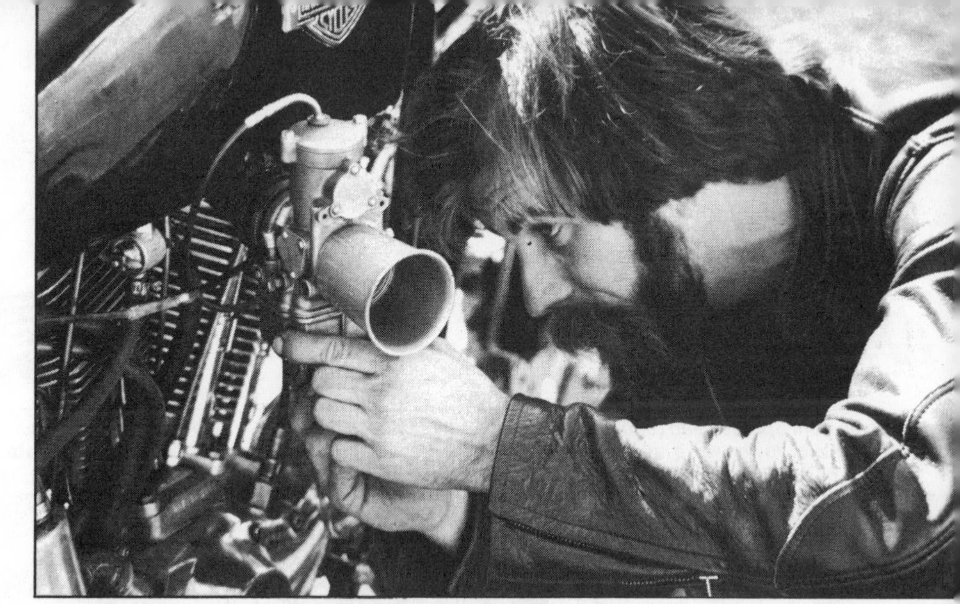

Breese performs last-minute jetting change on highly-accessible Dell'Ortos. Accelerator pumps are removed "for good gas mileage."

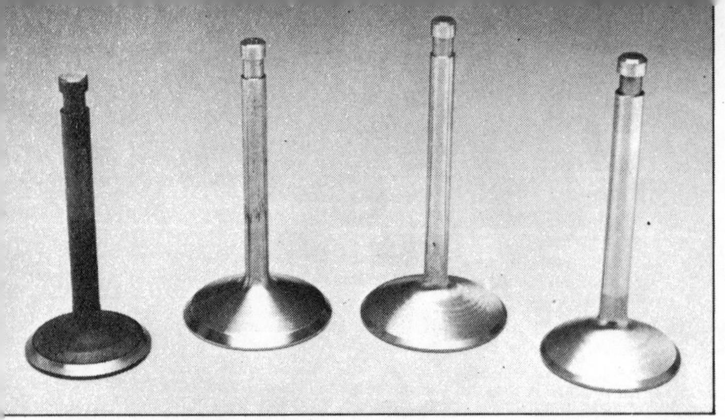

Valves from Sputhe head (right) are longer than stock Sportster valves because of lower valve angle, and are also lightened. Intake has same head diameter; exhaust is 0.115 wider than stock.

Sputhe calls this his "polyspherical bathtub chamber design." Stellite valve seats are shrunken into aluminum heads. Spigots at side are for oil return lines.

Even with larger bore, replacement barrel (left) is nearly 4 lb. lighter than stock. Aluminum is cast around manganese iron liner.

Engine uses 0.42-over S&S pistons (left) and a 9:1 compression ratio. At right is stock Sportster piston.

tank. Even if you stick your knee out it'll wobble." Ulrich went out, tucked in, and got around faster. After five or six laps he came in and handed it over to me. As I climbed on the bike he lifted his face shield and shouted over the exhaust racket from the straight pipe, "Whatever you do, don't take your knees off the tank or you'll get into a terrible tank-slapper. Also there's some oil in Turn Four."

"And the bad news is we're out of holy water," I mumbled to myself, clicking into gear and heading out pit lane. The Harley moved smartly down the road. Right side shift. Up for slow, down for go. The rearsets, adjusted for Breese who is less long of leg, were an extremely tight fit. I assumed the classic racing position of an Aztec grinding corn meal and heeled carefully into Turn One.

There was no way to hug the tank with my knees; they stuck out too far. One side made contact with a hot exhaust pipe (delayed reaction there; odor of burning leather before the pain) and the other knee ran straight into the foremost Dell'Orto. Sliding back in the seat, I held on as well as the bike permitted.

Concentrating not to shift wrong, I tried to pick up some speed. Initial reaction to the Harley is one of mild disorientation. Fresh off an ordinary street bike, it's hard to get a clear sense of how fast the Harley is traveling. Below 5000 rpm all speeds feel the same because of the wide, loafing powerband. The rearsets and slicks and the bike's general narrowness add to the sensation because cornering clearance seems limitless. I'd pass a bike easily in one corner, then be surprised to have him scratch by in the next. Opening the throttle a little more caused him to float suddenly backwards, peacefully and easily, like a fish in an aquarium. Nothing sudden or flashy, just awesome, useable power. The Harley lacks the usual ratio of commotion to speed. The commotion is constant; the speed infinitely variable.

Until you start revving the engine. Then engine and road vibrations begin to pick up and the world becomes more hectic. Things get faster and meaner. Above 5000 rpm in top gear the motorcycle is going genuinely fast. Too fast, maybe, when you can't hug the tank with your knees.

Before I went out Breese was telling me the Harley turns only 2000 rpm at 55 mph in top gear, describing the bike as "extremely peaceful" to ride. Peaceful? Maybe. If you have the self restraint to let the bike loaf, it chuffs along fairly well at low rpm. But a 347 lb. motorcycle with clip-ons, rearsets, a solo seat with a quarter inch of padding and more horsepower than a good Formula Ford does not lend itself to peaceful riding. With the wick turned up, the Harley becomes the embodiment of spartan, borderline-violent performance. Above 5000 rpm in top gear it's about as peaceful as a wounded rhino at a Landrover convention.

I brought the bike in and gave it back to its master. Breese went out that afternoon and won Open Superbike even though he had no front brakes because the pads somehow spit themselves out of the calipers. He stayed ahead of the second place full-house Kawasaki by pitching the Harley into corners and scrubbing off speed. Out on the track, the bike had that exaggerated time/distance look of a slot car on the wrong voltage. It reached a tremendous velocity down the main straight and always appeared to be going too fast to make the first corner. It would barely slow and then disappear around the turn, leaving only an exhaust note—which can be heard all the way around the track—as evidence it hadn't crashed into the mesquite and Joshua trees. In Open GP he finished second to Dave Emde, who was riding a TZ750.

After the race Breese looked at the Harley and told me, "We've really just started with this bike. There are a lot more things we could do to get real power out of it; hotter cams, high compression, and so on. But then it wouldn't be as much fun to ride on the street. The best thing about this bike is being able to pull up at a stoplight on a Harley and look CBX owners in the eye. I raced a guy with a turbo CBX up in northern California and it was just pitiful. He didn't have a chance."

Further information and pricing on the Sputhe heads and cylinders is available from:

Sputhe Engineering
6852 St. Estaban St.
Tujunga, Calif. 91042

HARLEY-DAVIDSON FXB-80 STURGIS

■ Harley-Davidsons, the factory tells us, are more than machines. It has to do with producing a motorcycle that isn't evaluated just on the basis of function, but on the way it makes a rider feel while functioning and the latest in a long line of not-quite machines is the Sturgis, or the FXB 80 to those familiar with Harley's letter designations.

Defined briefly, the Sturgis is a Low Rider with belt drive. Of course a Low Rider is a Super Glide in Sunday go-to-meetin' clothes and a Super Glide is an Electra Glide with a Sportster front end. What all that mechanical incest means is that the Sturgis has Harley's biggest motor, the 80 cu. in. V-Twin shared with the Electra Glide and Super Glide and all the other larger-than-Sportster machines, while having the trimmed-down styling of the Super Glide series, which includes Fat Bobs and the Low Rider and now the Sturgis and even something called the Wide Glide.

Confused?

Let's start over again.

First there was Harley's big bike, the FL that is today's Electra Glide, or FLH. Then there was the smaller model, the Sportster, or XL that uses a different engine of smaller displacement, ending up at 1000cc today as the XLH-1000. A third group of motorcycles has developed between those two basic bikes. That's the Super Glide series including the FXE Super Glide, FXE/F Fat Bob, FXS Low Rider and now the FXB Sturgis.

Calling it the Sturgis may be a bit confusing, too. After all, it's named after the famed Sturgis Rally in Sturgis, South Dakota and that would indicate that the Sturgis must be some kind of touring bike.

Well, it is some kind of touring bike, in its own way, but that way doesn't include giant fairings and plastic saddlebags. It's touring with a bed roll tied behind the short sissy bar and maybe a tent strapped to the forks and wind in the face. For that sort of touring, where the long-stroke V-Twin engine just rumbles along at a leisurely pace and you stick your feet out onto the highway pegs and set the throttle set screw and the highway just rolls backwards not too far underneath you, the Sturgis is every bit a touring machine.

Besides all the usual Harley-Davidson bits and pieces on the Sturgis, there's the novelty of belt drive, though no doubt Mr. Harley and the Davidsons wouldn't think it was much of a novelty as their first bike in 1903 used belt drive, too.

Belt drives aren't all that uncommon today, particularly to Harley riders who've seen lots of aftermarket belt drive kits fitted to Super Glides of all persuasions. Only the Sturgis is different from most of the kits and from Kawasaki's belt drive because the Sturgis has two belts. That's right. Two.

Both the primary drive and the final drive are handled by similar, though different size, toothed rubber belts that turn on large sprockets. Fitting a pair of belts to the Sturgis was more than a hammer and pipe wrench job. Because the belts are wider than chains, the starter mechanism had to be modified to clear the belts and new sprockets had to be fitted.

Up front on the end of the crankshaft a special compensator sprocket had to be designed, replacing the spring-loaded compensator sprocket used on the 74 and 80 cu. in. engines for so many years. In its place is a sprocket with rubber dampers inside the sprocket absorbing shocks from the engine. Because the belt doesn't wear as fast as a chain and change adjustment, there's no primary drive tensioner any more, that going away with the old duplex primary drive chain.

Harley's primary chain has always been outboard of the final drive chain with the clutch being outboard of both, but that was never a servicing problem until the belts arrived. Now, in order to change a final drive belt, the primary belt must first be removed. Yup. There's no way of changing the final drive belt without first removing the primary cover and pulling the primary belt. Figure two hours to change belts, says our H-D mechanic.

That shouldn't be a problem, we're told, because the final drive belt should last as long as the primary belt and the distance will be greater than if a chain were used. Add up all the time not spent adjusting the chain oiler and cleaning the mess of oil off the rear of the bike and the two hours every 20,000 mi. or so becomes time saved, the way Harley looks at it. Could be, too. Plus there's no primary chain oiling mess to worry about.

For the details, the primary belt is 1.125 in. wide, has 78 teeth spaced 13.8mm apart. The final drive belt is 1.5 in. wide, has 126 teeth spaced 14mm apart. A wide final drive belt has required a widened swing arm so there's room for the belt and its sprockets on the rear hub, but otherwise, things are straightforward.

An important question about the belt drive, is why? The obvious answer is that people wanted belt drives as evidenced by the many belt drive kits on the market. But there's more to it than that. There are real advantages of a belt drive and in the Sturgis' case there are very few drawbacks.

Not needing primary chain oiling means the dry clutch can stay drier and that should increase clutch life. It will also eliminate any primary chain oiling problems and primary drive maintenance will be simplified. The final drive belt doesn't need any lubrication so there doesn't have to be a chain oiler and the oil consumption of the bike is therefore lessened, plus making the back end of the motorcycle considerably cleaner. Belts are quieter, too, and in the Harley's case that's important because the motorcycles themselves aren't too quiet and meeting existing noise laws is a real challenge with a Harley. The belts also absorb some of the shock from the driveline and that makes the bikes smoother and makes shifting smoother, too. Then there's a reduction in unsprung weight with the belt and aluminum rear sprocket being lighter than a chain and steel sprocket. And finally, there's less adjustment with a belt. It doesn't stretch hardly at all and it doesn't change any more in the rain than the dry. With all those reasons, it's a wonder all motorcycles don't use belts rather than chains.

Harley riders being somewhat tradition-minded, it may be difficult to convince them that there aren't problems with the new system. The most notable problem is one of price; the Sturgis costs $261 more than the similar chain drive Low Rider. Plus, what do you do if a belt breaks just 85 mi. the other side of Truth or Consequences, New Mexico. There is no master link in an endless belt. Harley engineers say there is supposed to be an emergency belt kit with a pin-together fitting so it can be used to replace the standard belt in roadside repairs. Only several months after the emergency kit was described, our local Harley dealer has yet to see one. Hmmmm.

In normal Harley practice there are numerous tiny changes in this bike's basic internals. This year all the large V-Twins get a new Motorola electronic ignition that has an electronic advance mechanism replacing the centrifugal advance of pre-

Twin Belt Drive is New But it Hasn't Changed the Feel of Riding a Harley.

vious models. It's an interesting advance and firing system, operating with only one advance point. The Hall-effect magnetic triggering is provided by what Harley calls a Speed Cup and is, in effect, the triggering, distributing and half the advancing mechanism. This rotating cup has two notches, one for each cylinder, and those notches are what trigger the pickups on the ignition. Working with the cup are a series of storage chips in the microprocessor. The chips store information from the cup, switching information down the series as each is filled, each successive chip switching faster than the one before. The end result is that the leading edge of the cup's notches switches the ignition at high speed and the trailing edge of the notches trigger the ignition at low speed, 1600 rpm being the switch-over point. Below 1600 rpm the ignition has 18° of advance and above that there's 32° advance.

The huge jump in ignition timing causes occasional detonation even on the best pump gas, but careful throttle control eliminates most of the pinging. The large,>

3.498 in. bore is responsible for the pinging, Harley engineers say, because the large bore means it takes a long time for the flame to spread through the combustion chamber. The lengthy burning time makes an early spark necessary and even the low 8:1 compression ratio can't eliminate the need for premium fuel. A long 4.25 in. stroke keeps the bore size down somewhat, but that, in turn, limits maximum engine speed to 5500 rpm because of the great inertia forces of the huge engine.

Another major change for 1980 is a new transmission case and a new second gear ratio that's 10 percent higher than the previous model. Overall ratios on the Sturgis are slightly higher than the ratios on any other Harley-Davidsons because of the slightly different final drive ratio of the belt. With a top gear ratio of 3.27:1 for the Sturgis, 3.42:1 for the other Super Glide versions and only 3.36:1 for the five-speed Tour Glide, the Sturgis will run down the highway with the engine hammering along the slowest. And that suits it just fine.

Having about the same torque as an International Harvester Loadstar, the Sturgis is quite comfortable with the engine spinning 2700 rpm at 60 mph. That is, after all, only about half the maximum engine speed possible on the giant V-Twin.

Such high gearing doesn't lend itself to dragstrip performance and the Sturgis suffers in this regard because of the gearing. A 14.64 sec. quarter mile time and trap speed of 91.18 mph put the FXB-80 in company with the average Japanese 400cc Twin. Certainly Harley-Davidsons have had years of success drag racing, but the Sturgis is not intended as a dragster. It does manage a respectable 48 mpg in normal riding, a figure that would be good for a motorcycle with an engine half as big as the Sturgis'. But with a combined volume of 3.5 gal. for the two gas tanks on the Sturgis, cruising range is limited.

In stock tune the Sturgis is about as non-competitive a motorcycle as Harley-Davidson or anyone else could produce, it not having the power for any kind of racing or the suspension and handling to encourage that sort of activity.

What the Sturgis substitutes for handling agility is stability. With its 2 in. extended forks, 31.4° steering rake and over 64 in. wheelbase the Sturgis isn't going anywhere but straight unless a rider makes an extreme effort at moving the narrow 28 in. handlebars. A first time rider usually swings wide trying to turn the Sturgis until he learns to muscle the machine around corners sharper than the banking at Daytona. Once accustomed to the Harley's natural inclination to go straight, a rider can make the Sturgis turn reasonably sharply, as long as not too great an angle of lean is called for. At surprisingly gentle angles the Sturgis drags the folding footpegs on either side, followed soon thereafter by the exhaust on the righthand side and the sidestand on the lefthand side. Only when the Harley grounds down it's not like grounding a sidestand or centerstand on a small Japanese bike. On the Harley there's a feeling that it's not the motorcycle that's going to move, it's the road underneath. That same stability that keeps the Sturgis going straight keeps it going around corners, too. High speed sweepers are a natural for the Sturgis. It chugs around fast sweepers at the limit of its cornering clearance with no wiggle or wobble, as solid as a gold bar in a Swiss bank.

Should one want to slow the Harley at

Most obvious key that the Sturgis is different is the final drive belt and belt guard.

Propelling the Sturgis is the familiar 80 cu. in. ohv V-Twin used on other large Harleys. For 1980 it gets a new electronic ignition.

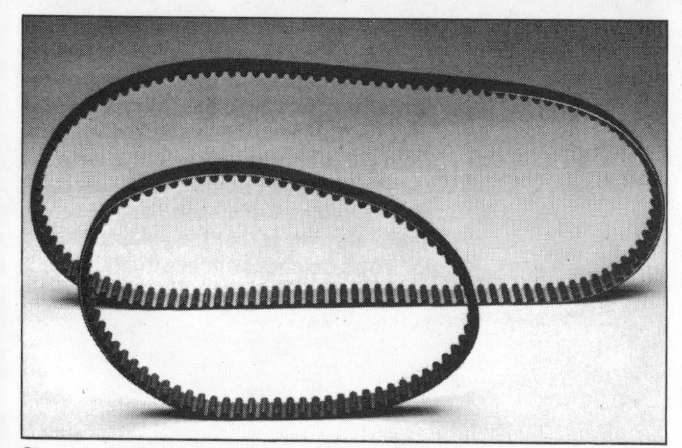

Shorter primary belt is 1.125 in. wide while the final drive belt is 1.5 in. wide. Both are made by Gates Rubber Co. for Harley-Davidson.

A rubber block compensator sprocket eases impact loads on the primary belt and replaces the spring loaded compensator sprocket used on chain drive Harleys.

the end of a fast ride it will require a vice-like grip and lots of room. Sure the Sturgis has triple disc brakes with lots of swept area. But in an effort to assure that Harley riders never find themselves grabbing too much front brake, the Sturgis (and most every other Harley-Davidson) has incredibly hard brake pucks. Even if the rider has biceps the size of watermelons and can squeeze the brake lever until it cries uncle and hits the grip the Sturgis still won't come close to locking the front tire. At least the rear brake is capable of providing all the stopping the tire can deliver, but it shouldn't have to work alone.

Thankfully other controls on the Sturgis are much easier to operate. The clutch pulls with a moderate amount of effort as long as the rider isn't one of those pencil-necked geeks with the tiny paws, but of course *those* types don't ride Harleys. The throttle is the easiest turning throttle made and the fat grips make it even easier so that the throttle set screw (nice touch) will hardly ever be needed. Shifting is, well, not easy, but serviceable. Shift as slow as molasses and things barely clunk. Shift as though this were a dragster and awful noises come from the transmission, though the belts may help smooth out the jerks.

Other features of the Sturgis are a mixture of good and bad. The locking sidestand is a model of simplicity and good design. It extends easily and once down doesn't allow the bike to roll forward off the stand. On the other hand, there's no centerstand, though hoisting a 610 lb. motorcycle onto a centerstand isn't much fun. Turn signals on the Harley are, as usual for a Harley, operated by pushing a spring loaded button on either side of the machine. The signals stay on as long as the buttons are pushed, making an automatic canceller needless, but making turn signal operation difficult should one try downshifting at the same time. Then there's the kickstarter. It takes a certain weight rider to be able to start the Harley by kicking it and that weight goes up dramatically if the engine is cold. Warm, a healthy 150 pounder can start it while a weak 150 pounder only floods the engine. Cold starts are best left to the fat man at the circus or the electric starter.

For its part the engine runs flawlessly. While the craftiest foreign bikes are adding air suction and accelerator pumps and even fuel injection the Harley manages to meet the same emission standards by proper carb jetting, its electronic ignition and nothing else. And the results are wonderful. Pull the choke knob under the seat, hit the starter button and the Harley eventually grinds itself into action, though accompanied by sounds of protest from the starter much of the time. Push the choke half-way in and the Harley can be ridden away instantly. A block down the street the choke can be pushed completely in and there are no rideability problems. No bucking or stalling. No coughs. It doesn't have to idle at 4000 rpm for 10 min. Nice what mild tuning and honest-to-gosh flywheels can do.

What the Sturgis can't do is provide the kind of comfort a more softly sprung motorcycle can provide. A ride to Sturgis from farther away than, say, Deadwood 2 mi. down the road would be a good test of a rider's toughness. The seat has little padding and there's only one riding posture that fits the combination of low 27 in. seat, short drag-style bars and footpegs. Thankfully there are highway pegs up front, but these only fit riders of a certain size and shape, due partially to the

HARLEY-DAVIDSON FXB-80

SPECIFICATIONS

List price $5687
Engine ....ohv V-Twin
Bore x stroke............88.8 x 107.9mm
Displacement 1340cc
Compression ratio 8:1
Carburetion ....(1) 38mm Keihin
Air filter..............oiled foam
Ignition ....electronic breakerless
Claimed power ....na
Claimed torque .....71.5 lb.-ft. lbs. @ 3800 rpm
Lubrication ....dry sump
Oil capacity ....4.5 qt.
Fuel capacity ....3.5 gal.
Starter ....electric, kick
Electrical power.........12v alternator
Battery 12v 19ah
Headlight 50/40w
Primary drive......toothed belt
Clutch ....dry multi-disc
Final drive ....toothed belt
Gear ratios, overall:1
- 4th 3.27
- 3rd 4.02
- 2nd......................5.42
- 1st 8.00

Suspension:
- Front ....telescopic fork
  - travel ....6.9 in.
- Rear...............swing arm
  - travel ....3.5 in.

Tires:
- Front ...MT90-19 Goodyear
- Rear....MT90-16 Goodyear

Brakes:
- Front........ dual 10 in. disc
- Rear ....10 in. disc

Brake swept area ..285 sq. in.
Brake loading (160-lb. rider ....2.0 lb./sq. in.
Wheelbase ....64.7 in.
Rake/Trail.......31.4°/4.9 in.
Handlebar width ....28 in.
Seat height ....27 in.
Seat width..............12.5 in.
Footpeg height...........11 in.
Ground clearance ....5.5 in.
Test weight (w/half-tank fuel) ...610 lb.
Weight bias, front/rear, percent...........43.5/56.5
GVRW ....1085 lb.
Load capacity ....475 lb.

ACCELERATION

Time to speed ———
Time to distance - - - -

speed in mph: 0, 25, 50, 75, 100, 125, 150
distance in ft.: 1500, 2000, 2500, 3000
time in sec.: 0, 5, 10, 15, 20
¼ mi.

CYCLE WORLD TEST

PERFORMANCE

Standing ¼-mile....14.64 sec. @ 91.18 mph
Top speed in ½-mile ....106 mph
Fuel consumption......48 mpg
Range (to reserve tank) ....135 mi.

Acceleration:
- 0–30 mph.......... 2.0 sec.
- 0–40 mph.......... 3.1 sec.
- 0–50 mph.......... 4.5 sec.
- 0–60 mph.......... 6.3 sec.
- 0–70 mph.......... 8.4 sec.
- 0–80 mph......... 11.5 sec.
- 0–90 mph......... 14.5 sec.
- 0–100 mph ....19.0 sec.

Top gear acceleration:
- 40–60 mph.........5.8 sec.
- 60–80 mph........7.9 sec.

Maximum speed in gears:
- 1st................... 50 mph
- 2nd.................. 74 mph
- 3rd...................99 mph
- 4th..................122 mph

Speedometer error:
- 30 mph indicated........28.4 mph
- 60 mph indicated........60.5 mph

Braking distance:
- from 30 mph........... 38 ft.
- from 60 mph......... 150 ft.

Engine speed at 60 mph.........2701 rpm

bulbous air cleaner. Passengers protested the tiny rear portion of the seat and the passenger pegs because of the vibration level. One passenger even claimed the seat gave her a hot seat from the vibration, though Harley doesn't claim any intent. The vibration, however, was never enough to bother riders.

Comfort and performance are easy enough to evaluate, but what about style? It's especially important on the Sturgis because the Sturgis has style and its style is a major part of what it has to offer. If you saw a Sturgis and were asked to describe it, you might say it's solid and straightforward, almost primitive, large and just slightly intimidating. At least that's what we'd say and its no doubt what Willie G. Davidson had in mind when the bike was styled. So. It looks like what it should look like and that's successful styling, never mind that forged frame junctions and steel brackets that look as if they were made in somebody's back yard aren't in keeping with the style of the other big bikes.

That style is created by the very blackness of the motorcycle. The engine cases and cylinders and heads and all the covers are black, mostly glossy black. So are the tanks and fenders and the spokes of the cast wheels. The tiniest bit of red trim identifies the Sturgis as a Harley and adds color to the rims of the wheels. Again, it's all part of that down-home look that Harleys have and others copy.

It's that look, combined with the staggered beat of the Harley's engine that manages to make a person on the bike a Harley rider. You don't need a leather jacket or primary chain holding up your pants, just arrive anywhere on the Sturgis and your presence will be felt. Okay, it may not get you respect.

But it gets you noticed.

Identification of the Sturgis is low key. This badge in front and the belt drive are the obvious points. Small Sportster headlight puts excitement in night riding.

If the electric starter doesn't work, there's always the kick starter, or a big hill for smaller riders.

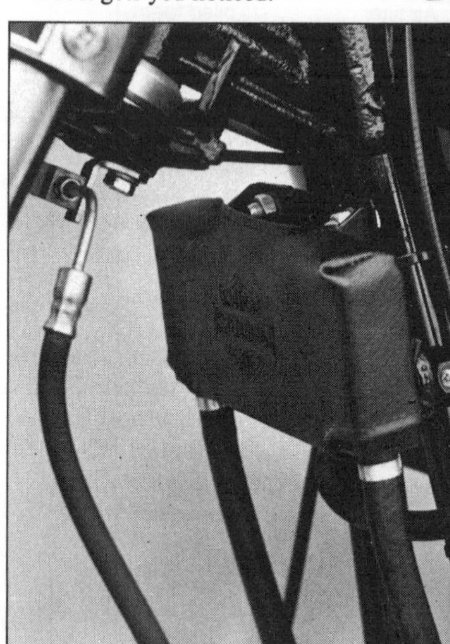

Like the Low Rider on which the Sturgis is based, there's an oil cooler included and it comes with its own vinyl cover for cold weather use.

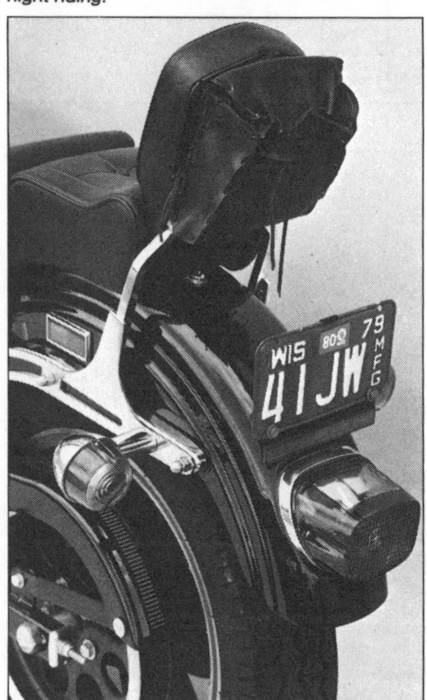

Part of the Sturgis and Low Rider styling is the leather stash pouch attached to the short sissy bar.

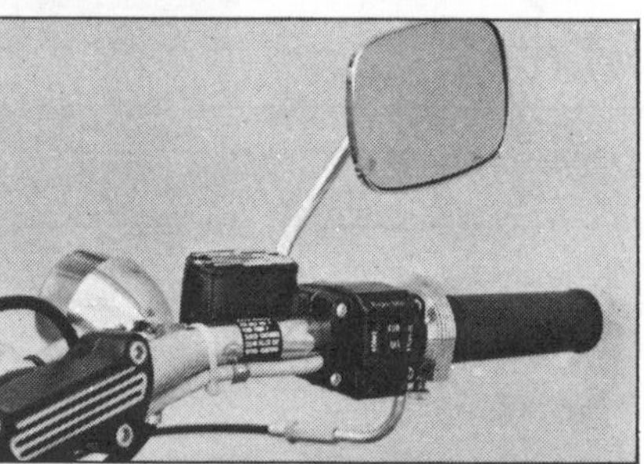

Short drag-style handlebars require lots of leverage to turn the long Sturgis. The mirrors don't stick out far enough for a rider to see past his elbows.

Dual gas tanks surround the tach and speedometer. The rubber mounted instruments are at times difficult to read because of vibration.

Despite the double 10 in. front discs, braking power is slight. The forks have 2 in. extensions and are mounted at 31.4° rake.

HARLEY-DAVIDSON FXRS

■ Look closely at the photos of the new Harley-Davidson FXRS and there's something you won't see. It's not as noticeable as the all-new frame or the rubber-mounted engine or the five-speed transmission or the extra oil drain lines. It doesn't even stand out as much as the raised white letter Dunlop K181 tires or the new controls. What makes this motorcycle significant beyond its features is the name on the gas tank. It says Harley-Davidson. There are no initials before Harley and, of course, there is no expletive before the Davidson.

This does not mean that in the few weeks after Harley-Davidson separated from AMF that the engineers feverishly came up with a new model. Instead, over the past few years Harley-Davidson's engineering staff (you'd be surprised) has been working on a number of new projects, some of which were introduced before the separation, some are being introduced now and others are still to come. That notion may get lost before the history books are written, though. As these things sometimes happen, Harley-Davidson Motor Company may very well be judged on the success of the new models to bear that name.

If so, the company is in luck.

The FXRS and its FXR twin were originally supposed to be stripped-down versions of the FLT, aka the Rubber-Glide. On the way to stripping the fairing and saddlebags and other pieces off the FLT, the design was changed. The FLT's frame has a huge square backbone that sticks way out front so the offset forks have room to operate.

Without a fairing to hide behind, the extended frame of the FLT looked peculiar on a sports bike. So the engineering staff was given permission to design a new frame for the FXRS.

Like the FLT the R-bike gets the rubber mounted engine. The locating arms are in the same places as on the T and they work just as well to isolate 80-cu. in. vibrations from the rider. And like the T, there are no cast iron junctions on this frame. It's entirely welded steel tubing, with plentiful gusseting around the steering head. Compared with the old frame of the FX series, the new frame is five times stiffer, according to Harley's chief engineer. Getting to start with a clean sheet of paper also meant that the R-bike's frame could be designed to provide the best handling for a stripped bike. The rear-set offset forks of the FLT are fine for the fully loaded touring machine, but the R gets to use the Sportster front end with 19-in. front tire and connect it at a 32° angle to the frame.

This frame might appear to be a copy of a non-Harley frame, but it's not. One look at the 64.7 in. wheelbase makes it clear that this is a Harley. It also uses square steel tubing for the swing arm. And when the one-piece gas tank is removed from the frame there is an enormous amount of steel welded up into a massive backbone, quite unlike the FLT or any other motorcycle.

Where this frame does reflect Harley design is in the relative positions of things like the seat and pegs. Harley's big motor is relatively tall, so the double downtube frame is deep. To keep the seat height down the top tubes dip low under the seat, enabling the bike to have a 29.5 in. seat height even with the overstuffed perch the RS provides. And the length of the frame and positioning of the engine and transmission leave plenty of room under the seat for the oil tank and battery, where they are easy to check and service.

Laid back is the seating position designed into the frame. The pegs are relatively high, but far forward. Highway pegs are mounted at the extreme forward end of the frame. But the pegs are narrow, folding and have scraping tips at the ends to warn the rider when cornering clearance no longer exists. (That is not a frequent message.)

At both ends of the FXRS are conventional Japanese suspension parts. The telescopic Showa forks provide a long 6.9 in. of travel, but little of that is used in normal use. Spring rates are stiff and stiction is high, so the forks move little. The shocks mount to the wheel-end of the swing arm, rather than half-way back as on the other FX models. Here, the spring and damping rates are well chosen for the weight and use of the machine, though passenger hauling may cause the shocks to bottom often.

Combining a long wheelbase and a none-too-steep steering head angle is normally a prescription for straight ahead stability and a resistance to turn without lots of muscle. In this case it doesn't work exactly like that. The bike also has a relatively low center of gravity and the engine is narrow, heavy and short enough so the mass is concentrated very heavily in the middle of the bike. In addition, the Dunlop K181 tires have a profile that makes for easy turning and good traction.

What results from the Harley's frame geometry and tires is excellent straight-ahead stability. Yet the bike turns easily, with reasonable effort required for moderate lean angles. The R-bike is capable of more than moderate lean angles. Apply more lever pressure and the bike leans over more and turns harder. It doesn't turn sharply, but it will lean over considerably, all the while being stable and predictable. What it doesn't do is fall into turns. Once put in a particular lean, it requires pressure to maintain that lean. Release pressure and the bike straightens up. Finding the limits of this bike's cornering clearance requires a strong desire to do so, because the high-mounted pegs are also narrow and beveled at the ends to keep from scraping. At speeds where a number of other large bikes will grind holes in the pavement the Harley just glides through corners with no drama whatsoever.

Not only is the FXRS an excellent handling big bike, it's also smooth and comfortable. The smoothness is deceiving. At idle the big Harley's front tire bounces around just like it does on any big Twin. The engine is visibly moving around in the frame and the frame passes the pulses along. What Harley had done is tune the rubber mounts to absorb vibration when the machine is being ridden, not when it's being parked. Out on the highway there is no vibration felt in the gas tank. The seat is soft and cushioned and very comfortable. The rubber-mounted handlebars do provide some buzz, depending on the engine speed, but they don't put hands to sleep at most highway speeds. At almost 70 the cushioned footpegs begin to dance some, but faster or slower it disappears. The highway pegs allow through the most vibration, though not a bothersome amount. This is a smooth running motorcycle. Better yet, the vibration from the machine is of low frequency, and high amplitude. There is no high frequency buzz that makes a machine feel nervous and tiring on the road. The quaking that comes through is more as though you put 25 cents in the motel bed. Or in the case of a long ride, about $300 worth of quarters.

Suspension doesn't help the comfort as much as the wheelbase. The rear shocks and spring rate are fine and do a good job of absorbing bumps on a wide variety of surfaces. But the forks just don't move unless there is a substantial jolt. Because the rider is sitting much closer to the rear wheel, the fork's resistance to movement isn't a problem unless the bike is ridden on repetitive bumps, such as concrete freeways that can cause the bike to act like the

One Small Step for Motorcycling
One Great Leap for Harley-Davidson.

Harley-Davidson's 80 cu. in. engine is still being refined. This year it has an oil control package consisting of longer valve guides, better valve stem seals and extra oil drain lines from the head. Oil consumption averaged 1500 mi. per quart even with the chain oiler turned on.*

rocker arm on a CX500. Outside Southern California it isn't a problem.

What makes the bike either comfortable or uncomfortable, and not all riders agreed, is the seating position. The FXRS rider sits as though he were in a chair, with his feet in front of him and his hands relatively close to the body. This is not the sort of bike on which the rider leans into the wind. Riders who can adapt to a laid-back riding style will find the FXRS to be supremely comfortable. The seat is much softer than the other FX models, the vibration is hardly felt at most speeds, the highway pegs provide a convenient perch for straightening legs and the large grips are comfortable for long periods of time. It's the seat that makes this machine work, though. During the test one rider took the Harley for a 4000 mi. trip and came back reporting that his seat never got tired of the Harley's seat. There was no squirming around after a few hundred miles. The legs didn't get cramped. And even without a windshield it was possible to ride 1000 mi. days without undue fatigue.

It wasn't a unanimous opinion, however. Other riders found the seating position uncomfortable for periods of more than an hour because the laid-back seating position caused backache.

Not everything contributes to comfort. The air cleaner housing is a large box on the righthand side of the engine. It sticks out far enough to interfere with the rider's right leg, particularly when the rider uses the highway pegs. If the box were smaller or didn't extend as far back as it does, it would be less of a problem. Also, the controls on the Harley still require Harley-size effort. This is not a motorcycle for pencil-necked geeks. They wouldn't be able to pull in the clutch lever.

New controls are attractive and relatively easy to use, but could be further improved. The new levers are more convenient to reach and are large enough to be gripped easily. But the effort required for clutch and brake levers is too much. Electrical controls are equipped with large buttons, but the pods are a bit large and require a stretch for thumbs. The throttle tensioner lock is inconveniently located between the two cables coming off the throttle grip, making it hard to use. It also doesn't hold the throttle in position at the most normally traveled speeds.

Other controls and ancillary items are a mixture of good and different. The push button signal lights work better the longer a person rides a Harley. With the larger buttons, they work especially well. The flat mirrors provide a good view for a long way back, despite some vibration that blurs the images. Having the ignition switch under the gas tank is more different than difficult. In any case it doesn't incorporate a steering lock. For that a padlock must be placed through the holes on the fork lock plate. The locking sidestand is difficult to reach at first, but becomes more convenient with practice. After a week of riding nothing but the Harley it's no problem, but the first-time rider may never find it. Instruments on the Harley are Japanese and look plastic and a bit out of place. They are canted back where they're easy to read and the nighttime illumination is excellent. A normal mechanical drive is used for the speedometer and odometer, but the tachometer is electronic. It shows a 6000 rpm redline, though the manual says the redline is 5400 rpm.

For years the small Sportster headlight used on the FX series was a problem for night riding because of the low light output. This year a 43,000 candlepower halogen headlight is used, still a 5.5 in. size, and the light output is excellent. Low and high beams are positioned perfectly and the beam is particularly steady, the headlight being hung from the small plate at the steering head and isolated from a lot of bouncing. >

HARLEY-DAVIDSON FXRS

SPECIFICATIONS

List price	$6990
Engine	ohv V-Twin
Bore x stroke	88.8 x 108.0mm
Displacement	1339cc
Compression ratio	7.4:1
Carburetion	(1) 38mm Keihin
Air filter	oiled foam
Ignition	electronic
Claimed power	na
Claimed torque	71.5 lb.-ft. @3800 rpm
Lubrication	dry sump
Oil capacity	3.5 qt.
Fuel capacity	4.2 gal.
Starter	electric
Electrical power	250w alternator
Battery	12v19ah
Headlight	35/50w halogen
Primary drive	duplex chain
Clutch	dry multi-disc
Final drive	530 chain
Gear ratios, overall:1	
5th	3.36
4th	4.13
3rd	5.38
2nd	7.43
1st	10.89
Suspension:	
Front	telescopic fork
travel	6.9 in.
Rear	swing arm
travel	3.5 in.
Tires:	
Front	MJ90-19 Dunlop K181
Rear	MT90-16 Dunlop K181
Brakes:	
Front	dual 10 in. disc
Rear	11.5-in. disc
Brake swept area	254 sq. in.
Brake loading (160-lb. rider)	3.01 lb./sq. in.
Wheelbase	64.7 in.
Rake/Trail	32°/5.7 in.
Handlebar width	28.5 in.
Seat height	29.5 in.
Seat width	12 in.
Footpeg height	13 in.
Ground clearance	6 in.
Test weight (w/half-tank fuel)	605 lb.
Weight bias, % front/rear	46/54
GVWR	1085 lb.
Load capacity	480 lb.

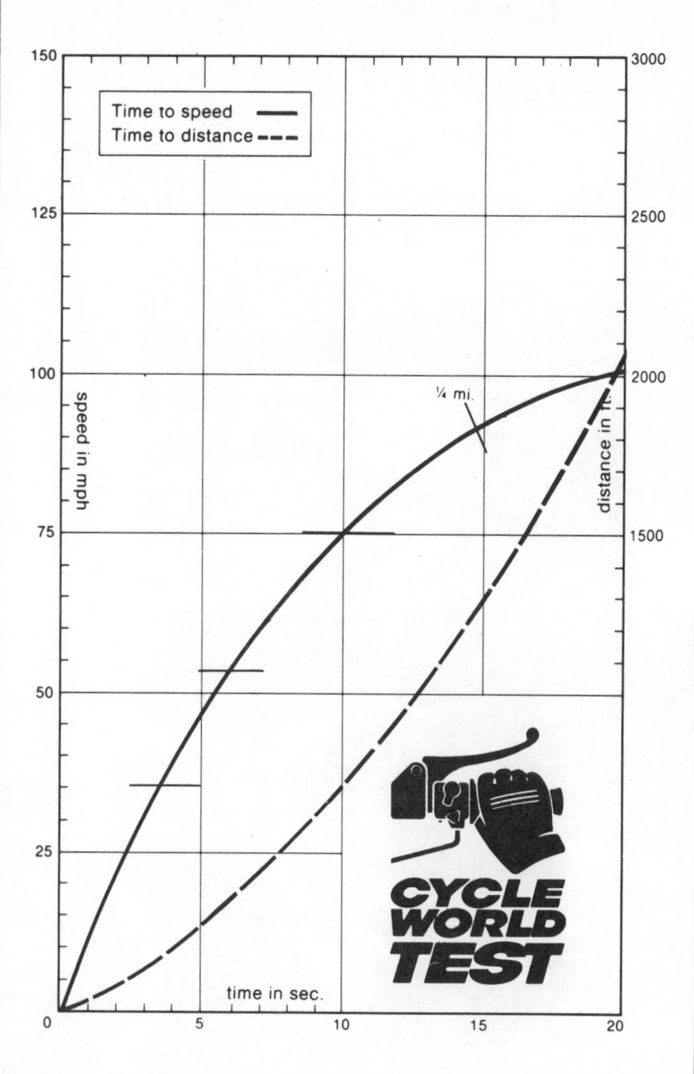

PERFORMANCE

Standing ¼-mile	14.26 sec. @ 91.46 mph
Top speed in ½-mile	99 mph
Fuel consumption	50 mpg
Range (to reserve tank)	190 mi.
Acceleration:	
0–30 mph	2.7 sec.
0–40 mph	3.8 sec.
0–50 mph	5.2 sec.
0–60 mph	6.9 sec.
0–70 mph	8.9 sec.
0–80 mph	11.0 sec.
0–90 mph	13.9 sec.
Top gear acceleration:	
40–60 mph	6.0 sec.
60–80 mph	10.3 sec.
Maximum speed in gears:	
1st	36 mph
2nd	53 mph
3rd	74 mph
4th	96 mph
5th	118 mph
Speedometer error:	
30 mph indicated	28 mph
60 mph indicated	59 mph
Braking distance:	
from 30 mph	32 ft.
from 60 mph	123 ft.
Engine speed at 60 mph	2747 rpm

HARLEY-DAVIDSON FXRS

A more significant change in the Harley way of doing things are the brakes of the R-bike. The most substantial change is the new Girling rear brake with a 11.5 in. disc. The long wheelbase and low center of gravity enable the Harley to use more rear brake than most other bikes and the RS has an excellent rear brake. A more curious change is at the front. The pair of 10 in. discs are the same size and configuration that Harley has used for several years now, but the new master cylinder provides a 10 percent better hydraulic leverage on the pucks. Harleys have always required very high lever pressures for the braking power that results, but the change makes a surprising improvement in braking power. It's still very difficult to lock the front brake on decent pavement, so a rider can just clamp the front brake as hard as he wants with little fear of retaliation from the pavement, but the stopping distances have been dramatically reduced. From 60 mph the FXRS stopped in 123 ft. And from 30 mph the stopping distance was 32 ft. The high speed stopping distance is particularly noteworthy, being the shortest stopping big bike we've tested. The initial rate of deceleration doesn't feel particularly strong when the brakes are applied, but as the brakes heat up the stopping power increases until the RS is stopping at an incredible rate.

Compared with other motorcycles, the Harley still requires greater lever pressure than average for all stopping. But the Harley's brakes work wet or dry, stop the bike in very short distances and aren't prone to locking up if used carelessly, which doesn't leave a lot of room for criticism.

The same conclusion applies to the engine. It isn't new, it doesn't have a radiato overhead cams, or even multiple carbure tors. Yet it provides excellent throttle re sponse hot or cold, starts easily, ha enough power to make grown men smile and gets excellent gas mileage.

As it has been since Pres. Taft could se his feet, Harley-Davidson means V-Twi engine. In this case it's a 45° V-Twin, ohv 3.498 in. bore and 4.25 in. stroke for 81. cu. in. of displacement (or 1338.6cc fo those who think God talks to Frogs.) Com pression ratio has been reduced from staggering 8:1 to 7.4:1 so even the bilgewa ter that passes for unleaded gas can bur controllably across acres of piston top This latest V-Twin also sports an oil con sumption control package consisting of ex tra oil drain lines for the cylinder heads longer valve guides and Kayline valv guide seals. Alternator output was raised

ear ago from 15 amps to 17.8 amps.

As motorcycle engines go this power-lant is distinctly out of step with its con-emporaries. There was a time when it 'asn't. This is not easy to say that the Iarley engine doesn't work. What's sur-rising is that in its present rubber-mount-d configuration it is a shining example of ow nicely an engine can work. The single Keihin carburetor doesn't have any flat pots, doesn't have to idle at 4000 rpm 'hen it's cold, doesn't gulp gas or quit 'orking at high elevations, doesn't, in hort, do all the things that have become lmost normal in 1981. As far as a device ɔ produce a reasonable amount of mooth, useable power with the least fuel, does an admirable job.

Harley's approach to engineering is a ig displacement engine, mildly tuned, ith lots of flywheel. This enables the bike to pull strongly from idle to redline with no discernable power peak or camminess at any speed. For normal riding the clutch can be let out with the engine at 1000 rpm and the bike will chug away. Shifting at 3000 rpm, or 2000 rpm or 4000 rpm or 5000 rpm works just fine. There isn't any reason not to shortshift because the engine has adequate torque and the compensator sprocket on the engine smooths out im-pulses to the drivetrain.

By the numbers, this isn't a particularly fast bike. With a 14.26 sec. quarter-mile time, it's about a half second quicker than the last 80 cu. in. Harley tested, probably due to the better gear spacing of the new five-speed transmission and the additional break-in miles on the bike when it was tested. Trap speed was 91.46 mph, a hair faster than the 91.18 sec. recorded by the FXB-80 tested last year, indicating very little additional power. As dragstrip times go, these are comparable to figures from 500cc Singles and 400cc Twins. Much of this can be attributed to gearing that en-ables the bike to cruise at 2500 to 3000 rpm on the highway. Lower gearing would help the FXRS off the line for dragstrip starts, but for other use would be less satisfying.

A number benefiting from the gearing is mileage. On the regular mileage loop the FXRS turned in 50 mpg, a creditable figure for any machine. Better yet was the highway mileage. On a 4000 mi. trip half-way across the country the Harley regu-larly ran 55 mpg when cruising at around 65 mph. At 70 to 80 mph the mileage dropped to 50 mpg, even at elevations of nearly a mile. Ridden at similar speeds and elevations the other over-1000cc ma-chines regularly dip into the 30 mpg range. This mileage enables the Harley to run 200 mi. before going on reserve under most highway use, even with the medium-sized 4.2 gal. gas tank. Oil consumption averaged 1500 mi. per quart with the chain oiler turned on.

While the gearing of the FXRS is relatively high compared with non-Harleys, it's not unusual for Milwaukee iron. The FXRS is even a tad lower geared than the last 80 cu. in. Harley tested. The five-speed transmission isn't used in this case to raise the gearing in 5th, it's used for a lower 1st and narrower gaps between gears. More important, the new transmission shifts smoothly and easily, something that couldn't be said about the old four-speed.

Functionally, the FXRS has made about 10 years of progress in one new model. It's taken the best features of the FLT, reduced the weight, improved the handling and refined more small details at one time than Harley's ever done. The changes make this bike more appealing to riders who aren't long-time H-D owners.

How this bike works, however, may not be what makes it a success or just another motorcycle. Like so many motorcycles before it, the FXRS may be limited by its styling. Other Super Glides may depend on this same basic styling, but the RS has other charms. Its highway aptitude alone is reason enough for its existence. But what motorcyclists of all backgrounds noticed first, last and at all times inbetween is that it looks like a Harley. To the rider who doesn't want to be a traditional Harley owner, the styling is an impediment. Of course the rider who's always wanted a Harley but has been put off by vibration or handling or braking can now have his Harley and enjoy the performance, too.

Riders who don't like puffy, overstuffed seats and sissy bars and Roadmaster styling felt compelled to complain about the FXRS even though they liked the way the machine worked. The standard model FXR is more subdued, with its wire spoke wheels and single-color paint and not having a sissy bar or highway pegs or polished covers. But the shape is the same and that's going to put off riders who would otherwise enjoy the bike.

For now, that doesn't matter. The FXR and FXRS are wonderful machines. The massive improvements are well thought out and successful. The bikes still look like Harleys and sound like Harleys and feel enough like Harleys that Harley riders won't mind the improvements. And the rest of us . . . we can enjoy the smoothest, most comfortable and easy to ride Harleys in history.

With machines like these under the Harley-Davidson decals, the Harley-Davidson Motor Co. is bound to succeed ◘

Front brakes benefit from better leverage on the master cylinder. Tires are raised white letter Dunlop K181, providing excellent traction and steering.

Lower 7.4:1 compression on the 1982 Harley Davidson enables the machine to run on low octane regular or unleaded gasoline.

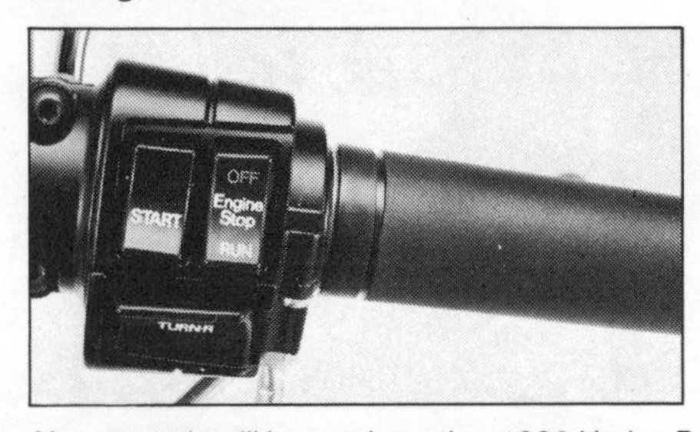

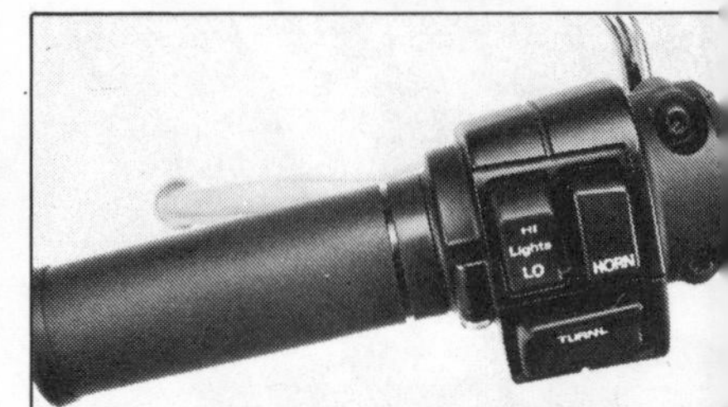

New controls will be used on other 1982 Harley-Davidsons. Pushbutton turn signals are convenient to use. Large size of the controls makes them a little awkward to use. Large diameter handgrips are comfortable.

Shocks on the FXRS aren't shared with any other Harleys. Dunlop K181 raised white letter tires are used, a 19 in. front and a 16 in. rear.

Instruments are canted well back for easy visibility. The pair of plastic-housed instruments looks out of place on the Harley, but work well. Tachometer is electronic.

New Girling rear brake is huge, has lots of stopping power and is easy to control. Long wheelbase of the FXRS enables the rear brake to be used more.

Access to the low-maintenance battery and the oil sump is convenient enough. The forward part of the seat hinges to reveal the battery and oil tank.

Adjustable control arms locate the Harley's engine on rubber mounts that absorb vibration.

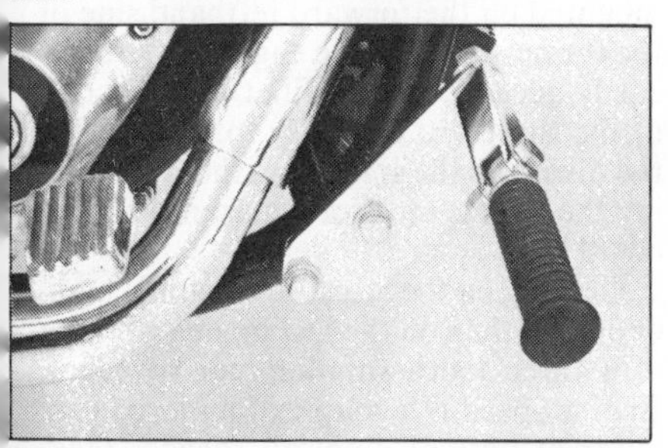

Highway pegs are standard on the FXRS, optional on the FXR version.

Footpegs are short and beveled on the end, with metal ends to contact the pavement during extreme cornering. New shift lever works with the five-speed transmission to provide easy shifting.

All-new frame on the FXRS uses no cast iron junctions. It's a double downtube design, with rubber mounts for the engine and swing arm. Backbone is a huge built-up collection of tubes and plates.

HARLEY-DAVIDSON XLS SPORTSTER 25TH ANNIVERSARY

Still the Essence of Motorcycle After All These Years.

■ No motorcycle has ever exuded toughness like a Harley-Davidson Sportster. The staggered beat of its 45° V-Twin engine is a strong, powerful sound, muffled or not. All the business pieces are hung out in the open, where riders and the less fortunate get to see them. There is as little plastic on a Sportster as on any product made in this decade. Sportsters are powerful, too, with a kind of chugging, tractor-like pull occurring at every engine speed, a power that high spinning smaller motorcycles can't duplicate. Most of all a Sportster is durable. For 25 years now Harley-Davidson has been building Sportsters, starting with the 900cc ohv conversion of the KH and continuing right up to the present 25th Anniversary Edition.

It's hard enough finding motorcycle manufacturers who were around 25 years ago, let alone models of motorcycles that have endured a quarter of a century. Twenty-five years ago the motorcycle industry was a mirror-image of its current self. Moto Guzzi was racing a V-Eight, the English and Italians were dominant, Japanese bikes didn't exist in this country and Harley-Davidson was surviving much as it had for years. Harley's smallest full-size motorcycle was the KH, a flathead V-Twin of 55 cubic inches. That was the basis for Harley's racing in this country, being used for roadraces or miles or TTs. The KR-series flathead Harleys remained the racing bikes after the Sportster was born because of size limitations in most competition. The Sportster was certainly competitive, being the fastest Harley made, and that made it among the fastest bikes in the world.

Originally the source of all that speed was a well-developed primitive engine. The overhead valve engine had a 3 in. bore and 3.8125 in. stroke, decidedly undersquare dimensions necessary because of the narrow 45° spread between the two cylinders. In 1972 the bore was increased 0.188 in. to make the Sportster a 1000cc bike. Lots of other changes have occurred in the Sportster's vertically split aluminum crankcase in the past 25 years, though the basic layout is essentially the same. There's still an enormous roller bearing crankshaft with a single crank throw. It's still a unitized engine and transmission, with a triplex roller chain primary on the left side of the engine connecting to a (now) multiplate wet clutch. The Sportster has had at some times in its life a dry clutch, but concern with keeping primary chain lubrication out of the clutch has led to the wet clutch, which is certainly strong though it has a tendency to drag some, especially when cold. Behind the engine in the cases is the four-speed transmission, lubricated with its own supply of oil. It's an easily serviced transmission, with lots of parts that can be removed without pulling the engine from the bike. It, too, has undergone various changes in detail over the years and has had a variety of gear ratios available.

On the righthand side of the engine is the timing case, filled with four separate cams linked to the crankshaft by gears. Lots of different cam profiles have been used in Sportsters over the years and lots more varieties are available to make the Sportster a much faster motorcycle than it is stock. These four cams push on roller followers that in turn push the pushrods and operate the valves. Unlike the larger Harleys, the Sportsters have mechanical adjustment of the valves, though these particular units have a habit of staying in adjustment for about 10,000 mi. usually.

Outboard of the cams is the electronic ignition pickup. The Sportster has gone from a magneto to battery and points to the electronic system, including electronic advance. Adjustment is possible for advance and retard, though regular maintenance doesn't call for anything more than checking the ignition timing. A gear-driven generator is mounted in front of the engine, and a starter is at the back of the engine, replacing the kick starter. On top of the aluminum cases are two giant, black cast iron cylinders. And on top of the cylinders are cast iron heads with rocker boxes bolted on top of those.

This year's change to the Sportster engine is the head gasket. It's thicker now, to reduce the compression ratio. According to the published numbers, the compression ratio has gone from 9:1 to 8:1, a substantial change. The reason for the change is to make the Sportster run on regular gas. Actually, the numbers are a bit exaggerated, as the old 9:1 ratio was more like 8.7:1 on most bikes and was rounded up to the next highest round number because people wanted to buy a high compression ratio. Sort of like calling the 730cc bike a 750. The result is an engine that can run on regular or unleaded gas, anything with 89 octane or higher on the pump, and still feel strong and powerful. This is also a change that owners of earlier Sportsters can perform to make their bikes run on regular.

Generator output has been increased this year, going from 10 amps to 13 amps. Other electrical system changes include a new low maintenance battery and a new halogen headlight. The battery is mounted prominently on the left side of the bike, under the seat, in plain view. On the 25th Anniversary Sportster it gets an etched metal plate around it, but there are no plastic sidecovers or plastic scoops on the Sportster. The headlight is still small in diameter, and the wattage of the bulb, 35 on low beam and 50 on high, isn't anything to write home about. But the amount of light from that small bulb is enormous, particularly on high beam.

Opposite the battery on the Sportster is the 3 qt. oil tank for the dry sump oil system. A small spin-on oil filter is now mounted on the forward lefthand side of the frame, ahead of the engine, where it is easily accessible. The filler and dipstick of the sump are also easy to reach when the bike is on the sidestand, though draining the tank is more of a nuisance than it could be.

Gearing on the latest Sportster is higher overall than on the last model, because of a three tooth smaller rear sprocket. Engine speed is a couple of hundred rpm lower at normal highway speeds. Maximum acceleration and top gear roll-on performance isn't quite as good with this gearing, but the 3200 rpm engine speed at 60 makes for easy cruising and relatively good gas mileage.

All of those are the minor changes, the things that only diehard Harley historians will remember 25 years from now. The important change is the frame, which is entirely new. Those big cast junctions that held the old Sportster frame together are gone, replaced by a steel tube frame made entirely of welded tubing. Weight is reduced and strength is increased, both changes that are universally appreciated in motorcycles. Other good things are designed into the new frame too, including a more laid down shock angle for greater rear wheel travel and an increase in cornering clearance from the higher ground clearance.

Some of the design features of this frame are similar to the new frame on the Super Glide II series, a frame that has also eliminated cast junctions, but the Sportster doesn't use a rubber mounted engine. Everything is bolted together solidly, the big hunk of iron in the middle tying everything together and adding rigidity. The tubes all run in fairly conventional places, with a large single backbone extending back from the top of the steering head and a pair of double downtubes extending down from the steering head to wrap under the engine. The backbone bends down behind the engine, headed for a cross tube just above the swing arm pivot. The double lower tubes bend up under the back of the engine, hold the swing arm pivot, then bend back and hold the top of the shocks, where they fasten to double top tubes extending along from the gas tank to the rear fender.

Onto this new frame are attached suspension units with some improvements of their own. The long travel forks now get DU bushings to reduce static friction. The shock damping and spring rate are changed for a softer ride. Front brakes are carryover items, but the rear disc is a new 11.5 in. disc with a Girling caliper that reduces braking effort and provides more stopping power with longer pad life.

New controls make operating the brakes and other parts of the bike easier. Dogleg levers have pivot points arranged for a greater mechanical advantage on the front brakes and clutch. The change is most noticeable on the clutch, which is now easy to pull. Front brake effort is still way above that required on most Japanese bikes, but it has been improved. Light switches and controls have larger buttons this year for easier operation, while the traditional push-button signal lights remain, even with larger buttons.

As always, there is not just one Sportster. There are two basic models, the XLH standard Sportster and the XLS Roadster. Lots of options and colors are available for both. What we have here is an XLH 25th Anniversary Sportster, hold the options. It has maroon and silver paint with the name Sportster written across the silver sides of the 2.2 gal. gas tank. A polished cover over the battery gets a 25th Anniversary logo etched into its surface. Another 25th Anniversary badge covers the electronic ignition pickups on the other side of the bike. The last badge of honor is a small Harley-Davidson emblem on the front fender. That's what makes a 25th Anniversary Special. The Roadster, with a softer seat, small sissy bar, larger 3.6 gal. gas tank, extended forks and black painted engine also is available in 25th Anniversary trim.

Styling touches on the Anniversary model are attractive and subdued. This isn't a copy of the 1957 Sportster, and it isn't a custom-looking motorcycle. It looks a lot like the original 1000cc Sportster, but with some parts that are more modern and other parts that date back farther. The styling is as close to timeless as any modern motorcycle is going to come. No one was offended by the Sportster's looks, though few people commented on the styling. It didn't draw crowds or turn heads. Outside Harley shops no one noticed this was the 25th Anniversary model.

What makes the styling successful is that it is appropriate for this motorcycle. The only plastic on the bike is surrounding the round instruments. That's it. There are no artificial sidecovers trying to look like an oil tank or a wing. There's no giant swoop at the back of the bike to create any artificial line or imagined V-shape. Parts that should be chromed are chromed and parts that should be painted are painted. Few of the mechanical components are covered up on the Sportster. This is as it should be. Call it essence of motorcycle.

Keeping the Sportster looking like a Sportster is an important part of the new frame. The last time the Sportster frame was changed there was some resistance from customers. It didn't look right. The latest Sportster may not look exactly like its predecessors, but it is identifiable enough not to hurt. And the improvements in handling make it all worthwhile.

Frame geometry on the Sportster is fairly typical for a modern big bike. The wheelbase is about 60 in. long, rake is 30° without a rider aboard. Weight is 515 lb. with a half tank of gas. These would be average figures for a lightweight Japanese 750. But the Sportster doesn't feel like a Japanese 750. It feels smaller and lower. The distribution of mass is apparent as soon as a rider sits on the Sportster and picks it up off the sidestand. It balances easily, with little effort. The claimed 29 in. seat height really is 29 in. off the ground. For that matter, all the figures in the owners manual perfectly match the figures obtained with tape measure and scale, something entirely unheard of in this business. The Harley's claimed dry weight isn't taken with the tires and battery missing. >

HARLEY-DAVIDSON

Keeping the rider's weight low, along with the weight of the bike, makes for agile handling. Relatively light pressure is needed on the pull-back handlebars to turn the Sportster. It can change direction easily and quickly. Good suspension control helps make the Sportster easy to handle and stable. Spring rates are appropriate for a solo rider and the damping is stronger than on many recent bikes, resulting in less wallowing of the bike in sudden handling maneuvers. High speed stability is good, but the bike is just as willing to change direction when the speedometer is pegged. This is wonderful fun for a rider who likes quick, responsive steering, but it can be disconcerting to riders who climb off Gold Wings.

Using the good handling is easy because of the abundant cornering clearance available. It's possible to scrape the folding pegs on the Sportster, but it doesn't happen under anything that can be called normal riding. Even fast mountain road riding doesn't bring the pegs down into contact with the road until the rider makes a conscious effort to lay the Sportster down farther than usual. This isn't just a very good handling Harley, it's a very good handling motorcycle.

Seat of the pants sensations take on new meaning for the Sportster rider. You feel the road surface and the suspension and the vibration of the engine through the Sportster's hard seat. It's about like sitting on a church pew, only a lot easier to stay awake.

As uncomfortable as the seat is, it wasn't bad enough to keep us from riding the Sportster to Daytona and back for Motorcycle Week. Okay, we know it isn't a touring bike. There are better Harleys for riding across country. But a Sportster somehow adds something to a trip that more comfortable bikes can't supply. There are sensations that make people feel they're riding a motorcycle, not a high-efficiency transportation device.

Equipped with the Harley-Davidson Compact windshield, a sheepskin saddle cover, and a connection to plug in an electric suit, the Sportster was aimed at the other coast when it had 37 mi. on the odometer. The sheepskin cover cut the vibration through the seat to a manageable level. At around 60 mph or over 70 mph the vibration level was noticeable but not oppressive. At around 65 it was disconcerting. With the 2.2 gal. gas tank, gas capacity was about equal to ass capacity. Both needed some attention at 100 mi. intervals. Crossing western states means frequent stops for gas because towns often aren't located exactly 100 mi. apart. Cruising at 70 mph the Sportster would usually run on reserve at 90 mi., but that could be stretched by slowing down. Reserve is good for about 20 mi. The standard Sportster tank is a 3 gal. peanut tank; the Roadster tank holds 3.6 gal. We managed to get where we wanted to go without difficulty, but we would rather have the larger tank. Even Sunday rides frequently need more than a 100 mi. range.

Vibration, the hard seat and the small gas supply are the shortcomings of the Sportster on the highway. It also has a surprising collection of good features for a highway machine. Geared as high as it is, the Sportster was comfortably relaxed at highway speeds. It didn't feel or sound as though it was thrashing itself to pieces. And with 6000 mi. on the odometer at the end of the test it appears to be as sturdy as it feels. Four days after leaving California the Sportster was running just as well as it had with 37 mi. on the odometer. With the chain adjusted once en route, again at Daytona, and an oil change at Daytona (it needed one quart added between coasts) the Sportster was ready for the trip back. The large grips were especially comfortable. The throttle stop was more difficult to use than it should have been, but it was better than having to hold the throttle open all the time. The small Harley windshield kept the air blast off the rider, though it reflected light from the headlight back to the rider at night. The small, 43,000 candlepower headlight took the terror out of night riding. No stock motorcycle headlight has worked better on high beam. The combination of handlebars, low seat, forward-

mounted pegs and windshield makes for a comfortable seating position. After four 700 mi. days the Sportster rider was still ready for more miles on the Sportster. There is something enchanting about the bike.

Where the Sportster works best is off the Interstates. Winding through two-lane country roads in Mississippi the Sportster provided a motorcycling euphoria, and a feeling of control. It was a participant in the ride, instead of an inert mechanical carpet that so often whisks people around the country. That feeling of toughness always comes through the machine. This is a man's motorcycle never mind the ladies who have ridden one. The sensations are strong and physical.

Part of that character comes from the power. Okay, the numbers on the last page don't convey that power. The low 14 sec. quarter mile time does not make this Sportster one of the great dragstrip machines of all time. That time is a little slower than the last Sportster tested, reflecting the lower compression and higher gearing. Sportsters have always been low 14 or high 13 sec. bikes in the quarter. That used to be as fast as anything on wheels could go, when Sportsters were the fastest of the fast. Now small Twins provide times like that. Objectively, the Sportster is not fast. What it is, is powerful. The powerband begins as the key on the left side of the engine, below the gas tank, is turned and the button on the right handgrip is pushed. From the loping 1000 rpm idle up to the 6200 rpm redline the power feels the same. It is strong and positive and the throttle response is instantaneous. The butterfly-throttle carb with accelerator pump works perfectly. The cams are tuned for low speed and mid-range power. Harley no longer releases horsepower claims, but the power is probably around 50 bhp. Torque is a claimed 54 lb.-ft. at 4000 rpm. The torque curve could be drawn with a ruler and a pencil. The ruler would be held level.

Under the enormous chromed air filter is essentially the same 1000cc V-Twin Sportster engine in use since displacement was increased in 1972. This year a thicker headgasket lowers compression so the engine can run on regular gas.

Low maintenance battery is new for '82. On the Anniversary model it is covered by this polished plate. On the standard Sportster it's not covered by any sidepanels or plastic.

Combined with the perfect throttle response, good low speed power and ample flywheel make for lots of lugging power. Pull in the clutch lever, push on the shift lever and listen to the clunk of the transmission move big gears around. Then let out the clutch lever. If the throttle is open a little the bike moves out faster. But it always moves out. Give the Sportster some throttle and speed picks up. It doesn't matter what gear the bike is in or how fast the engine is spinning, there's always the same strong push forward.

If more push is needed, there are dozens of people around the country who will sell the Sportster owner pipes with less restriction and bigger pistons and different carbs and better cams. There is virtually no limit to the amount of speed that can be pumped into the Sportster motor.

One modification any Sportster owner is likely to make is to replace the air filter.

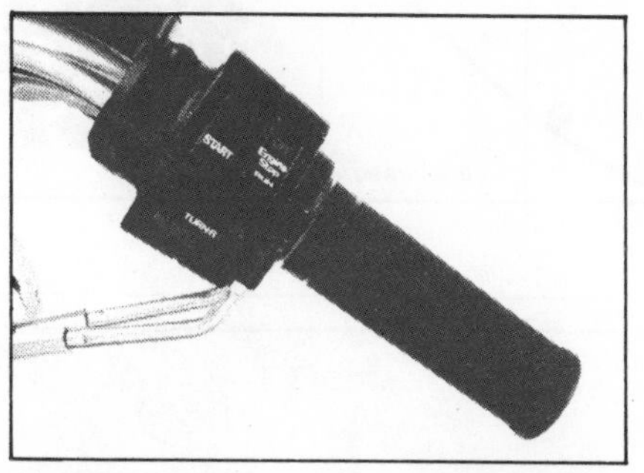

All Harleys get new controls this year. Buttons are larger and easier to reach. Large diameter handgrips are comfortable and durable. Throttle set screw was difficult to use, but return spring pressure is light.

Instrumentation on the Sportster is an antithesis to current Japanese trends. Speedometer, tachometer, odometer and lights for low oil pressure or charging current are the only instruments. No blinking lights, light emitting diodes, safety check panels or plastic handlebar covers are provided.

It sits on the right side of the bike and extends back far enough so it forces the rider's knee out into an uncomfortable position. That big breadbox of an air filter is needed to get the bike through noise tests. Fortunately Harley-Davidson knows it is inconvenient and there are a variety of smaller, less obtrusive air filters in the Harley catalog that bolt right on. And to make it all legal the catalog tells the purchaser that these air filters are intended for off-road use only. So in case your parts man asks, tell him your Sportster is only going to be used for motocross, so it's all right to sell the filter.

Brake improvements have helped the Sportster. It is now able to stop as quickly as most motorcycles, but the effort needed for that stopping power is much higher than average. Locking the front brake is impossible for most riders because of the amount of lever pressure necessary. This does prevent the front tire from locking in panic situations, but a little easier lever effort would make the bike easier and more fun to ride.

Once upon a time the Sportster transmission was a model of perfection. It shifted easily and precisely and quietly. The transmission has been improved over the years, but it is no longer perfect. Clutch drag makes shifting into neutral difficult. When the bike first arrived it wouldn't go into neutral unless it was rolling at least 20 mph. Gradually it was able to be shifted into neutral at a stop, but it requires much care. First and top protest when engaged. Second and third are silent, though one rider reported missing third on occasion. The transmission works best shifted fast and hard.

Modification is an important part of a Harley-Davidson. Harley makes lots of parts and accessories and H-D dealers carry hundreds of other brands of accessories for Harleys. In contrast to some other companies that go out of their way to keep owners from modifying bikes, Harley expects it. The latest Sportster fits into this nicely. Get the Roadster version for the big tank and soft saddle, put on the XLH forks for better handling, add the small round air filter and maybe the small windshield and it becomes a pleasant highway bike. Go to the performance shop for a set of Sputhe cylinders and heads, two big carbs and hot cams and you've got a dragstrip terror.

As delivered by the factory, the Sportster is a wonderful, big, strong motorcycle. It is fun to ride, but rewards skill in shifting and braking and steering. Ours has proved as trouble-free as any motorcycle we've had, while exuding a great sensation of strength. It isn't particularly comfortable or fast, it's not cheap with a $4670 list price, and it's not an effortless bike to ride.

But somehow it manages to be fulfilling to ride as much in 1982 as it was in 1957. ■

HARLEY-DAVIDSON XLS SPORTSTER

SPECIFICATIONS

List price $4670
Engine ....ohv V-Twin
Bore x stroke....81 x 96.8mm
Displacement 997.5cc
Compression ratio 8:1
Carburetion..............38mm Keihin
Air filter ....oiled foam
Ignition ....electronic
Claimed power ....na
Claimed torque........54 lb.-ft. @ 4000 rpm
Lubrication ....dry sump
Oil capacity................3 qt.
Fuel capacity ....2.2 gal.
Starter ....electric
Electrical power..........182w alternator
Battery......................12v
Headlight ....35/50w halogen
Primary drive......triplex chain
Clutch ....multiplate wet
Final drive ....530 chain
Gear ratios, overall:1
4th 3.97
3rd 5.49
2nd......................7.25
1st 10.02
Suspension:
Front ....telescopic fork
travel ....6.9 in.
Rear...............swing arm
travel ....4.0 in.
Tires:
Front ...Goodyear MJ90-19 Eagle A/T
Rear....MT90-16 Goodyear Eagle A/T
Brakes:
Front........ dual 10-in. disc
Rear............ 11.5 in. disc
Brake swept area ..248 sq. in.
Brake loading (160-lb. rider) ....2.72 lb./sq. in.
Wheelbase ....60 in.
Rake/Trail ....30°/4.75 in.
Handlebar width ....27.5 in.
Seat height ....29 in.
Seat width ....10 in.
Footpeg height.........11.5 in.
Ground clearance ....6.5 in.
Test weight (w/half-tank fuel) ..515 lb.
Weight bias, % front/rear 46.6/53.4
GVWR ....900 lb.
Load capacity ....385 lb.

ACCELERATION

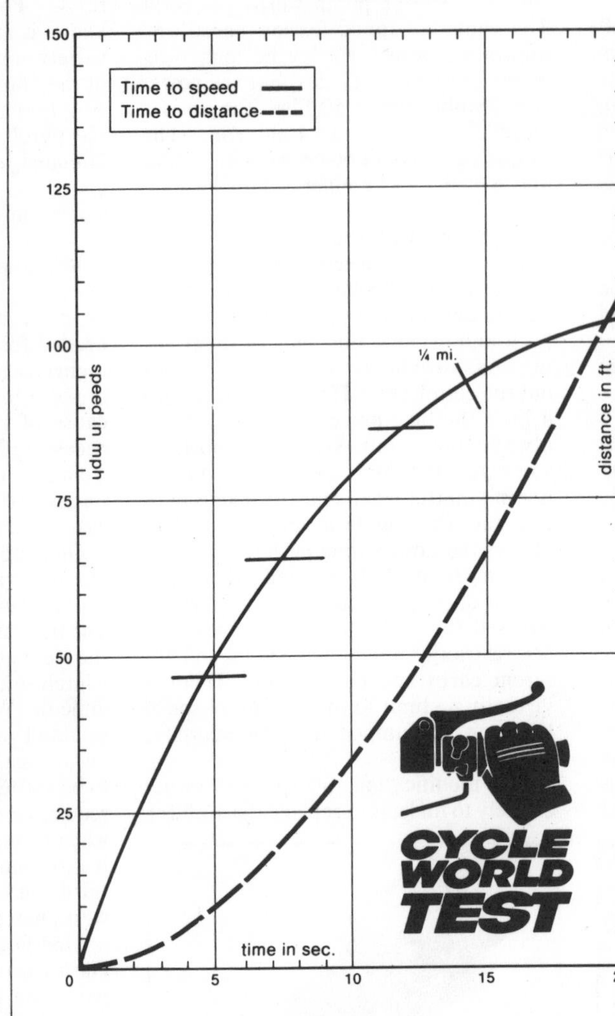

PERFORMANCE

Standing ¼-mile....14.26 sec. @ 91.18 mph
Top speed in ½-mile ...99 mph
Fuel consumption......52 mpg
Range (to reserve tank) ....93 mi.
Acceleration:
0–30 mph.......... 2.7 sec.
0–40 mph.......... 3.8 sec.
0–50 mph.......... 5.2 sec.
0–60 mph.......... 6.9 sec.
0–70 mph.......... 8.9 sec.
0–80 mph......... 11.0 sec.
0–90 mph ....13.9 sec.
Top gear acceleration:
40–60 mph.........5.8 sec.
60–80 mph ....8.5 sec.
Maximum speed in gears:
1st.................... 45 mph
2nd.................. 63 mph
3rd....................83 mph
4th..................115 mph
Speedometer error:
30 mph indicated... 29 mph
60 mph indicated ...59 mph
Braking distance:
from 30 mph...........36 ft.
from 60 mph......... 135 ft.
Engine speed at 60 mph.........3225 rpm

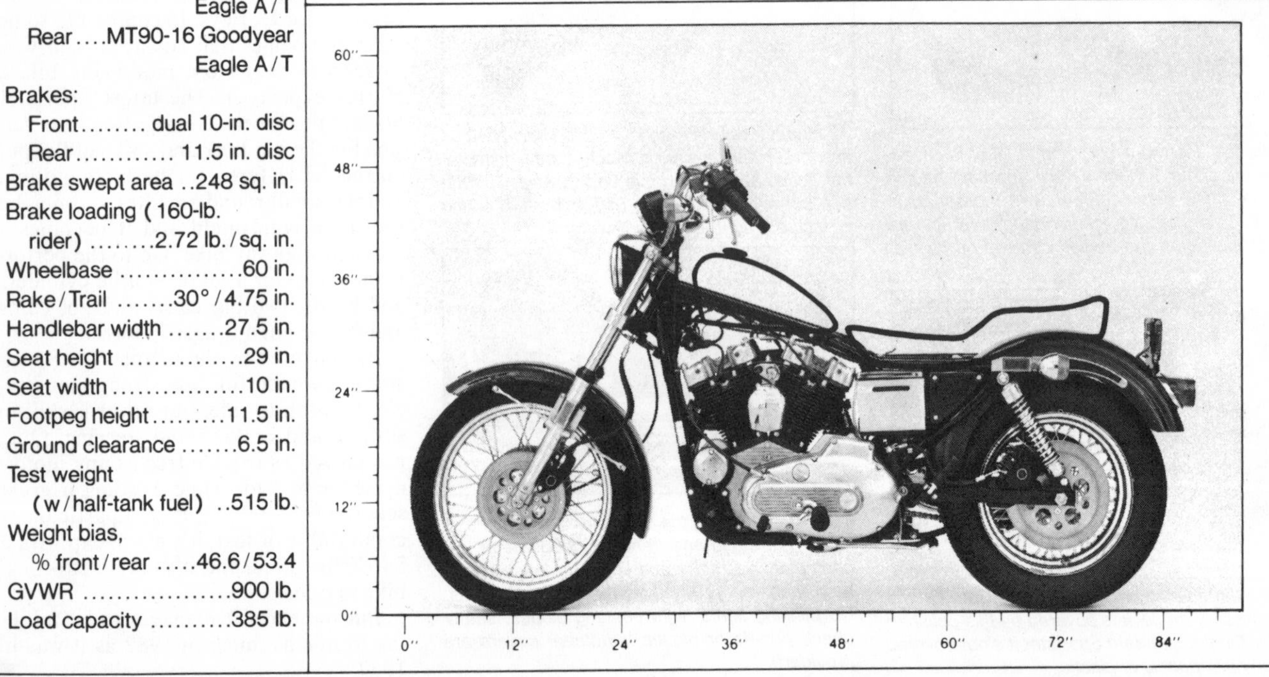

Shooting the Coast

Or, Travels With Harley

by Peter Egan

"Forget the airline tickets," I told my wife, Barbara. "No decadent air travel for us. We're going to Seattle on a Harley-Davidson."

A Harley?" Barb looked up from brushing our eldest cat, an animal who is especially well-groomed because she's too feeble to resist. "Why a Harley-Davidson?" There was an edge of gravity and uneasiness in her voice. Barb's last Harley ride had been on a Sportster with a passenger seat about the size and density of an upholstered Gideon Bible. She hadn't forgotten.

"Because we just got a new one in for a test bike and we've never taken a long trip on a Harley before. Anyway, this one is different. It's out in the driveway. I brought it home." Temporarily unhanded, the cat slunk off beneath the sofa and we went outside for a look at the motorcycle.

Sitting in the diffuse sunlight of the late afternoon was a 1981 FLH Heritage. Eighty cubic inches of V-Twin all done up in the style and trappings of Early American touring. It had a buddy seat and saddlebags fringed in black leather, spangles, floorboards, car tires, a split gas tank with a filler cap on either side, a big windshield and a front fender that appeared to weigh as much as two Honda 50s. It was painted in slightly misted shades of green and orange, colors lifted right off an antique poster for a daredevil air show. A large round speedometer was lodged in the middle of the gas tanks.

Barb circled the bike, stared at the saddlebags for a moment, felt of the fringe around the seat, stood back and folded her arms. I felt like Bogart introducing Hepburn to the leaking African Queen. "It's very interesting," she said after a few moments, "but a little . . . strange."

Strange?

Hmmmm . . . The bike looked historical, old fashioned, and pleasantly dated to me, but not really strange. The Suzuki Katana was strange. Electronic Space Invader games were strange and one-bedroom condominiums for $150,000 were strange, but to my own eye Harleys that looked like the Heritage were almost an American institution. It was clearly a question of age and familiarity. To appreciate the Harley, to look forward more than anything to riding this particular machine all the way up the West Coast and back, you had to remember a time when nearly every motorcycle on the road looked very much like the '81 Heritage.

Like most people too young to have planted Victory gardens but old enough to remember Ike and Dick in their prime, I grew up thinking a Harley-Davidson and a motorcycle were essentially the same thing, like a carbonated cola beverage and a Coke or a facial tissue and a Kleenex. The first motorcycle I ever saw close up was a Harley.

It was a huge machine belonging to Buford, our next door neighbor. I was only about seven at the time, but I remember the bike clearly. It had a two-tone windshield, Vicks-bottle blue at the bottom and clear at the top. The brake and throttle cables were red and white striped in a barber pole pattern and there were black leather saddlebags with silver diamond-shaped studs and fringe that almost swept the ground. It had a giant version of an upholstered tractor seat, also fringed and bestudded, with cracks in the leather and foam rubber stuffing falling out like dried chunks of angel food cake. The handgrips trailed colored plastic streamers and the engine was kick-started with a bicycle pedal. The tankshift knob had been replaced by an eight-ball. The bike was blue and had at least three headlights. Maybe more.

Buford himself was a quiet youth recently returned from Korea and given to spells of moping. He wore dungarees with 12-inch cuffs rolled up to expose the buckles on his engineer boots (to this day I've never seen an actual engineer wear a pair of these forbidding boots—they all look as though their mothers dressed them). He also wore khaki T-shirts stretched out at the neck and never went anywhere on the Harley without first lighting a cigarette and placing a hat on his head. The hat looked like something a yacht captain would wear but was slightly soiled and had wings on the front. When he motored down the street the cigarette sparkled like a short fuse on its way to his mouth.

He rode off every evening leaving his mother on the back porch shouting after him in a one-way discussion of jobs, drink and the kind of friends he hung out with. When Buford thundered back into the driveway in the wee hours of the morning and the Harley gasped to a stop his mother mechanically reappeared on the porch and resumed shouting where she'd left off. Buford himself never said anything. Except once.

I was out in the back yard admiring his Harley and he suddenly took me by the shoulders and looked down at me, squinting fiercely through his cigarette smoke, and said, "Don't ever buy an Indian. Buy a Harley."

Being seven I was in no position to buy either brand, but I agreed to buy a Harley if it came down to a choice.

The Indian threat was well under control by the time I could afford motorcycles, as the company went out of business, but the image of that big road cruiser in Buford's back yard stuck with me as some sort of woolly emblem of the era. With its saddlebags, streamers, chrome pipes, buckles, and fringe it looked like a cross between Roy's horse Trigger and a carnival ride. Friendly, yet exciting; the kind of machine that would inspire Buford's pure loyalty. The 1981 Heritage in our driveway was cleaned up and modernized, but styled in the same spirit, and it struck some responsive chord in the grinning and riding portion of my brain, which occupies nearly all of the cranium except for a small, walnut-sized lobe that warns me when I'm cold or hungry for Mexican food. The Heritage looked more friendly than strange.

I had some misgivings about taking a Harley up the coast from L.A. to Seattle. We'd never made the trip before, but somehow it didn't seem like the right outing for a bike like the Heritage. Certain bikes belong on specific kinds of trips, and the Harley seemed more suited to a ride across Nebraska or elsewhere in the heartland than a winding run through the quiet, chic little villages of seaside California and points north. Steve Kimball, managing editor and seasoned Western vagabond, set our minds to rest (while not actually putting us to sleep). He looked at our planned route, which took us all the way up the Coast Highway to Seattle and back down through central Washington, Oregon and California. "Your trip up the coast will be one thing," he said cryptically, "while the trip back will be something else entirely. The coast might be better for a sport bike, but the inland return is Harley country."

We left L.A. early in the morning, sharing the road with bread trucks and paper boys. The city had been tremendously hot for two weeks so we'd packed sweaters and jackets almost as an afterthought. But in the morning it was cool and foggy on the coast and when we rode past the barely visible Queen Mary it appeared to be ar-

riving in Liverpool rather than docked in Long Beach. We stopped north of the city, at Malibu, for breakfast.

The fishing pier at Malibu attracts some strange folks early Saturday morning, and they were having a convention in the diner where we stopped. An elderly gentleman with a two-day growth of beard spotted us and walked over to our table. He had a fishing pole and was wearing an old mailman's uniform with a loud necktie. He had that earnest but slightly crazed look common to tent preachers and people who collect string. He pointed to our helmets on an empty chair. "I don't believe in those," he thundered. "You might as well put your head in a box. The people who sell them should be put in jail forever."

"That seems rather severe," I offered.

"Not in this case. Danger is everywhere."

Apparently danger was even in the diner, because he suddenly spun around as though someone had been sneaking up on him and then left, slamming his fishing pole in the door on the way out. "Salt of the earth," I said to Barb. "The chamber of commerce hires them so out-of-state tourists won't go home disappointed."

We paid our bill and joined the growing flow of traffic headed north for its weekend in Santa Barbara, which is to L.A. more or less what Pompeii and Herculaneum were to Rome; a nearby retreat from the heat and the largeness of the city. We lunched on tacos in Santa Barbara, made a mandatory stop at California Guitar, purveyors of collectable used electric guitars, mostly of Fifties and Sixties vintage, and climbed back on the Harley.

North of Santa Barbara you finally clear the lingering sprawl of L.A. and its surrounding cities, and parts of the landscape become genuinely rural. Where the road loops inland you see farms and ranches that would look right at home in Kansas, except for the occasional pineapple palm in the front yard. Near some of the small Italian communities the cemetaries are filled with winged archangels on monuments, a part of the stoneworking tradition from the old country.

By the time we made our first gas stop, (41 mpg) we'd discovered a couple of things about touring with the Harley. First, the traditional buddy seat doesn't really work very well for two people. Harley makes an optional dual seat for this bike, but I had insisted on the original sprung pillar saddle because nothing else fit the character of the bike so perfectly. The sprung saddle was wonderfully com-

shooting the coast

fortable for one, but crowded for two, so Barb spent about half her time perched back on the soft duffel bag full of clothes we'd thrown over the luggage rack. As long as we had soft luggage, seating was no problem, though all my shirts soon looked as though I'd been sleeping in them.

Second, the Harley is an immensely stable bike, even in slow traffic. The Shriners who ride these things in parades know what they're doing because you can torque along at about 3 mph in slow traffic without ever weaving or putting your foot down. On the highway the Heritage is equally stable, if a little ponderous. The Harley makes you feel more like a ship's captain than a rider, and you begin to understand the significance of Harley hats. You pilot the bike down the road and changes in direction have real meaning and require a mature sense of responsibility. It takes only a full morning in the saddle to realize that nothing thuds down the road with as much upright majesty, or is less boring to ride than a Harley. Cornering clearance is nil, but it doesn't matter much because it's more fun to thunder along and look at the scenery then it is to make time through the corners. Healthier too. The bike molds you to its own pace, rather than the other way around.

Leaving the station, a third facet of its personality surfaced. Filling the tanks full is a mistake. Unless the right hand tank is left about 3 or 4 in. low, gasoline will jitterbug out of the filler cap as you motor down the road and blow a fine mist of gas into the wind and onto your pants. Buford may have smoked while riding, but I didn't.

A tenacious fog had moved over the coastline and was holding on. The weather was cool and dark and jackets and sweaters came out of the saddlebags. By the time we got to Morro Bay for the night we'd begun to feel like figures in a Bergman film, riding in and out of the mist with the cloud ceiling at about 200 ft. We got the last motel room in town, stashed our luggage and went out to look for a restaurant.

Morro Bay is a small resort town on a pretty bay with a huge Gibraltar-shaped rock in it. The town was filled not so much with tourists from afar, as we'd expected, but with nearby locals escaping from hot, arid places like Bakersfield and Merced in the San Joaquin Valley, searching for shade and cool, damp air. The coast has a peaceful hush about it that makes people calm and subdued. The fog absorbs noise and color. As you go north in California the beaches become less and less like the boisterous beer and bikini beaches of the south; activity becomes more measured and introspective. They are places for quiet walks, not volleyball and Pepsi commercials. Just a few miles inland the sound and brightness returns, but the beaches more often have a moody and brooding quality.

In the morning we passed the gates and parking lots for tours of San Simeon, the lavish hilltop home and estate of the late William Randolph Hearst. All tours were booked until late afternoon, and because we'd been through the place a year earlier we rode on toward Big Sur.

Big Sur is a spectacular stretch of coastline where steep green mountainsides plunge down into the ocean. A road has been carved into the high slopes and it makes a wonderful ride, maybe one of the best in motorcycling. It winds along roadcuts hundreds of feet above the ocean, with vista points where huge chunks of excoastline have fallen into the sea from high cliffs. The air smells like bay leaves, gorse and salt water, like something from the coast of Wales or Cornwall.

We stopped for gas in Big Sur and two guys at the station felt compelled to walk out and sneer at the Harley for a while. They couldn't help themselves. They wanted to be sure everyone understood they had Good Taste and knew that fringe was Out. We soon discovered on the trip that the Harley had a way of bringing these people out of the woodwork. There are few chances in life to show off your good judgment, and the loud, colorful Harley provided one. It was tiresome having the bike a target for people who didn't understand, but it was also a nice test of humor and flexibility, a barrier against people you'd rather not talk to anyway.

We stopped at a place called Nepenthe for lunch, a restaurant built next to the old weekend retreat of Orson Wells. Nepenthe is a lovely restaurant out on a cliff over the ocean, a place where tourists and local beautiful people can mingle to have various foods with sprouts on them, a place where bleached white bread is unknown. Many patrons wore clothes of gingham and feathers and wrinkled Egyptian cloth fashioned into the garb of Gypsies, fakirs and camel drivers; the essential stained glass and Mercedes crowd. The food and the coffee were excellent.

Big Sur descends into the Hansel and Gretel-like village of Carmel, once a small artists' colony and now a place where golf shirts can be bought for fairly high prices. Little stores sell $2000 rocking horses, Scottish woolens and English tea and marmalade. We decided to pay our $4 and ride the famous 17-Mile Drive, a private drive along a very scenic stretch of beach north of Carmel. We waited in line and were turned back at the gate by a man who said, "No motorcycles. If it were up to me I'd let you through, but those are the rules. Sorry. You can turn around over there."

I put the $4 back in my wallet and rode away, left with the same speechless emptiness I remember feeling when I was kicked out of a high school dance for wearing "beatnik sandals".

Barb patted my knee. "Always causing trouble," she said.

"Right. Born to raise hell."

Goodbye Carmel, hello San Francisco.

Around Carmel and to the north real trees appear in the valleys and along the riverbeds, not the rain-starved runts of the sunny South, and near San Francisco the hills are forested. We cut across from the coast on Highway 84 from San Gregorio to Palo Alto, where my aunt and uncle live. Being kind people, they took us in and fed us despite the bugs and road dust.

The next day we rode into San Francisco, past the old pastel-colored row houses of the surrounding hills and across the bay from Oakland Army Base, site of the Best Day of My Life when I got out of the Army 11 years ago and threw my fatigues into an incinerator and bought some starchy new PX civilian clothes and stepped out onto the street, free at last. We chugged up and down the hills of the city and wound down the famous serpentine bricks of Lombard St., putting the Harley brakes to a hard test.

Hungry for lunch, we headed over to North Beach, an old Italian area of the city famous for its good food, coffee houses and long-standing Bohemianism. We parked the bike and found ourselves just around the corner from the Trieste, probably the best known of the city's many coffee houses. Every folk singer, poet and musician who is anybody has hung out or performed in this small cafe, and pictures of patrons like Gregory Corso and Ferlinghetti are on the walls.

We walked up to the copper bar and each ordered an espresso. If strong coffee can be said to put hair on your chest, espresso will turn you into a flaming werewolf. It is the distilled essence of the bean, half solid and half fluid; a drink to frighten Turks. We sat down and shared a window table with a six-foot four-inch tall black man who wore a black cloak with half moons embroidered on the cuffs and a fez cap with a tassel. His name was Alonzo, and despite his distinguished and slightly mystical presence he turned out to be an avid motorcyclist with a past of Triumphs and BSA Rocket Threes, as well as a licensed airplane pilot and a violin and flute player. Not the sort of person you meet at Tupperware parties. We had a good talk about bikes and planes, a few more coffees, and left.

Before crossing the Golden Gate Bridge we stopped at a lookout over the bay, where a few hundred Japanese tourists were trying to take photos of the bridge while their buses idled, though the towers were nearly obscured by fog. We crossed over to Sausalito with the Harley's exhaust rhythmically echoing off alternate beams of the bridge. We turned into the empty hill country toward the coast and passed a farm with several greenhouses and windmills. A sign at the gate said Green Gulch Zen Center.

"I'll bet that's a lively bunch of pranksters," I told Barb. "Always laughing and telling Zen jokes."

North of San Francisco the coastline quickly becomes primitive and sparsely populated, broken only by small villages and occasional clusters of architect-designed weekend homes, done in the rough wood treehouse-on-the-ground style. The coast highway is narrow and precipitous as it runs along the mountain slopes. It looks like a good place for an accident in a gangster film or a murder mystery. They wouldn't find you for weeks, what with the pounding surf hundreds of feet below the highway. A high and lonely road. Most corners were marked 20 or 30 mph, and the Harley wasn't really happy on corners slower than 35 mph. Below that it sort of thuds and shudders around curves, scraping its floorboards and underpinnings unless ridden gently. Repeated gearshifting on tight roads is not terribly pleasant either because the cogs change with a brutal precision that sounds like a 45 caliber slug slamming into a piece of boiler plate. The motor pulls like a train, of course, from very low rpm so shifts come less often than with other bikes. And in the Harley's defense, this was the first time we'd taken a winding road slowly enough to enjoy the scenery instead of holding our breath and watching the pavement speed by.

The coast remained cold, dark and misty, but we headed inland toward the village of Olema, where the sun was shining. We stopped for lunch at the Olema Inn, a reconditioned hotel and stage stop where both John Steinbeck and Jack London had stayed. We had their eggplant parmesan and voted it Best Restaurant Meal of the Trip So Far. We could see the sunbreak between the marine clouds and the mountains from our table. Rhapsody in Blue was playing in the dining room.

Back on the Coast Highway it was cold and wet and we arrived well chilled in Mendocino by nightfall. We checked into the Mendocino Hotel, a 109-year old establishment with dark wood rafters and paneling, a warm fire in the lobby fireplace, and brass beds and fixtures from the gaslight era. We took hot showers, stood by the hot fireplace, and then went out in search of a hot meal and some hot coffee. By 10 we started to thaw. Mendocino, like so many north coast villages, was an old logging and fishing town that fell into economic ruin and was revitalized in the late 60s by businessmen, artists, etc. escaping San Francisco and other cities in search of rural living. Many of the old hotels and shops are now restored and it's a popular tourist town. Back in the hotel lobby we sat around the fireplace drinking until midnight with a crowd of other hotel guests, among them a real German psychiatrist who looked like Freud himself and had a very good German or Austrian accent. I half expected to hear horses and carriages clopping by outside instead of cars honking. The most modern touch in the hotel was Rhapsody in Blue playing on the stereo. Gershwin was becoming the patron saint songwriter of inns and hotels.

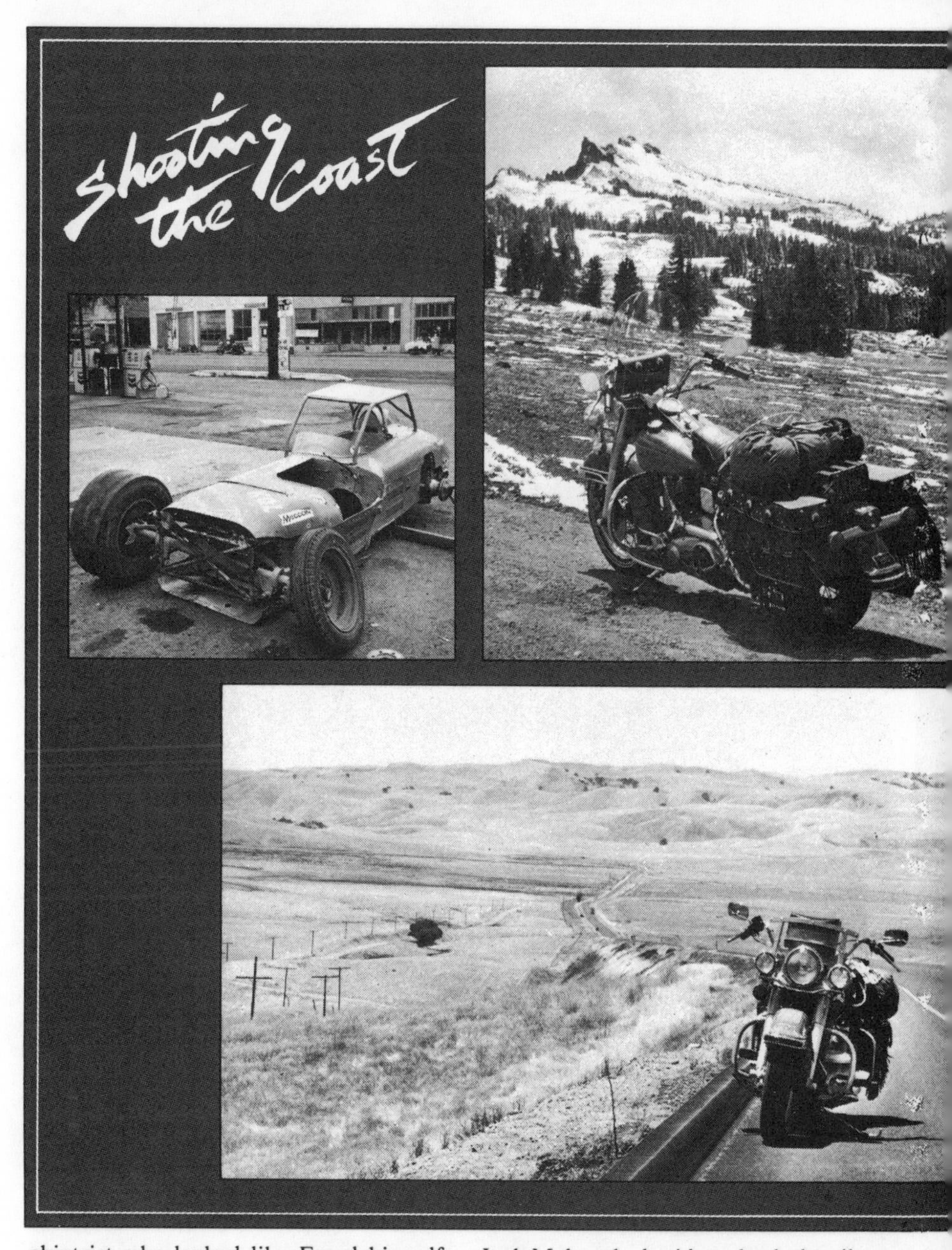

The morning brought more cool gloom, beautiful wild coastline and smooth winding road through spectacular scenery. The coast highways, 1 and 101, were shaping up as a perfect, continuous motorcycle route. We'd traveled more than three days without a single straight, boring, dull mile of road, and the traffic was light. More than a thousand miles of one breathtaking vista after another; too good to be true. The Harley thundered on without complaint, its only requirements so far being a couple of quarts of oil during the early break-in miles.

For the first time in my life I hadn't brought any tools along on a motorcycle trip. When we picked up the bike Harley's Jack Malone had said to check the oil occasionally, oil and adjust the chain as needed and to adjust the primary chain when we got to Seattle. "I never carry any tools," Jack said. "You can adjust almost anything on the bike using a few hand tools at a gas station, if you have to. The valves have hydraulic lifters, so you can forget about those. The bike shouldn't give you any trouble." There was something infectious about this relaxed attitude, so I left my took kit home. Out on the high wire without a net.

North of Ft. Bragg we began to meet logging trucks with huge redwood logs, only three or four to a truck, chained to the trailers. We turned inland through Redwood National Park. The size of the trees there is staggering, even if you've seen them before, and it is almost incomprehensible that anyone would want to cut them down. Yet there is a constant battle in this area over some of the last and oldest redwood stands. ("Father, what ever became of the largest, most beautiful trees

on earth?" "They cut them down, child. Your mother and I wanted a redwood deck around the jacuzzi.") I am no naturalist—the only tree I can positively identify, other than the redwood, is the Christmas tree, and only then if it has plenty of lights and a large pile of gifts beneath it—but I worry over the motives of people who can walk up to a 2000-year-old giant redwood and sink an axe blade into its trunk.

We drove out of the park and its giant trees and past a large redwood lumber mill surrounded by clearcut, which is a little like visiting Arlington National after reviewing the troops at West Point. We stopped in Miranda for lunch and a sign on the restaurant door said, "No animals, backpacks, petulia oil or drunks."

"They forgot pinkos and Trotskyite revisionists," I told Barb.

"And motorcyclists."

"Let's eat at the restaurant across the street." We had hamburgers and listened to the country station on the radio. There are county stations in L.A. too, but between songs the ads are for Jordache jeans and Toyotas. Here the ads were for Ellen's Star-Lite Cafe, Tru-Way Hardware and the Methodist Church supper, which adds credibility to the song lyrics.

The coast of Oregon was open, sweeping and windy, more to the Harley's liking. Huge, rugged chunks of rock stick out of the surf and every so often the rocky coastline is cut by the wide mouth of a river coming down from the mountains. Then the road crosses a long bridge or winds around the bay to a narrower part of the river and a smaller bridge. The coast seems wilder and more remote and the villages less commercial and polished than those in California. North of Coos Bay the road is protected from the sea by massive sand dunes. Amusement spots offer dune buggy rides and rentals. We stopped for the night in Tillamook in a very pink motel and had a good seafood dinner nearby. I asked for wine and the waitress looked at me as though I'd requested some dope and a couple of young virgins. "We don't sell wine here, sir," she said calmly. A few hundred miles closer to the Napa Valley a restaurant would go broke without wine, but here it was not in the picture.

We crossed the wide mouth of the Columbia River at Astoria and headed inland toward Olympia and Seattle at Aberdeen. There was a strange copper glint to the sunlight and the smell of wood smoke in the air. A man at a gas station explained that nearby clearcut areas were being burned over for new planting. We rode up the east side of Puget Sound, through Olympia and Tacoma and into Seattle. It was an unusually clear, sunny day and Mt. Ranier was beaming its awesome presence over the whole city. We found the home of our friends, Lyman and Kathy Lyons, without any trouble. They were in the garage, putting the finishing touches on an old wooden boat they'd restored.

The next day they took us for a boat ride on Lake Washington. The boat was an 18-ft. Mukilteo, an open wooden craft built in the tradition of old Norwegian fishing boats. Lyman and Kathy had spent the rainy Seattle winter (as distinct from the rainy Seattle summer) restoring the boat; long months of stripping, caulking, painting and varnishing. The completed project was beautiful to look at.

"A wooden boat," Lyman explained, "is not so much an object as a process. It's always changing—shrinking, swelling, weathering—you're never completely done working on it. You can buy aluminum or fiberglass boats that get the job done without any maintenance, of course, but there's no satisfaction in having them. They don't look right and they don't sound right when the waves slap against the hull."

Lyman was talking about boats, but I knew he had hit upon the exact reason people buy things like Morgans, Waco biplanes, oversized Victorian houses and bikes like the Harley Heritage. There are easier, cheaper things to own, but they don't always sound right or look right, or have any history behind them. People who couldn't see the advantage the Lyons' Mukilteo held over a fiberglass motor launch would never understand.

Before leaving Seattle we washed and waxed the Harley and adjusted the drive and primary chains. I tightened the bolts on one exhaust flange which had begun to work loose and stopped at the Harley shop to get a pair of passenger peg rubbers. Both of ours had slid or vibrated off somewhere on the road. The Harley was then ready.

Steve Kimball was right about the trip back. It was something else entirely. It was an inland return, down Highway 97 through central Washington and Oregon, to I-5 in northern California, and Highway 101 to I-5 in southern California. Coastal towns, particularly in warm regions like southern California, draw people, wealth,

shooting the coast

tourism and industry rather easily. Property values are high and newness predominates, while anything old, quaint or restored is something of a find. But inland towns work a little harder for a living and count their losses and profits more carefully. Tourism is thinner and agriculture is more important. Roads, buildings, houses, main streets and cars are not torn down or traded in lightly. Objects are used until they are worn out, or kept usable indefinitely through care and thrift. Trends take hold more slowly, and a bike like the Heritage looks more at home on the landscape.

I'd always believed the Northwest was all lush timber and mountains, but Highway 97 through Washington and Oregon ran to the east of the Cascade Mountains' rain shadow. The country was high and cold and arid with snow-capped mountains in the west and rolling desert and wheat country to the east. The land looks alternately like Kansas, Wyoming and Utah. There are large towns like Yakima, Bend, and Klamath Falls, but the towns between them are often small, windswept places where you check your gas and hope the next name on the map has an open gas station. Many of the farms have a lonely, lost look with weatherbeaten buildings tilted by the strong, constant wind that blows down from the mountains. It is stark, beautiful country to ride through.

We circled up into the mountains to see Crater Lake, the world's most perfectly blue body of water, then descended into California with the lone peak of Mt. Shasta growing on our horizon. South of Shasta the hills immediately assume the unofficial state colors of oak leaf green on a wheat yellow background and the sun becomes markedly warmer. We followed I-5 through the hot agricultural lands of the Sacramento Valley and south of San Francisco took Highway 101 down the Salinas Valley; Steinbeck Country, East of Eden and just east of Cannery Row and Tortilla Flats.

With the shopping centers, franchise motels, condos and mobile home parks sprouting up outside Salinas, Steinbeck and the Trask boys might have a hard time recognizing their home territory, and Kate's place is probably buried under a parking lot now. All of them would have approved of Rosita's Armory Cafe in downtown Salinas, however, because it had the best Mexican food in the state.

We took a slightly northern diversion to Hollister, a thriving farm town whose main claim to national fame is that hundreds of motorcyclists rode into town in the early Fifties to attend a motorcycle race at the city park one weekend and accidentally became drunk and disorderly and ran amok of the local and state police and tore up Main Street. This story, complete with 8 x 10 low-life photographs made it into Life Magazine, and later into the movies with Marlon Brando as the Wild One, securely fixing the image of the leather-and-hot-chrome motorcyclist in the public's mind for the next 20 years.

We stopped for coffee in the New China Cafe in Hollister and found ourselves sitting at the counter next to a man named Floyd Perry who remembered the whole thing. "There were hundreds of bikes parked on both sides of Main Street and so many people milling around the traffic was stopped. I drove home from work at the hospital early that day and my car was one of the last to make it through. Later I took a walk down the street just to have a beer and look at all the bikes. That evening things got pretty wild and I was called back to the hospital to help dress cuts and injuries. It wasn't any big thing; just a lot of people drinking and having a good time. I don't know if the police were really needed or not."

When we left there was so much highway traffic rumbling through downtown Hollister and so few parking spots on Main Street it would be hard to imagine large numbers of bikers gathering there today. They'd have to wait for the WALK sign at the corner or be flattened by speeding semis.

At Paso Robles we decided to cut over to the Interstate on Highway 46. Highway 46 runs for about 65 mi. across some of the most desolate, sun-baked hills in southern California. At about the halfway point stand a gas station, a few houses, a restaurant called Stella's Country Kitchen and a post office the size of a phone booth. This is the town of Cholame, and just outside of town James Dean was killed on September 30th in 1955. Dean was on his way from Ventura to a sports car race in Monterey, driving his Porsche Spyder with his German mechanic as a passenger. They came down a long hill outside Cholame, going about 85 mph at dusk, when a Ford driven by a Cal Poly ag student named Donald Turnipseed ran a stop sign and turned in front of them. Dean's last words to his mechanic were, "That guy has got to stop."

There is a roadside memorial to Dean in Cholame, built by a Japanese fan and wealthy businessman named Ohnishi. If ever there were a Godforsaken, unlikely spot for a person like James Dean to die in a car accident it's out on Highway 46; truly in the middle of nowhere. It looks like the landscape from *Giant*, Dean's last film, in the west of Texas. On the highway marker is chiseled the young actor's favorite quote from St. Exuperay: "That which is essential is invisible to the eye."

South of Bakersfield the San Joaquin Valley was oven-hot and dusty, the sunlight so bright I kept checking to see if my sunglasses were still in place. We pulled off I-5 for water at a rest stop, where the poorer people without AC and eight-tracks to keep their minds off the heat were lying about resting under the tiny lollipop-shaped trees found at all rest stops; grandmothers, grandchildren and traveling families in large Detroit hardtops from the late Sixties; cars with bald tires and all the windows open and hissing radiators.

Once you've decided you're no longer touring but just waiting to get home, the miles drag out. But even on hot, dull roads like I-5 the Harley was fun to ride, right down to the last. We'd been on these roads with more sophisticated bikes and wanted the ride to be over, pushing the speed limit and wanting to go faster. On the Harley, however, just rolling down the road and listening to the motor and looking at the bike around you is an entertainment. There was no need to hurry the Heritage—there were faster, smoother Harleys like the Tour Glide for that—and we spent little time watching for police because the big Twin's loafing gait was so pleasant between 55 and 60 mph.

We were hoping to cruise all the way home without stopping again, but we ran onto reserve coming up the Grapevine to Tejon Pass just outside of L.A. so we pulled into an oasis.

At the gas station a balding man in his fifties got out of his car and walked over to look at the Harley. After inspecting the bike for a few minutes he said, "You sure did a nice job of fixing that thing up. It looks like new." He ran his hand along the top of the leather saddlebag. "My uncle used to have a bike just like this. He gave me rides on it when I was a kid. Too bad they don't make motorcycles like this any more."

I didn't want to intrude on his reverie, so I just said, "Yes. It really is a shame."

You couldn't blame the man for not knowing. There were so many things they didn't make any more. The Harley's styling, after all, was a throwback to a simpler age of two-lane roads and small towns; an era when you had to drive your Porsche Spyder down State Highway 46 through Cholame just to get from L.A. to Monterey, or a time when there was so little traffic in downtown Hollister you could actually hold a riot in the streets, or when Salinas was a town surrounded by bean and lettuce fields instead of shopping malls and apartments; when small towns held motorcycle races in the city park or sports car races in the streets and nobody worried about insurance or lawsuits. Older people looked at the Heritage and remembered those things.

There were a lot of things they didn't make any more, and it was just a crazy, colorful stroke of good fortune that the Harley wasn't among them. ◘

Harley-Davidson for 1983

FLH Belt Drive Electra Glide

FLHT Electra Glide Classic

FXSB Belt Drive Low Rider

Evolution in action. That's what could be seen at Harley's new model show in Milwaukee. A V-Four wasn't shown there. There wasn't a street legal XR750 flat tracker. The big Twins hadn't grown to 1500cc. In comparison with some other motorcycle companies, which sometimes seem to belong to the engine-of-the-week club, the Harley show might seem anticlimatic. While there is some truth to that impression, it's neither fair nor totally accurate. What was in evidence in Milwaukee was the continued change of the Harley V-Twins as the company strives to bring its performance into the motorcycle mainstream without diluting those qualities that make them Harley-Davidsons.

When confronted with the 11 bike Harley-Davidson range, the non-Harley expert is left with the impression of alphabet soup. Just two engines and all those letters! FLH, FLHT, FXRS, FXWG, XLX, XLS . . . how do you distinguish between all these different but similar looking models?

The first clue is the first letter of the model designation. The F implies an 80 cubic inch V-Twin, and the X is used for the smaller, unit construction 61 cubic inch engine. After that, the important thing is which of four frames the model uses.

The FLH Electra Glide is the classic Harley-Davidson dresser. It uses a lug construction frame with the engine mounted rigidly, and has followed an evolutionary line of development that dates back at least to the 1930's. For 1983 the chain final drive has been replaced by a Gates Polychain belt but otherwise the FLH is unchanged.

The XLH is the Sportster. The 61 cubic inch V-Twin is rigidly housed in a frame welded from tubes and steel stampings. This frame was introduced for the 1982 model year, and dramatically improved the way the bike handled. This year the news is engine improvements. Horsepower is up by more than 10 percent due to a compression increase (allowed by a new, vacuum-advance ignition) and a less restrictive exhaust system (allowed by the Federal noise laws). Additional changes are a new, larger 3.3 gal. gas tank, and a new seat.

The XLS bears the Roadster name. Mechanically identical to the Sportster, the Roadster offers mainly styling differences, many of them new for this year. The tank capacity and look have changed with the addition of a 3.8 gal. Fat Bob gas tank. The tachometer has moved from in front of the handlebars to atop the tank console. Previous Roadsters were fitted with 2 inch extended front forks, but the 1983 model comes with forks in the standard Sportster length for improved handling. The Roadster, like the Sportster, has a new seat for the new model year.

The XLX-61, a new model for 1983, is the nameless Harley. If the Roadster is a dressed up Sportster, the XLX is a Sportster with every non-essential piece removed. This reduces the dry weight to 486 lb., and gives the XLX a stark, tough look of its own.

The original FX series is represented by three motorcycles this year. The Super Glide started it all in 1971 when the factory duplicated the work of many custom builders and grafted the Sportster front end onto the big V-Twin engine and frame from the Electra Glide. Hence the designation: F for the big V-Twin, X for the Sportster heritage, and E for electric start.

The other two models of the FX series are the FXSB Low Rider and the FXWG Wide Glide. The Low Rider is a Super Glide with trim changes and slightly longer front forks. For 1983, the Low Rider is only offered with Gates Polychain belts for both primary and final drive. Previously, a separate Low Rider model named the Sturgis came with the belts, but now that the belts are proven, all Low Riders will come with them. The Sturgis designation has been dropped. The Wide Glide is

Sportsters Get More Power, Dressers Get New Options and Harley-Davidson Rolls Into Another Year.

another Super Glide relation, and comes as close to being a factory chopper as any motorcycle ever has. The 80 cubic inch engine and Electra Glide frame are used as on the other FX models, but are mated with long front forks widely spaced on their triple clamps and a 21 in. front tire. The foot pegs and controls are located in the highway position, and a larger (5 gal.), twin cap fuel tank is fitted. The 1983 model features new paint colors, and the previously offered black gas tank with red and orange flames is available only on special order.

The FLT Tour Glide was first released in 1980, and was the beginning of Harley's entry into modern motorcycling. A welded frame of tubes and stampings replaced the lugged frame construction used on other models, and a rubber engine mounting scheme similar to Norton's Isolastic mounting was adopted. The frame succeeded in combining light handling and stability simultaneously, and the rubber engine mounts reduced engine vibration from the 80 cubic inch V-Twin to a non-issue at highway speeds. Changes to the Tour Glide for 1983 definitely fall into the evolutionary category. Modifications to the seat and suspension have been made to drop the seat height by 1.5 in. while improving the seat shape.

Harley-Davidson has a long history and loyal customers, and these virtues sometimes require a careful balancing of tradition and new design. The new for 1983 FLHT Electra Glide is a product of this balancing act. After the Tour Glide was released, Harley discovered that some Electra Glide owners liked the idea of the reduced vibration of the rubber mounted engine, but didn't like the bulkiness of the frame mounted fairing of the Tour Glide, or the styling that went with it. The new Electra Glide is Harley's attempt to reconcile the benefits of the Tour Glide design with the preferences of its customers. It is a Tour Glide chassis in an Electra Glide outfit, and might be better called the Electra Glide II to distinguish it from the still available FLH Belt Drive Electra Glide. The FLHT uses the Tour Glide frame but substitutes the Electra Glide handlebar mounted fairing and lights. The five-speed transmission and the enclosed chain operating in an oil bath are retained from the Tour Glide, as are the rubber engine mounts.

The final Harley frame configuration is used on the FXR and FXRS Super Glide IIs. The original Super Glide was based on the FLH frame and engine; the Super Glide II is more loosely based on the Tour Glide. Because the Tour Glide has unusual steering geometry that places the forks behind the steering head and looks unusual when not covered by a fairing, the factory elected to design an all new frame preserving the Tour Glide rubber engine mounts while possessing more visual appeal. The new frame managed to make the Super Glide II in either the base FXR or the higher trim FXRS model a very good handler. The rubber engine mounts filter out vibration to the extent that the Super Glide II feels smoother than a number of four cylinder machines. Since the design was new for 1982 and no problems have turned up requiring immediate solution, the two Super Glide IIs remain unchanged for 1983.

That seems to sum up the Harley-Davidson design philosophy—fix what needs fixing, preserve your strengths, and minimize your weaknesses but certainly don't make changes for the sake of change. This philosophy may be forced on them by their size and lack of financial resources, but Harley has followed it to produce motorcycles like the Tour Glide and Super Glide II that can compete on their own merits, and don't need any special allowances because they're Harleys or made in America. And the evolution of the Harley V-Twins hasn't stopped with this model release. Programs are underway to improve engine performance of all models, and to do things such as reducing the amount of effort the front brake requires. ◘

XLH Sportster

XLS Roadster

FXR Super Glide II

The Electrically Equipped HARLEY-DAVIDSON SPORT MODEL

"Great Distances Can Be Covered In a Single Day by Riders of the Harley-Davidson Sport Model, Because This Machine Can be Driven Continuously Without Fatigue."

For a motorcycle engineer, it was a fabulous opportunity. The world's biggest motorcycle company wanted an all-new motorcycle, something lighter and quicker, more comfortable and quiet and easier to ride. The state of the art in engine design had just taken a quantum leap because of the research in aviation. All of a sudden an engineer knew so much more than any one had known just a few years before, that a motorcycle could be drastically improved.

That was the position of the engineers at Harley-Davidson in 1916. World events had an enormous effect on motorcycles at the time and those in the near future. The war in Europe had forced aviation and aircraft engines to be developed from the barely flyable to high performance. Motorcycle engineers were learning about overhead valves and camshafts and better oiling and ignition systems all from the air wars. The demand for fuel was hurting the quality of gasoline in this country as refiners turned out more low quality gasoline. This kept combustion pressures down on cars and motorcycles, even though engineers knew of the benefits of higher compression.

If the war increased the possibilities for motorcycle design, the economy and Henry Ford limited it. Ford was an important man to the motorcycle industry because motorcycles were competing against cars as basic transporation in the first part of this century and no one made more cars cheaper than Henry Ford.

Equipped with lots of clean paper, a rapidly growing body of engineering knowledge, and all the freedom they could ask for, the Harley-Davidson engineering department created the most unusual new motorcycle in the company's history. It was introduced in 1919 and called the Sport Model, the letter designation was WJ for the electrically equipped Sport Model, or just W for the magneto-equipped.

The Sport Model didn't break new ground in design so much as it assembled ideas that were being tried and fit them together in a neat, lightweight package. Instead of making a V-Twin or a Single, the designs Harley-Davidson and the other big American companies had always produced, the Sport Model engine was an opposed Twin, a configuration that was being used by several motorcycles of the day. The opposed Twin engine was much smoother than a Single or V-Twin, and this was important because Harley intended to spin the engine faster for more power than was typical for 1919.

y Steve Kimball

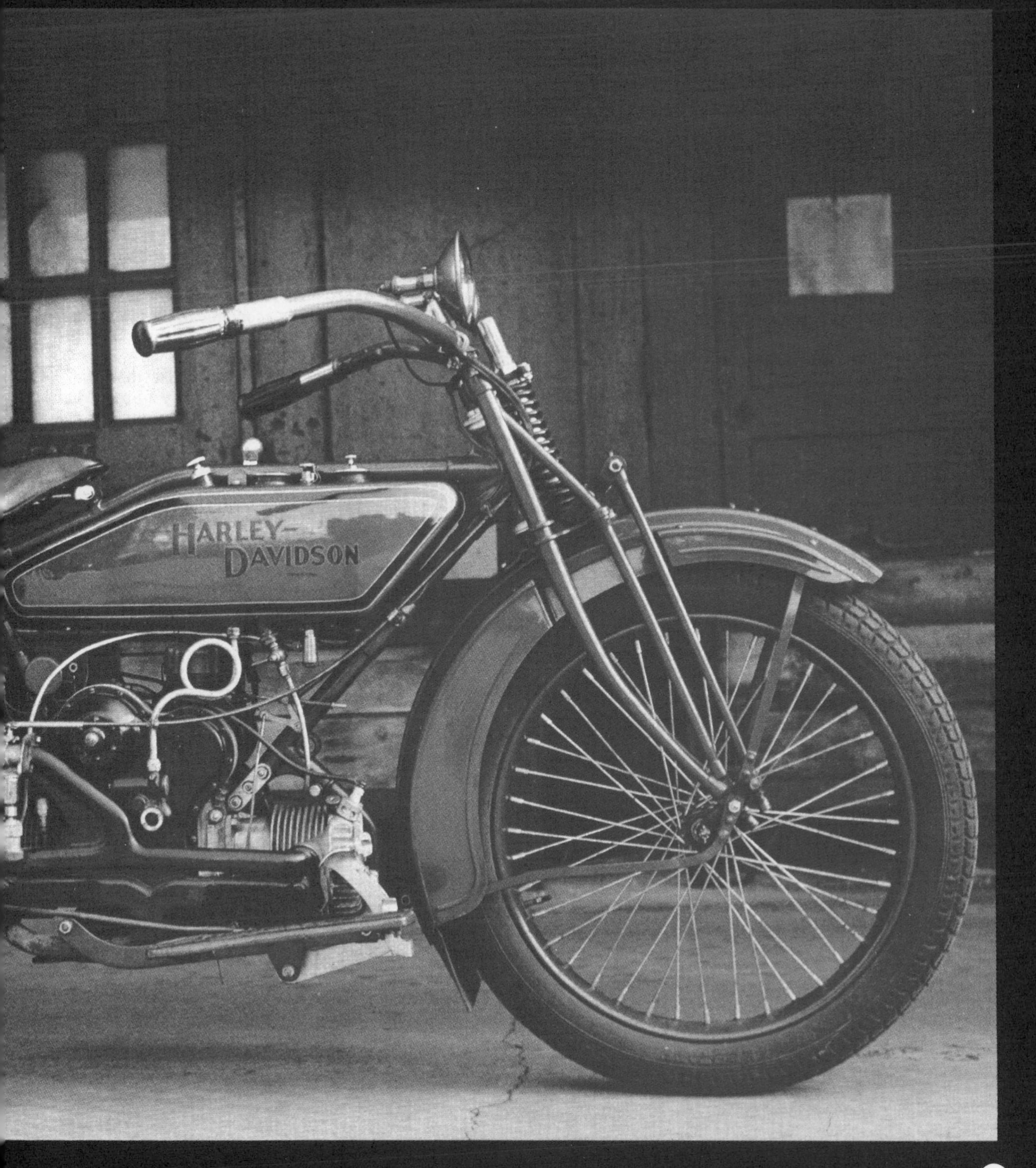

hotos by Steve Kimball

As a Harley-Davidson brochure of the period explained, "The perfect balance of the opposed cylinder motor means that there is no vibration at any speed."

Unlike the current opposed Twin motorcycles, the Sport Model engine doesn't have the cylinders sticking out the sides of the motorcycle. Cylinders go fore and aft and the entire engine is mounted extremely low for the lowest possible center of gravity. Engine and transmission are housed in the same case, with the transmission mounted directly on top of the engine, primary drive is through helical gears operating a multiplate wet clutch. The only chain on the motorcycle is the final drive chain and it's housed in an oil bath full enclosure.

For a company that had become the world's largest manufacturer of motorcycles by selling mostly V-Twin motorcycles of around 61 cubic inches, this was a drastic departure. With a bore of 2.75 in. and stroke of 3 in., displacement works out to 35.64 c.i., or 584cc. According to the factory literature, "This motor develops well over 6 horse power." With its three-speed sliding gear transmission in high gear, the Sport Model could hit a top speed of about 50 mph. That works out to about 3200 rpm, a fast engine speed for 1919.

As important to performance as a high speed engine was light weight. The word *plastic* wouldn't have meant any more in 1919 than the word *television*. Aluminum pistons were five years away and any other aluminum parts were unheard of. Motorcycles were made of iron. Even so, the Sport Model weighs 264 lb. That's measured on a certified scale. For comparison, that's less than any of the current 250cc dual pupose bikes. It's about on a par with a current 185cc street bike, or a large two-stroke enduro bike. The Sport Model doesn't weigh 264 lb. because there was nothing more to add, it weighs 264 lb. because there was nothing more to take out.

Besides the light weight, there is the low center of gravity, supposedly about as high as the axles. This extremely low center of gravity makes the Sport Model feel lighter than an equivalent 264 lb. modern motorcycle. Just pushing it around for the photos, it didn't take any steering effort. It's about like pushing a shopping basket, or almost as if the motorcycle was built to be pushed, or pulled or carried. And considering the roads of 1919, it probably was. Traveling anywhere outside a major city meant riding through mud and sand and rocks and following narrow trails in dirt roads. Today this would be called off-road riding. In 1919 it was motorcycle riding. And that's why the special solo motorcycles like the Harley-Davidson Sport Model were built.

Harley-Davidson wasn't the only company that knew what roads were like. So did Indian, and at the same time the Sport Model was introduced, Indian was coming out with the equivalent sized Scout, which also had a unit construction engine and transmission and had a more conventional V-Twin engine and maybe a little more speed.

That didn't keep the Sport Model from becoming the biggest selling solo motorcycle within a year after its introduction. Of course some of Harley-Davidson's success wasn't due just to the machinery. During WWI Indian committed a larger share of its production to War Department motorcycles, and that allowed Harley-Davidson to take over more dealers. That made the Milwaukee brand a bigger motorcycle company when the war ended and helped the Sport Model get off to a good start.

Big motorcycles, the 61 c.i. models, were often equipped with sidecars, which made them useful competition with cars as transportation, though they cost just as much. The idea of the small machine was for solo use. "It is the snappiest, liveliest motorcycle ever built," according to the brochure from Harley-Davidson. "At the same time it is the quietest and most economical, the easiest starting, the sturdiest, and by far the most comfortable."

With a pitch like that, how could a young man not buy a Sport Model? One who couldn't turn down the motorcycle was Leon Landry, a 14-year-old Massa-

1.

2.

3.

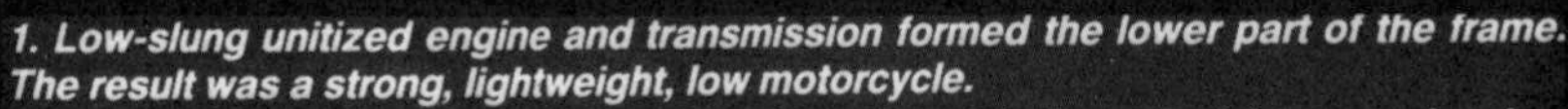

1. Low-slung unitized engine and transmission formed the lower part of the frame. The result was a strong, lightweight, low motorcycle.
2. Long intake manifold was heated by the exhaust to keep fuel from condensing. Intake and exhaust manifolds were cast together.
3. A brake, 7 in. by 1 in., wrapped around the rear hub. It was tightened by pushing on the pedal on the right side of the motorcycle. Front brakes were several years away.
4. Built by Harley-Davidson, the electrical system was optional.

husetts youth who plunked down the 335 for a magneto-equipped Sport Model in 1919. It was his first motorcycle. Three years later he was a Harley-Davidson dealer. With his friend Bill Lang, who also had a Sport Model, Landry stripped his bike of such unneeded parts as fenders and seat post and equipped the Harley for hillclimbing. Both Lang and Landry were successful in the local hillclimbs and Landry was successful as a motorcycle dealer.

"I've always been partial to that model," recalled Landry, now retired. "I lost track of mine. It's somewhere in New Jersey now, but the owner won't sell it." So Landry looked around and found another Sport Model, this one a 1920 model with electrical system built by Harley-Davidson. It had sat in a field for 15 years in New Hampshire and was, like most pieces of equipment left to sit in fields for 15 years, well rusted. But at his dealership in Florida Landry started work restoring the bike, building the parts that couldn't be bought. A few changes had to be made. Aluminum pistons were fitted. He couldn't find the original single headlight that came with the electrically-equipped Sport Model, so his bike got Kay-Bee spotlights, a common modification of the period.

According to Landry, his original Sport Model was competitive with the Indian Scout 37 in. machine in hillclimbs and flat track races. Sport Models weren't used in most competition because they didn't fit the classes of the period. Racing classes were sanctioned for 30.50 in. machines (500cc) or 61 in. motorcycles (1000cc). The AMA's Class C rules didn't exist then, so the racing machines were works bikes, most equipped with four-valve heads on the Singles or a pair of four valve heads on the Twins.

4.

Sport Models were successful in cross country events and hillclimbs. A Sport Model was the first motorcycle to climb Mt. Baldy near Los Angeles when it carried Jack Fletcher up the 10,080 ft. mountain on July 10, 1919. Soon Hap Scherer was setting a new Three-Flags record for small motorcycles with a 64 hour run for the 1716 mi. of almost roads. Harley-Davidson had never competed in the major long distance trials like the Three Flags, but the Sport Model was ideally suited for such competition. Its 28 in. seat height was about 4 in. lower than most other motorcycles, which made it easy to handle the lightweight machine on the roughest roads. The "double bar trussed frame" used the engine as the lower stressed member, a style then known as "keystone construction." The sprung fork used trailing links and a coil spring at the steering head.

According to the factory claims, the Sport Model would get 50 to 90 mpg of gas and 800 to 1200 mpg of oil. Servicing was easy. The valves could be ground without removing the cylinders from the engine or the engine from the frame. Even the cylinders could be pulled without removing the engine. Although the Sport Model was equipped with a hand oil pump, it wasn't needed for normal operation, the automatic oiling system taking care of all engine lubrication.

A look at the stories in Harley-Davidson's owner publication, the *Enthusiast*, illustrates the kind of motorcycling done in the Twenties. "Cheaper to Ride a Harley-Davidson than to Walk," proclaimed one headline. "Girl Motorcyclist Makes Long Trips on Sport Model," said another. "How I Cut 11 Hours off the Boston to Chicago Record" explained another Sport Model record. Motorcycle adventurer John E. Hogg wrote,"Caught in A Desert Death Trap." Another head: "Six Motorcyclists Go Coon Hunting." Or, "Motorcycling in Hula-Hula Land."

Motorcycles were for the adventurous. But cars were for transportation. In 1910 a Ford Model T roadster cost $900. By 1919 an improved version of that same car cost $500 and over half a million were sold. The next year the price of a Model T dropped to $395 and nearly a million were sold. When a Sport Model with generator cost $380, a 61 in. V-Twin Harley cost $418 and a Model T cost $395, it became harder to sell big motorcycles.

In his speech to dealers in November, 1920, Walter Davidson told the H-D dealers, "We might as well all recognize that the so-called prosperity that we have been enjoying has come to a very sudden stop." The post-war economic boom was over. Deflation was occurring in prices for a variety of products, but sales weren't picking up. Henry Ford was blamed, in Davidson's speech, for the difficulties experienced by the motorcycle industry because he was selling a car that "has no features" and must be sold on low cost alone. Ford depended on a great volume of sales and this meant people who would have bought motorcycles for transportation were buying cars.

Most of the 143 known motorcycle manufacturers in this country built bikes before this period. This is when most of them went out of business. In such a harsh economic climate, the Sport Model did not succeed. It became "The most popular solo motorcycle in the world," almost immediately, according to the factory claims. But it was out of production by 1923. Henry was selling Fords for $265 then, making $50 profit on each one and selling about 2 million. Harley-Davidson sold its last Sport Model in England and New Zealand and elsewhere that conditions demanded a lightweight, durable motorcycle. For the U.S. H-D offered the 61 in. V-Twin and the new 74 in. model, a bored out 61, with prices of $285 and $310. A sidecar cost $98.

Leon Landry wasn't the only person to learn to ride a motorcycle on a Sport Model during this period. A lad named William H. Davidson also had his first ride on a Sport Model. His father, William A. Davidson was in charge of engineering at Harley-Davidson and in 1942 young Bill became President of the Harley-Davidson Motor Co., a title he kept until 1971. Landry, as a dealer, knew the Davidsons and so when he finished his restoration project on this 1920 Sport Model, he gave the motorcycle to Bill Davidson.

It's not in the Harley-Davidson museum at York, Pennsylvania, though. This Sport Model is kept at the Harley-Davidson headquarters in Milwaukee. It's part of a smaller museum, of sorts, a museum that only has two motorcycles. It's the Styling Department museum because the two motorcycles are kept in the same area with the stylists, where they can look at it, the most unusual Harley-Davidson built. The other bikc is the XLCR, the unusual cafe racer-style Sportster.

The Styling Department, of course, is run by another William Davidson, this one known as Willie G. When he works on the design of a new Harley-Davidson, he can occasionally look back at the motorcycle that taught his father how to ride, and the motorcycle that taught his grandfather what to design. ◘

HARLEY-DAVIDSON XR1000

For The Jay Springsteen In All Of Us

■ Racing improves the breed, everyone knows, but most of the people building street bikes long ago quit racing the motorcycles they sell the public. After all, who needs a bike like Kenny Roberts or Freddie Spencer?

There is, however, one racing motorcycle that could be—make that should be—a street bike. It's light and fast and controllable and reliable and beautiful and has a racing heritage second to none. A roll of the drums now, and . . . here's the Harley-Davidson XR1000.

Like everyone else who's ever gone to an AMA dirt track race and seen the thundering Harley XR750s racing, some of the people inside Harley-Davidson have wanted to build a street version of the XR. Easier said than done, said the Engineering Department. Easier done than said, said Dick O'Brien of the Racing Department.

O'Brien, known as O.B. on the racing circuit, knows racing, he knows Harley-Davidsons and he knows how to get things done. Christ, does he know how to get things done. He asked for 60 days to build a street legal XR. That was last June. Sixty days later he presented the completed XR1000 to the management and the project was on.

A Harley-Davidson XR is not quite like anything else in the Harley-Davidson line. It traces the roots of its engine back to the same roots that grew into the Sportster. Both are 45° ohv V-Twins with a row of four separate cams geared together on the right-hand side of the engine. Both use similar fork-and-blade connecting rods rotating on a single throw crank spinning on ball and roller bearings. Both grew out of the old 45 cu. in. flathead K-model Harley-Davidsons, the Sportster turning into an overhead valve motor in 1957, the XR turning from an iron flathead to an iron overhead valve to the alloy 750cc ohv racing motor a dozen years ago.

Although both the Sportster and the racing XR750 are descended from the same design, they are substantially different. When the XR became an all-alloy motor, it received a better shaped combustion chamber, a carburetor for each cylinder, much different rocker boxes and rockers, lighter aluminum pushrods, shorter connecting rods and no concessions to street operation. The XR motor made more power, under tougher conditions, and did so because of a superior design and better materials. The narrower angle between the valves and flatter pistons made for faster combustion, so more compression could be used and more power extracted.

Early on in the project it became clear that a racing XR750 could not be converted to a street bike without enormous cost and compromise. The frame of the XR750 was not built to have lights or a sidestand mounted. The shape of that beautiful orange fiberglass is fine for going around circles of dirt with a left foot sliding along in a steel shoe, but it takes more than that to be a good street bike. So the XR1000 became mostly a Sportster, styled like the latest XLX1000 Sportster, with all the Sportster pieces that work, plus it has the power-making pieces from an XR750 added.

That adaptation is an especially good answer now, because in 1982 the Sportster received a new frame. Light and strong, the new frame provided more cornering clearance and excellent handling to the old Sportster. It replaced all those cast junctions with welded steel tubes. All it needed was an engine with more power, and maybe some more powerful brakes.

That's the XR1000. Bolting on a set of XR cylinders and head turned out to involve some redesign. The Sportster motor has an 81mm bore and 96.8mm stroke. the XR750 motor has a 79.5mm bore and 75.5mm stroke, and uses shorter rods with the shorter cylinders and stroke. No combination of existing parts would allow the XR heads to fit on a Sportster crankcase.

New cylinders and rods were needed to mate the alloy heads on the big displacement engine, and the new cylinders are iron, not aluminum alloy with liners, as the XR750 uses. The difference is about 10 lb., a little less cooling for the big iron cylinders and more strength. According to O'Brien, the iron cylinders work as well as the alloy cylinders for power, have no cooling shortcomings because of the alloy head, and retain their shape better than lightweight cylinders. They could also be developed in less time.

The new cylinders are noticeably larger across the fins, with much greater cooling area. They also use through-bolts instead of the old Sportster's separate bolts holding the cylinders to the cases and the heads to the cylinders. This also adds strength, something the XR1000 appears to possess in great amount. New rods a half inch shorter than the old rods were used to reduce the height of the engine, so it would fit in the new frame.

What remains of the racing XR are the important parts. The heads are the same, at least the same as the latest batch of XR750 heads. In detailing the production specifications and finding machining services for the larger production run, some improvements have been made. There is more strength around the valve guides and the latest heads are a different alloy that works better than the old alloy. Valve sizes are 1mm larger on the XR1000 than on the XR750 (45mm intake and 38mm exhaust), but are made of the same material.

When the heads have been machined they are sent to California for assembly. Why ship parts to California and back to Wisconsin? Because all the heads are assembled by Jerry Branch. Assembling, in this case, means porting and polishing the ports and combustion chambers, shimming the double valve springs to the correct height and installing the titanium collars and keepers.

XR heads use different rocker boxes than the iron heads. Valve lash is adjusted by eccentric rocker shafts, easily set by twisting the shaft from outside the box, after checking the clearance through inspection holes. The Sportster used adjustable cam followers. Aluminum pushrods are used on the XR, and the rockers are individually spliced at the correct angles for each valve. This last operation was developed for the racing engines. Instead of having separate rocker arms made for each valve, with the optimum angle between arms of the rocker, the long tubular center of the rockers are cut, then mounted in jigs at the correct angle and welded together.

Valves are set at a 68° included angle on the XR head, instead of the 90° angle of the iron Sportster heads. This makes for a flatter combustion chamber, which in turn makes a shorter distance for the flame to travel during combustion, improving power and reducing the tendency to detonate. Compression ratio

BELL

will be 9:1 for the stock XR1000 engine, which requires nearly flat-top pistons. Cast aluminum pistons are used, machined down on top to achieve the desired compression ratio.

Where the rocker boxes bolt to the head, the threads have helicoil inserts. When Project Engineer Gary Stippich was asked if the production engines would still get the helicoils, he explained that the racers needed them because of the number of times the rocker boxes get pulled on racing heads, and there wasn't time to experiment without the inserts, so all the heads will retain the inserts.

Stock 1983 Sportster cams will be used in the XR1000. These are called Q cams in the Harley-Davidson list of camshafts, and have moderate lift and duration, though because Harley measures cam timing at 0.005 in. of lift, the figures don't look particularly mild. Lift is 0.284 in. on intake and 0.267 in. on exhaust. Duration is 368° exhaust and 361° intake. They give a broad, flat torque curve and have been relatively easy to work with on emission tuning, which is important when you're working with a 60 day lead time.

Most noticeable of the XR characteristics are the dual carburetors and the exhaust climbing up the left side of the bike. The racing bikes have these, and so does the XR1000. Dell'Orto carburetors are used, 36mm, with accelerator pumps. K&N air filters tuck in to the side of the bike, requiring an indentation to be made in the oil tank. That's one of the problems with this design. Packaging the engine and carbs and filters so a rider can sit on the motorcycle requires some extra work fitting things around the engine. The exhaust is just like the racebikes. Length and shape are the same, and the pair of pipes run up the left side of the bike just like on Springsteen's bike, but there are mufflers inside those pipes so the bike can pass sound tests.

Actually, the XR1000 has a lower sound level on the tests than the Sportster, because having the intake and exhaust on separate sides of the bike means the loudest side doesn't have two sources of sound raising the sound level. It's all a matter of how the tests are run, and no one without a sound meter will ever be able to tell.

Performance is the reason for adding the racing part to the Sportster. It used to be the fastest and quickest stock bike made, and it remained one of the quickest for many years. But since the big Fours from Japan were developed, the Harley has lost some of its performance image. With the new heads, cylinders, intake and exhaust, the XR1000 puts out about 70 bhp on the Harley dyno, measured at the crankshaft.

Power is increased through the rpm range, particularly at lower engine speeds. Using individual carburetors makes jetting easier, explained Stippich, because the irregular firing of the 45° engine forced the carburetion to be a compromise with a single carb, jetting richer in spots than ideal to cover up leanness in the other cylinder at that speed.

While this is a sizeable increase in power and can cut more than a second off the quarter mile time of the XR1000 compared with an XL1000, the performance potential is even greater. Remember, this project was developed in the racing department.

And in case any Harley customer wants to race an XR1000 on pavement, there will be factory speed parts available. The first level of performance increase is the addition of 10.5:1 compression pistons and longer duration, high lift, cams. With only these parts changed power jumps up to over 80 bhp. Peak power is reached at 5600 rpm with the stock cams and pistons, and this increases to 6300 rpm for the high compression, high overlap combination, but still with plenty of low and mid-range power.

For a full racing version, with an open exhaust and perhaps larger carburetion, there is the potential for about 100 to 105 bhp, according to O'Brien. Where and when such a Harley-Davidson will appear is anybody's guess, but in the back room of the racing department Carroll Resweber was busy welding up a Cal Rayborn replica frame to fit the new motor. O'Brien wasn't talking about that.

Elsewhere in the Harley plant a couple of production prototypes were being assembled. One had a couple of hundred pounds of lead bolted to the underside of the frame so it would be at gross vehicle weight rating for the emission tests. The other was mailed to California where it found itself on these pages. When the assembly line turns these out, the choke levers on these carbs will be replaced by a pull, the breather hose may be stainless steel, the tach will be redlined at 6200 rpm, the lower frame lug on the right-hand side will be gone, the cylinder hold-down studs on the left side won't be visible and the primary cover will be flat and silver with an orange decal.

When it arrived, it didn't gather dust. The XR is a particularly captivating motorcycle, and to a broad variety of riders. It was spotted on city streets and open freeways. It couldn't be parked for more than a minute at any motorcyclist hangout without a crowd forming around it and the rider subjected to interrogation. One consultant who works in the motorcycle industry and can have his pick of any new motorcycles from Japan begged us for a ride on the XR. Admittedly this is the first XR1000 released for tests, but the response was still staggering.

It is a very mechanical bike, with every

Assembled cylinder, head and rockerbox of the XR1000 has much greater fin area for cooling than Sportster cylinder and head. Marks on rocker shafts and the rockerbox indicate limits of valve lash adjust, set by turning eccentric shafts.

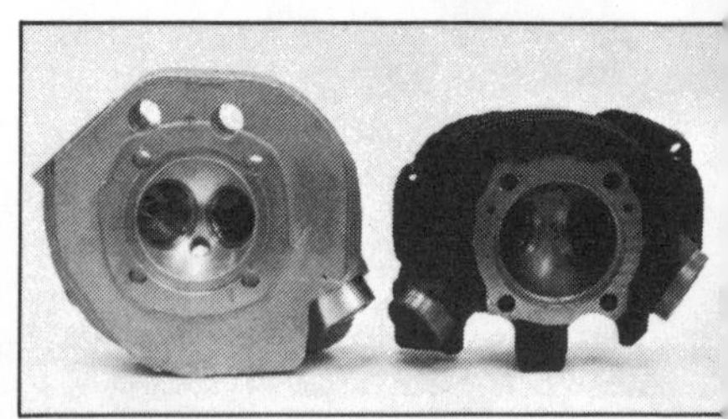

Combustion chamber in the old iron head (right) was deeper, which required high peak on the piston. This slowed flame travel during combustion. XR head is shallower and has intake and exhaust ports on opposing sides for the left-side exhaust and right-side intake.

Power output of the Sportster is limited by combustion chamber shape and heat dissipation. XR head, on left, eliminates any overheating problems in full-throttle loads.

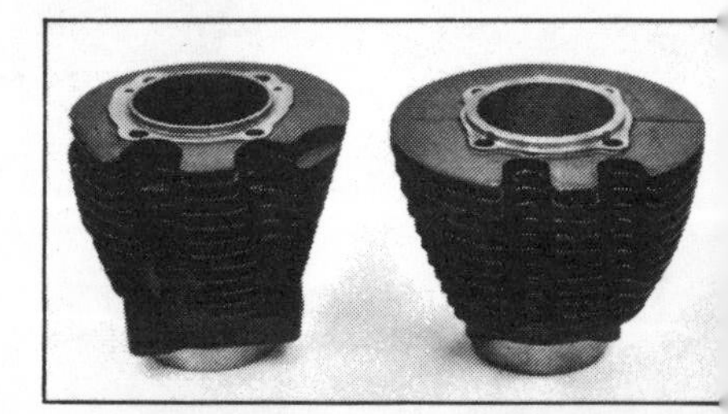

New iron cylinder for XR, right, has more fin area than Sportster cylinder and uses through bolts instead of separate bolts holding cylinder to the cases and the head to the cylinder.

All the mechanical parts are out in the open. Production carbs will have adjustments more accessible than these.

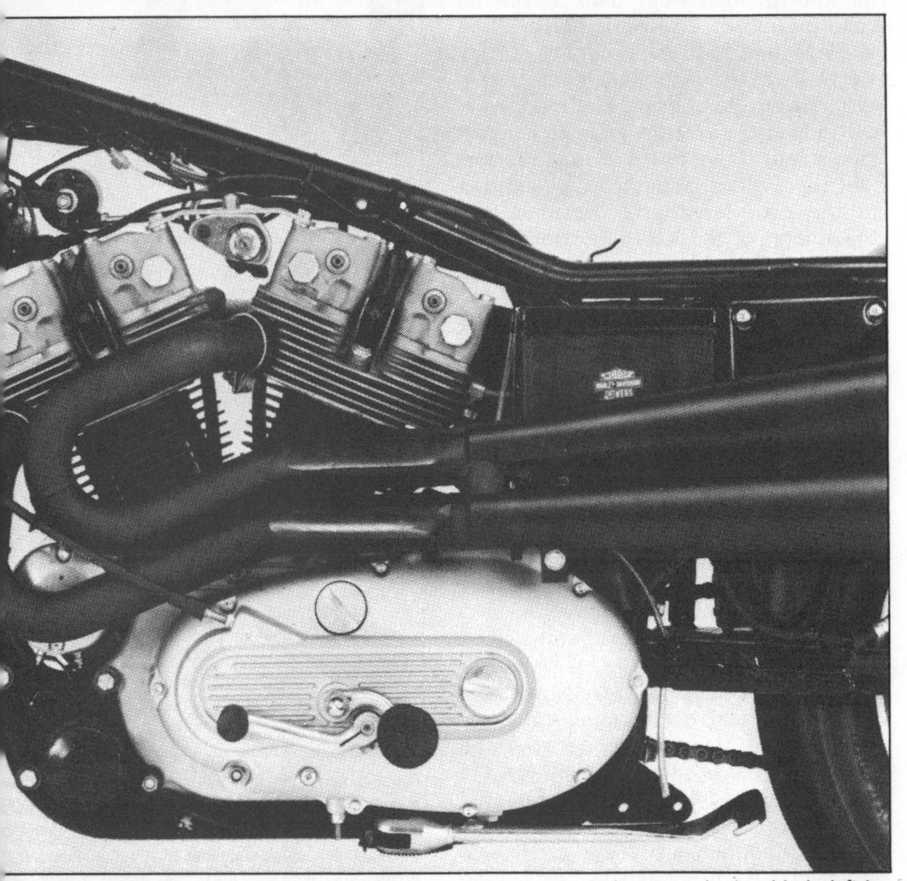

More heat shielding is needed on the high-mounted exhaust. At low speeds the rider's left leg begins feeling like the Colonel's best drumstick.

working bit hung out in the open. There are no plastic panels covering anything. The tires, especially the rear tire, are huge. Fenders are so real and simple on the XR it makes everything else in the parking lot look like a toy. Why all the scoops and fins and chrome and plastic and tailpieces when a couple of carefully curved and painted metal pieces can look so attractive and work so well? A solo seat, more padded than the seat on the XLX Sportster, is mounted well forward of the rear fender. The tiny 2.2 gal. gas tank, as narrow as it is, can be touched with both knees when the rider is aboard, because everything is so narrow. Handlebars are simple and low, but wide. There is no plastic covering them, and the two simple round instruments bolted to the steering head are held with more steel. All very businesslike. All exuding a visual strength, a presence, that draws eyes like some kind of ocular magnet.

As much as anything, it's the exhaust that does it. Wrapping around the left side of the engine, climbing up the side of the motorcycle, the double tapered mufflers look just like they do on the racing XRs. On the other side of the bike there are the two carbs and an even clearer view of that engine.

Because this new Harley has a good amount of power and big brakes and it handles well, don't think it is anything like an Orientaloid. Throw a leg over the bike and the first thing you notice is that your leg doesn't need to go so high. The motorcycle is low, with a low seat, low fender and a reasonably low steering head. The sidestand holds the bike at more of an angle than most other bikes, and it locks into position when it's down so the bike won't roll forward. Put your hands on the ends of the handlebars and there are big smooth grips under them. Diameter is noticeably larger than any other brand, and there is room for big hands. Big hands make it easier to reach the clutch and brake levers, though the clutch pull on this XR was much lighter than most Sportsters.

Starting the XR doesn't require any choke with the pumper Dell'Ortos, though there are choke levers there, hidden beside the K&N filters. The ignition is hidden below the gas tank on the left side, turn it one click, pump the tremendously stiff twist grip a couple of times and touch the starter button and the XR rumbles and hammers itself into motion. The sound is lively, strong, and not like anything else, including a Sportster. The exhaust is a little louder and there is a mechanical pounding not muffled as much by the aluminum heads at it is by the iron Sportster pieces. It's a wonderful, soul stirring sound. Turn the volume up 50 percent and you couldn't keep from roaring off into the night, trying to be the kind of person your mother warned you about.

Riding the XR is not particularly difficult. The clutch works easily and smoothly, but that throttle must be some kind of test. Are you strong enough to ride a Harley? Dell'Orto carbs normally have too-stiff return springs, plus the single throttle cable from the twist grip goes to a roller mounted beneath the gas tank, where it spins the roller, which in turn pulls double cables that operate the two carbs. More than anything else, the stiff throttle pull makes shifting difficult. Pull in the clutch, touch the shifter and back off a little on the throttle, and the engine speed goes to idle, but doesn't come back up.

Lurch on through to fourth gear and things are a little easier. It doesn't matter much what speed the engine is spinning when the bike is shifted. It can run along in top gear just above idle, and it pulls strongly at that engine speed. Normal riding calls for engine speeds between 2000 and 3000 rpm. At that rate, engine vibration is hardly noticeable, except that the bike feels inordinately smooth. Above the 3000 rpm the XR1000, like the Sportster, starts vibrating excessively. This peaks about 3500 rpm, and then recedes slowly. Because of the gearing, the smoothest engine speed results in a highway speed of 55 to 60 mph, with the most vibration occurring around 65 mph. Taller gearing would help, and the XR1000 could certainly handle higher overall gearing. A better improvement would be the addition of a five-speed transmission, with a wider range or ratios.

Horsepower the XR1000 has. It also uses a lot of gas. With the stock 2.2 gal. gas tank filled to overflowing it would just stagger to a halt at the end of the 100 mi. test loop. Actually, because no one got the XR to run that far on a test under other riding conditions, the test was shortened to one 50 mi. loop. Reserve, one out-of-breath tester reported, was good for 14.1 mi. The larger gas tank is an essential option.

Like so many other parts on the XR1000, the transmission goes way back in Harley history. It is a four-speed because the Sportster was a four-speed because the K-model was a four-speed. Some five-speed transmissions have been made for roadracing, but aren't available through the factory. This version of the Sportster transmission shifted better than the last one tested, but it is no longer a superior transmission. The throws are long and some riders thought there was less feel in the shift lever than they were used to, though there were no missed shifts.

Harley-Davidson controls are in other ways unusual, too. Turn signals are controlled by push buttons. Hold down the button on the side to be lit, and the signals flash. Take your thumb off the button and the light stops. This makes the combination of downshifting, braking and signaling more work, but few Harley riders leave the turn signals on after a turn. Harley hand grips, like Harley everything else, are large. Diameter tapers from about 1.5 in. to 1.4 in., and the surface is not ribbed or bumped. In addition to the extra-large grip diameter, the brake lever of the XR1000 extends farther from the grip than is normal. Add a distant lever with a fat grip and it becomes difficult to reach and control the brake lever. This criticism is not unanimous. Riders who liked the stretch to the lever were quick to identify their smaller-pawed brethren as quiche-eating wimps. A little machining work on the cylindrical push block in the brake lever would move the lever closer to the grip.

Adapting intake and exhaust systems from a racebike to a street bike requires a little compromise. On the XR1000 the compromise must come from the rider. By tucking the carbs and air filters closely into the side of the bike, the rider's right leg can be held very close to the bike, if the rider is tall enough. Shorter riders found interference between the forward carb's air filter and their leg. On the left side there's that high-mounted exhaust. It tucks as close to the engine as possible, and there are small heat shields attached, but still enough heat gets to the rider's leg to make cooking possible on

Every XR head is ported and polished by Jerry Branch, who assembles the valve parts on the head. New head casting has more support for valve guides than previous alloy XR head.

Sportster piston is shown on the left, new XR piston is on the right. Cast aluminum pistons are cut to the desired height to control compression ratio. Stock piston produces 9:1 ratio.

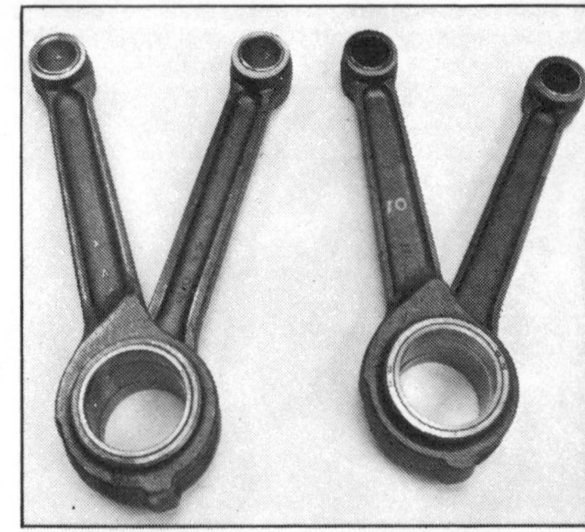

Connecting rods on XR1000 are half an inch shorter than rods on XL Sportster, though both have the same bore and stroke. Rod to stroke ratio is very close to 1.8:1 on the XR1000.

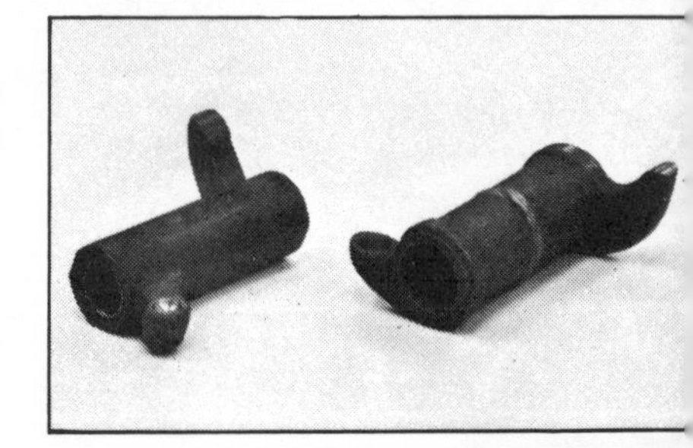

Rocker arms of Sportster (left) and XR show the welded section in the middle of the XR rocker. Only one rocker is forged, but by cutting the rocker, adjusting the angle between the arms, and welding together, each valve has optimum angularity from the rocker.

HARLEY-DAVIDSON XR1000

SPECIFICATIONS

ist price	$6995
ngine	ohv V-Twin
ore x stroke	81 x 96.8mm
isplacement	998cc
ompression ratio	9:1
arburetion	(2) 36mm Dell'Orto
ir filter	oiled felt
gnition	electronic
laimed power	70 hp @ 5600 rpm
laimed torque	48 lb.-ft. @ 4400 rpm
ubrication	dry sump
il capacity	3 qt.
uel capacity	2.2 gal.
tarter	electric
lectrical power	182w alternator
attery	12v
eadlight	35/50w halogen
rimary drive	triplex chain
lutch	multiplate wet
inal drive	530 chain
ear ratios, overall: 1	
4th	3.97
3rd	5.49
2nd	7.25
1st	10.02
uspension:	
Front	telescopic fork
travel	6.9 in.
Rear	swing arm, dual shocks
travel	4.0 in.
ires:	
Front	100/90-19V Dunlop Sport Elite
Rear	130/90-16V Dunlop Sport Elite
rakes:	
Front	(2) 11.5 in. disc
Rear	11.5 in. disc
rake swept area	.301 sq. in
rake loading (160lb. rider)	2.2 lb./sq. in.
heelbase	59.3 in.
ake/Trail	30°/4.75 in.
andlebar width	32 in.
eat height	29 in.
eat width	9 in.
ootpeg height	13 in.
round clearance	6.5 in.
est weight (w/half-tank fuel)	500 lb.
eight bias, % front/rear	47/53
VWR	900 lb.
oad capacity	400 lb.

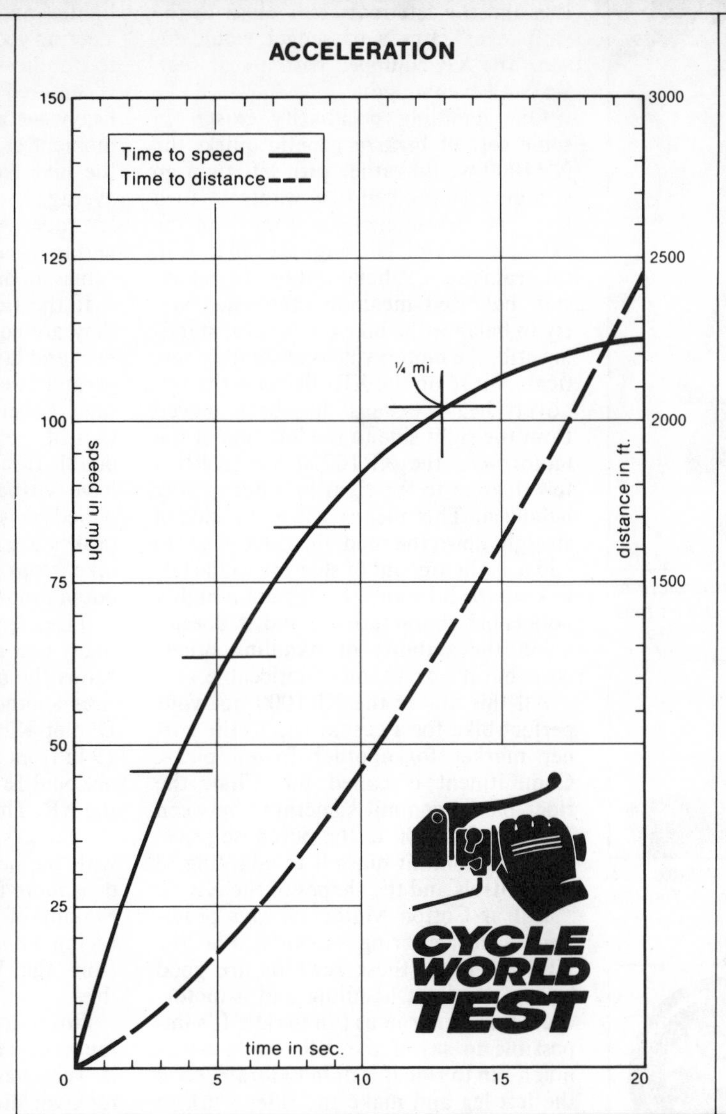

PERFORMANCE

Standing ¼-mile	12.88 sec. @ 101.23 mph
Top speed in ½-mile	112 mph
Fuel consumption	46 mpg
Range (to reserve tank)	83 mi.
Acceleration:	
0–30 mph	2.0 sec.
0–40 mph	2.8 sec.
0–50 mph	3.8 sec.
0–60 mph	4.9 sec.
0–70 mph	6.2 sec.
0–80 mph	7.5 sec.
0–90 mph	9.3 sec.
0–100 mph	12.6 sec.
Top gear acceleration:	
40–60 mph	4.1 sec.
60–80 mph	4.3 sec.
Calculated speed in gears @ 6200 rpm:	
1st	46 mph
2nd	63 mph
3rd	83 mph
4th	115 mph
Speedometer error:	
30 mph indicated	29 mph
60 mph indicated	58 mph
Braking distance:	
from 30 mph	36 ft.
from 60 mph	117 ft.
Engine speed at 60 mph	3220 rpm

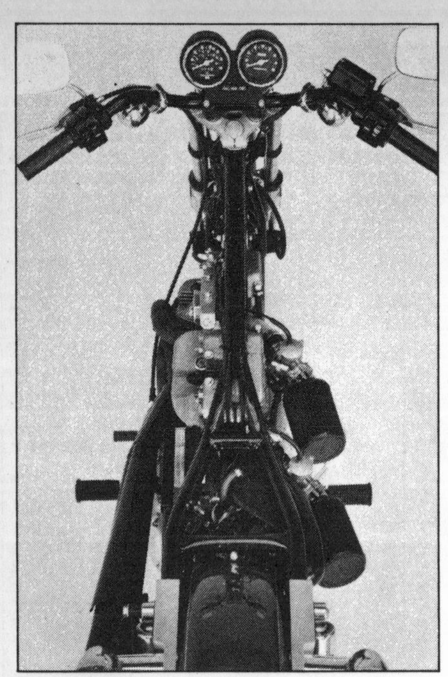

Engine and frame are narrow. Carburetors fit behind the rider's leg, while the exhaust fries the left leg.

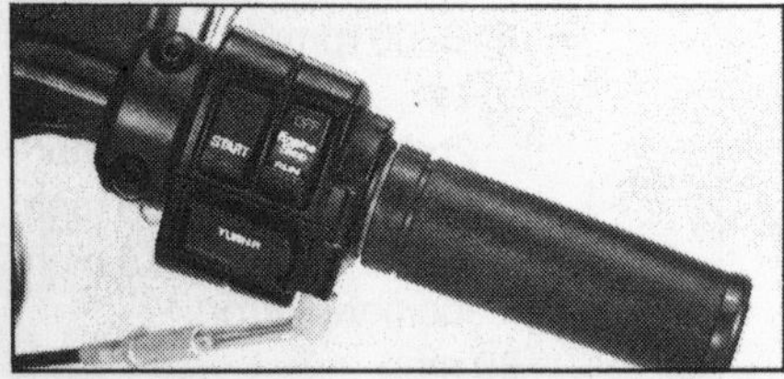

Larger than average grips are comfortable, but make the brake lever hard to reach. Throttle locking screw is under twistgrip. Push button turn signals require some adaptation.

Instruments are simple and effective. Warning lights indicate high beam, low oil pressure or low charging. There is no neutral indicator light or signal light indicator.

New calipers and large diameter brake discs have enormous stopping power. Standard equipment Dunlop Sport Elite tires take full advantage of the braking force.

the left shin. More heat shielding is needed here. On the road it's less of a problem, but around town the air flow is less and the left foot stays close to the shift lever. How a passenger would fit, were the XR equipped with a rear seat, we can't even imagine.

One handling peculiarity exists. In some sort of bizarre genetic quirk, the XR1000 would rather turn left than go straight. That's right, it wants to turn left. The characteristic is a result of the exhaust system. The engine is placed in the frame so it is balanced on the Sportster, balanced meaning that when you try to balance the bike on its tires, standing still, the motorcycle is absolutely vertical. Not so on the XR. Because the relatively heavy exhaust has been moved from the right side to the left side of the motorcycle, the XR10000 has to list a few degrees to the right in order to stay balanced. This means when it's ridden straight down the road, the rider needs to add a slight amount of steering to the left to keep the bike upright. It's not a highly noticeable characteristic, and it doesn't affect the stability or handling otherwise, but it was, to some, noticeable.

All this makes the XR1000 not your perfect bike for a casual trip to the corner market for another frozen pizza. Commitment is called for. First, the rider has to commit something between $6000 and $7000 to the purchase price. He must commit himself to adapting to the controls and the shapes of the XR.

But as Cotton Mather always promised, sacrifice bring rewards. For the XR1000 rider, those rewards are good power, excellent handling and a motorcycle that's enormous fun to ride. It's impossible to say if the XR would be as much fun to ride if it didn't vibrate, cook the left leg and make the rider work to use the turn signals.

Some of the fun of riding the XR undoubtedly comes from its heritage. Unlike most motorcycles, the XR has a heritage. All those bright orange flat track racers and famous names may not make it go faster or run smoother, but they have intrinsic value, nebulous though it may be.

On the right kinds of roads, the XR has other strengths. Take away city traffic and straight roads and it comes into its own. Nothing but a large displacement, mildly tuned motor can have a powerband like the XR. From idle to the 6200 rpm redline the motor is powerful and responsive. It feels best from 3000 rpm to 5000 rpm, though there isn't much difference above or below these engine speeds. Leaving the bike in high gear on a country road and exercising this wonderful engine is the most satisfying.

This good power combines with excellent handling to make the XR1000 a top notch sports bike. The handling doesn't come from extraordinary light weight or quick steering geometry, because the XR weighs about the same as some of the lighter and faster 750 Fours and has steering geometry that is more conducive to stability than quickness. But the mass is centered on the bike, with little of the heavy metal wide or high. A low polar moment of inertia makes it easy to flick the bike from side to side. Wider than average handlebars help, providing more leverage. Add better-than-average cornering clearance and the XR1000 becomes an outstanding handling bike.

If the rider can adapt to the brakes, they are equally outstanding. New calipers and larger front discs provide much greater swept area and hydraulic advantage. Lever effort is now comparable to that of most Japanese motorcycles with double front discs, but the Harley brakes have virtually no flex. The lever gets pulled in slightly and it stops, as the brakes are applied. Pull harder and the bike stops quicker, but the lever still doesn't move.

Tires have been getting better on many new motorcycles, but the XR1000 raises the quality of original equipment tires another notch with the addition of Dunlop K291S Sport Elites, a 100/90V-19 in front and 130/90V-16 in back. An optional 18 in. rear wheel is available on the XR. The only other option is a larger 3.3 gal. gas tank. Equipping the XR1000 with the best street tires Dunlop makes does more than benefit the handling and braking of the Harley. It is part of the racing image. All parts are first class from the Branch-ported heads to the tires.

Not so long ago some of the hardware found on Harley-Davidsons looked as if it were hammered out of iron ore by rock-wielding natives along the shores of the Milwaukee river. All the hardware on the XR is beautiful, though. Aluminum brake pedal and shift lever are nicely shaped, the paint is perfect and the welds are well done. The exhaust looked a little cobby, but that's expected to be more finished on the final production bikes.

Production numbers on the XR1000 will make it something of a limited edition. Starting in February, 200 will be built each month, making a run of 1000 bikes for this year. That could go up if there is enough demand, and most of the Harley-Davidson people expect there will be a demand. Within the Harley factory, employes have been asking about buying XR1000s, according to O'Brien.

That's understandable. The XR1000 is an exciting motorcycle. It's fun to ride, satisfying to look at, and it has performance potential built on a successful racing past. Best of all, there isn't an artificial piece of plastic or metal on or in the beast. In every sense, it is an honest motorcycle. ■

new ideas for today's crochet

Jean Leinhauser & Rita Weiss

Sterling Publishing Co., Inc.
New York

Technical Editor: Susan Lowman

Photo Stylist: Christy Stevenson

Photography: Marshall Williams
James Jaeger

Book Design: Graphic Solutions, inc-chgo

Produced by: The Creative Partners,™ LLC.

Library of Congress Cataloging-in-Publication Data Available

10 9 8 7 6 5 4 3 2 1

Published by Sterling Publishing Co., Inc.
387 Park Avenue South, New York, NY 10016

Distributed in Canada by Sterling Publishing
c/o Canadian Manda Group, 165 Dufferin Street
Toronto, Ontario, Canada M6K 3H6
Distributed in the United Kingdom by GMC Distribution Services
Castle Place, 166 High Street, Lewes, East Sussex, England BN7 1XU
Distributed in Australia by Capricorn Link (Australia) Pty. Ltd.
P.O. Box 704, Windsor, NSW 2756, Australia

Printed in China

Sterling ISBN-13: 978-1-4027-2306-3
ISBN-10: 1-4027-2306-7

For information about custom editions, special sales, premium and corporate purchases, please contact Sterling Special Sales Department at 800-805-5489 or specialsales@sterlingpub.com.

INTRODUCTION

The exciting fashions in this book are definitely NOT your granny's crochet!

Let's face it! No longer do we crocheters have to hide our assets under a shapeless poncho or a bulky granny square jacket The crochet of today is a whole new kind of crochet—exciting, glamorous, and daring!

Today's crochet makes use of the same stitches we've always known, but those stitches are used in entirely new and daring ways. We've searched out innovative designers daring enough to use those stitches in novel ways to create wearable crochet that sets a fresh standard for design, and we've collected those wonderful new patterns in this book.

Beautiful new yarns—from faux fur to suede-like textures—helped our designers create young fashions with a fresh look—the look so many of today's crocheters have been yearning for.

So throw away your old ideas about crochet, grab your hooks and your yarn and have a great time creating these exciting designs.

And once granny sees what you are doing, there will be no stopping her either!

Rita Weiss

Jean Leinhauser

CONTENTS

FLORAL CASCADE

Designed by Margaret Hubert

Richly-colored flowers cascade down the wide collar of this elegant shell, adding a subtle touch of excitement that's perfect for an evening event. A variety of textured yarns adds interest.

FLORAL CASCADE

SIZES	Small	Medium	Large
Body Bust Measurements	34"	36"	38"
Finished Bust Measurements	34¼"	36½"	38¾"

***Note:** Instructions are written for size Small; changes for sizes Medium and Large are in parentheses.*

Materials

For shell

Sport or DK weight yarn, 10 (10, 12½) oz black (MC)

For floral trim (for all sizes)

Worsted weight mohair, 2½ oz brown (A)

Worsted weight metallic yarn, 1¾ oz bronze (B)

Sport or DK weight yarn, 2½ oz dark brown (C)

***Note:** Photographed model made with Lion Brand® Micro-Spun #153 Ebony (MC), Imagine #126 Cocoa (A), Glitterspun #135 Bronze (B) and Wool-Ease® Sportweight #403 Mushroom (C)*

Ten ⅜" diameter round black shank buttons

Black sewing thread and sewing needle

Straight pins

Size E (3.5mm) crochet hook

Size G (4mm) crochet hook

Size I (5.5mm) crochet hook (or size required for gauge)

Gauge

14 sc = 4" with Size I crochet hook and sport weight yarn

INSTRUCTIONS

BACK

Beginning with bottom ribbing, with Size E hook and MC, ch 11.

Row 1: Sc in 2nd ch from hook and in each rem ch: 10 sc; ch 1, turn.

Rows 2 through 70 (72, 74): Working in back lp only of each st, sc in each sc, ch 1, turn.

BODY

Row 1 (right side): Working across long edge of ribbing in ends of rows, work 60 (64, 68) sc, ch 1, turn.

Rows 2 through 4: Change to Size G hook and working from now on in both lps of each st, sc across, ch 1, turn.

Change to Size I hook and work in sc rows until piece measures 13" (13½", 14") from bottom of ribbing, ending by working a wrong-side row.

SHAPE ARMHOLES

Sl st across 6 sts, ch 1, sc to last 6 sts, ch 1 turn, leaving last 6 sts unworked: 48 (52, 56) sc.

Continue to work in sc rows, decreasing 1 st each side every other row 5 times. Work even on the rem 38 (42, 46) sts until armhole measures 4" (4½", 5").

SHAPE LEFT SHOULDER

Sc across 9 sts, ch 1 turn. Working on these 9 sts only, dec 1 st at neck edge every other row 2 times. Work even on rem 7 sts till armhole measures 7½" (8", 8½"). Finish off.

SHAPE RIGHT SHOULDER

Skip the center 20 (24, 28) sts; join yarn at neck edge, working on rem 9 sts, dec 1 st at neck edge every other row 2 times. Work even on rem 7 sts until armhole measure 7½" (8", 8½"). Finish off; weave in all ends.

FRONT

Work same as back until 5 armhole

decreases are completed: (38, 42, 46) sc; ch 1, turn.

SHAPE NECK AND SHOULDERS

Sc across 11 sts, ch 1 turn, leaving rem sts unworked. Dec 1 st at neck edge only every other row 4 times. Work even on rem 7 sts until piece measures same as back to shoulder, finish off.

Skip center 16 (20, 24) sts; join yarn at neck edge, ch 1, sc in rem 11 sts, ch 1, turn. Dec 1 st at neck edge only every other row 4 times. Work even on rem 7 sts until piece measures same as back to shoulder, finish off.

ASSEMBLY

Sew shoulder and side seams. Starting at underarm seam, work 2 rows sc around each armhole, adjusting sts as needed to keep work flat. Starting at shoulder seam, work 1 row sc around neck edge, adjusting sts to keep work flat.

COLLAR

With size E crochet hook and MC, ch 131.

Foundation Row: Dc in 7th ch from hook; (ch 1, skip 1 ch, dc in next ch) 6 times; (ch 1, skip 1 ch, tr in next ch) 47 times; (ch 1, skip 1 ch, dc in next ch) 9 times; ch 1, turn. Change to size G crochet hook

Row 1: Skip first st; (sc in next ch-1 sp, sc in next dc) 7 times; ch 2, dc in next tr; *ch 2, in next tr work (tr, ch 2, tr); ch 2, tr in next tr; rep from * to last tr, dc in last tr; ch 2; **sc in next dc, sc in next ch-1 sp**; rep from ** to ** across, ending sc in top of turning ch; ch 1, turn.

Row 2: Skip first sc, sc in each sc to first tr, sc in tr; 2 sc in next ch-2 sp, sc in next tr, ch 1, dc in next tr, ch 2; * in next ch-2 sp work (tr, ch 2, tr); ch 2, skip next tr, tr in next tr, ch 2; rep from * to last 3 tr, dc in next tr, ch 1, sc in next tr, 2 sc in ch-2 sp, sc in next tr, sc in rem sts; ch 4, turn.

Row 3: Skip first 2 sts, dc in next st; (ch 1, skip next st, dc in next sc) 8 times; ch 2, dc in next dc, ch 2; (dc in next tr, ch 3) 15 times; (tr in next tr, ch 3) 35 times; (dc in next tr, ch 3) 14 times; ch 2, dc in next dc; (ch 1, dc in next sc) 10 times, ch 4, turn.

Row 4: Skip first st, dc in next dc; *(ch 1, skip next st, dc in next dc) 13 times*; **(ch 3, dc in next dc) 10 times **; (ch 3, tr in next tr) 48 times; rep between ** and ** 10 times; rep from * to * across, ending dc in 3rd ch of turning ch-4, ch 1, turn.

Row 5: * (Skip 1 st, 7 dc in next st, skip 1 st, sc next st)* 3 times; (skip 1 st, 9 tr in next st, ch 2, skip 1 st, sc in next st, ch 2) 15 times; rep from * to * 3 times, ending sc in 3rd ch of turning ch-4. Finish off, leaving a long yarn end for sewing.

Sew collar ends tog into a ring. Fold collar at seam and mark center at opposite edge. With wrong side of collar facing right side of garment, pin center to right shoulder, pin seam to left shoulder; pin in place around neckline, easing to fit. With right side of garment facing, and with size G crochet hook, working through both collar and the sc row around garment neckline, work 1 row sc all around, attaching collar to garment. Finish off; weave in all ends.

FLOWERS AND LEAVES

Note: *Use size G crochet hook for all flowers and leaves.*

Small Flower (make 2 with Color B)

Ch 4, join with sl st to form a ring.

Rnd 1: Ch 1, 10 sc in ring, join in beg sc.

Rnd 2: (Ch 2, 3 dc in next sc, ch 2, sl st in next sc) 5 times. Finish off, leaving a long yarn end for sewing flower to garment.

Large Flower (make 4 with Color A and 4 with Color B)

Ch 4, join with sl st to form a ring.

Rnd 1: Ch 1, 10 sc in ring, join in beg sc.

Rnd 2: (Ch 3, 3 tr in next sc, ch 3, sl st in next sc) 5 times. Finish off; leaving a long yarn end for sewing flower to garment.

Leaf (make 4 with Color B, 3 with Color A and 3 with Color C)

Ch 20.

Rnd 1: Sc in 2nd ch from hook and in next 5 sc; hdc in next 6 chs, dc in next 6 chs, 9 tr in last ch; working now in unused lps on opposite side of ch, dc in next 6 lps, hdc in next 6 lps, sc in last 6 lps; join in beg sc. Finish off, leaving a long yarn end for sewing leaf to garment.

Following arrangement shown in photos, sew flowers and leaves on back and front of collar on right shoulder, using matching yarn. With sewing thread and needle, sew one button in center of each flower.

IT'S SUEDE ROUND-UP TIME

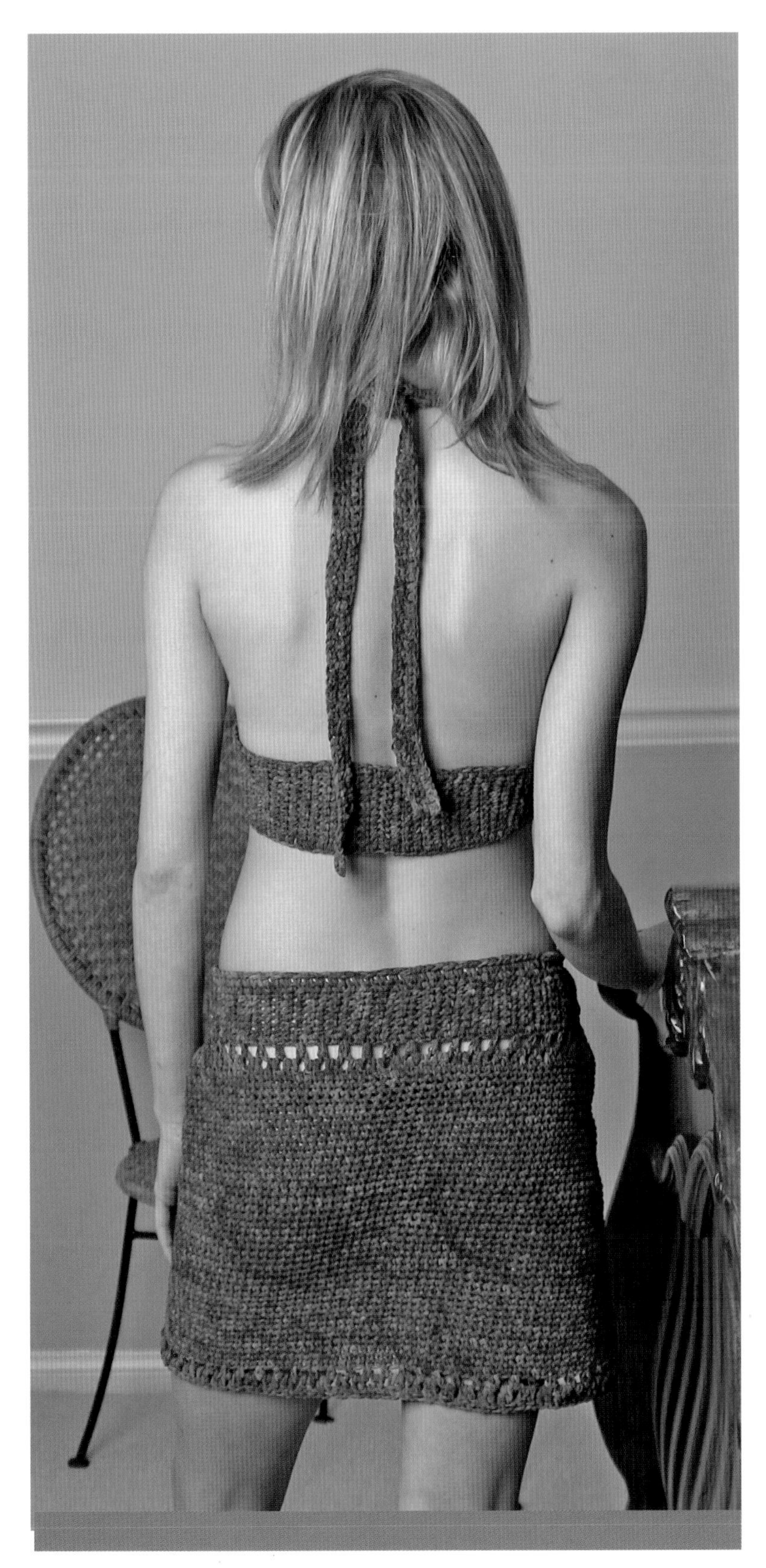

Designed by Tammy C. Hildebrand

In this outfit you are sure to catch the eye of the shyest cowboy. Soft sensual suede-type yarn helps to create the perfect outfit to glorify the wild West. Wear the fringed halter top over jeans, or, if the halter is too daring, wear the skirt with your western shirt.

SIZES	Small	Medium	Large
HALTER:			
Body Bust Measurements	30"-32"	34"-36"	38"-40"
Garment Bust Measurements	28"	32"	36"
SKIRT:			
Body Hip Measurements	30"-32"	34"-36"	38"-40"
Garment Hip Measurements	29"	33"	38"
Body Waist Measurements	23"-25"	27"-29"	31"-33"
Garment Waist Measurements	23"	27"	31"
Garment Length	14½"	14½"	14½"

Note: *Instructions are written for size Small; changes for sizes Medium and Large are in parentheses; garments stretch to fit.*

Materials

Suede type yarn,
- 3 (3½, 4) oz brown (for halter)
- 8½ (8¾, 9½) oz brown (for skirt)

Note: *Photographed models made with Berroco® Suede™ #3717 Brown*

3 gold metal craft rings, 2" diameter
1 yd ¼" wide elastic
Sewing needle and thread
Tapestry needle
Size G (4mm) crochet hook (or size required for gauge)

Gauges

Halter:
15 sc = 4"
15 sc rows = 4"

Skirt:
15 sc rows in waistband = 4"
14 sc in skirt rnds = 4"
17 sc rnds = 4"

INSTRUCTIONS

HALTER (right half)

Row 1 (right side): Starting at bra center front, work 12 sc over a ring: 12 sc; ch 1, turn.

Rows 2 through 4: 2 sc in first sc, sc in each sc to last sc, 2 sc in last sc: 18 sc at end of Row 4; ch 1, turn.

Rows 5 through 16 (20, 24): Sc in each sc; ch 1, turn.

Row 17 (21, 25): Skip first sc, sc in each rem sc: 17 sc; ch 1, turn.

Row 18 (22, 26): Sc in each sc up to last sc: 16 sc; ch 1, turn, leaving last sc unworked.

Rows 19 through 22 (23 through 26, 27 through 30): Rep Rows 17 and 18 (21 and 22, 25 and 26) two times more: 12 sc at end of last row.

Rows 23 through 48 (27 through 56, 31 through 64): Sc in each sc across; ch 1, turn. At end of last row, do not ch 1. Finish off, leaving a long length for sewing.

HALTER (left half)

Row 1: With right side facing, working in opposite side of same ring, work 12 sc over ring: 12 sc; ch 1, turn.

Rows 2 through 4: Rep Rows 2 through 4 of right half.

Rows 5 through 16 (20, 24): Sc in each sc across; ch 1, turn.

Row 17 (21, 25): Sc in each sc up to last sc: 17 sc; ch 1, turn, leaving last sc unworked.

Row 18 (22, 26): Skip first sc, sc in each rem sc: 16 sc; ch 1, turn.

Rows 19 through 22 (23 through 26, 27 through 30): Rep Rows 17 and 18 (21 and 22, 25 and 26) two times more: 12 sc at end of last row.

Rows 23 through 48 (27 through 56, 31 through 64): Sc in each sc across; ch 1, turn. At end of last row, do not ch 1. Finish off and weave in ends.

Matching sts on last row of each side, sew back seam with suede yarn and tapestry needle.

TOP HALTER EDGING

With right side facing, sc in ring, sc in edge of each row starting on right half and ending on left half, sc in ring: 98 (114, 130) sc. Finish off and weave in ends.

RIGHT STRAP

Row 1: With right side facing, join with sc in 11th (13th, 15th) sc of top halter edging on right half, sc in next 4 sc: 5 sc; ch 1, turn.

Rows 2 through 18: Sc in each sc; ch 1, turn.

Row 19: Sc in next 4 sc: 4 sc; ch 1, turn, leaving last sc unworked.

Rows 20 through 31: Sc in each sc; ch 1, turn.

Row 32: Sc in next 3 sc: 3 sc; ch 1, turn, leaving last sc unworked.

Rows 33 through 44: Sc in each sc; ch 1, turn.

Row 45: Sc in next 2 sc: 2 sc; ch 1, turn, leaving last sc unworked.

Rows 46 through 57: Sc in each sc; ch 1, turn.

Row 58: Sc in first sc: 1 sc; ch 1, turn, leaving last sc unworked.

Rows 59 through 89: Sc in sc; ch 1, turn. At end of Row 89, do not ch 1. Finish off and weave in ends.

LEFT STRAP

Row 1: With right side facing, join with sc in 84th (100th, 116th) sc of top halter edging on left half, sc in next 4 sc: 5 sc; ch 1, turn.

Rows 2 through 18: Sc in each sc; ch 1, turn.

Row 19: Skip first sc, sc in next 4 sc: 4 sc; ch 1, turn.

Rows 20 through 31: Sc in each sc; ch 1, turn.

Row 32: Skip first sc, sc in next 3 sc: 3 sc; ch 1, turn.

Rows 33 through 44: Sc in each sc; ch 1, turn.

Row 45: Skip first sc, sc in next 2 sc: 2 sc; ch 1, turn.

Rows 46 through 57: Sc in each sc; ch 1, turn.

Row 58: Skip first sc, sc in next sc: 1 sc; ch 1, turn.

Rows 59 through 89: Sc in sc; ch 1, turn. At end of Row 89, do not ch 1. Finish off and weave in ends.

STRAP EDGING (work on both straps)

With right side facing, join with sc in edge of Row 1 on strap, sc in edge of each row, sc in sc on Row 89, sc in edge of each row on opposite side: 179 sc. Finish off and weave in ends.

BOTTOM HALTER EDGING

With right side facing, join with sl st in ring, ch 3 (counts as dc), 2 dc in ring, sc in edge of each row; join with sl st in 3rd ch of beg ch-3: 96 (112, 128) sc and 3 dc. Finish off and weave in ends.

MIDRIFF

Row 1: With right side facing, join with sc in 23rd sc of bottom halter edging before 3 dc in ring, *ch 3, skip next st, sc in next st; rep from * 23 times more: 25 sc; ch 1, turn.

Rows 2 through 24: Sl st in first ch-3 sp, ch 1, sc in same sp, *ch 3, sc in next ch-3 sp; rep from * across: 2 sc at end of Row 24; ch 1, turn. At end of Row 24, do not ch 1. Finish off and weave in ends.

FRINGE

Following Fringe instructions on page 190, cut 16" lengths of yarn. Using 3 lengths in each knot, tie one knot in each ch-3 sp at both edges of Rows 1 through 23, and one fringe in ch-3 sp on Row 24: 47 fringe knots.

SKIRT

First Waistband Side

Row 1 (right side): Work 7 sc over second ring: 7 sc; ch 1, turn.

Rows 2 through 35 (43, 51): Sc in each sc across; ch 1, turn.

Row 36 (44, 52): Sc in each sc and in third ring at the same time. Finish off and weave in ends.

Second Waistband Side

Row 1: With right side facing, work 7 sc over opposite side of second ring: 7 sc; ch 1, turn.

Rows 2 through 35 (43, 51): Sc in each sc across; ch 1, turn.

Row 36 (44, 52): Sc in each sc and in opposite side of third ring at the same time. Finish off and weave in ends.

Top Waistband Edging

Rnd 1: With right side facing, join with sc in either ring, 6 sc in ring, sc in edge of each row, 7 sc in next ring, sc in edge of each row; join with sl st in beg sc: 86 (102, 118) sc.

Cut elastic to 22" (26", 30"). Join ends to form a circle and with sewing thread and needle, sew ends tog, being careful not to twist circle.

Rnd 2: Ch 1, working over elastic circle, sc in same st as joining and in each sc around; join with sl st in beg sc. Finish off and weave in ends.

Skirt

Rnd 1: With right side facing, working along bottom edge of waistband, join with sc in either ring, 13 sc in ring, sc in edge of each row, 14 sc in next ring, sc in edge of each row; join with sl st in beg sc: 100 (116, 132) sc.

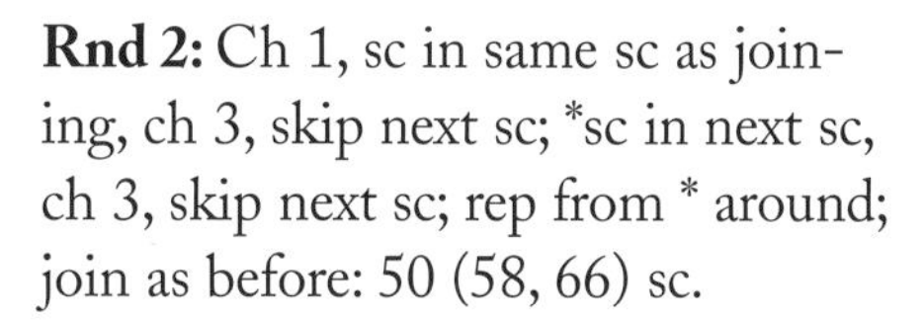

Rnd 2: Ch 1, sc in same sc as joining, ch 3, skip next sc; *sc in next sc, ch 3, skip next sc; rep from * around; join as before: 50 (58, 66) sc.

Rnd 3: Sl st in next ch-3 sp, ch 3, dc in same sp, 2 dc in each ch-3 sp around; join with sl st in 3rd ch of beg ch-3: 100 (116, 132) dc.

Rnd 4: Ch 1, sc in same st as joining, sc in each dc around; join with sl st in beg sc: 100 (116, 132) sc.

Rnd 5: Ch 1, sc in same st as joining, sc in each sc around; join with sl st in beg sc.

Rep Rnd 5 until skirt measures 14½", or desired length. At end of last rnd, do not finish off.

Bottom Skirt Edging

Rnd 1: Rep Rnd 2 on Skirt.

Rnd 2: Rep Rnd 3 on Skirt.

Rnd 3: Ch 1, sc around joining sl st, ch 1, skip next 2 dc; *sc in sp before next dc, ch 1, skip next 2 dc; rep from * around; join with sl st in beg sc: 50 (58, 66) sc. Finish off; weave in ends.

LITTLE BLACK DRESS

Designed by Doris Chan

For the experienced crocheter

The star of every woman's wardrobe is the Little Black Dress — that wonderful, versatile garment that clings to the body and takes its owner everywhere in style! This version is made in a beautiful black yarn with a built-in glisten, and trimmed with a deep faux fur border.

LITTLE BLACK DRESS

SIZES	Small	Medium	Large
Body Bust Measurements	28"-30"	32"-36"	38"-42"
Finished Bust Measurements	30"	36"	42"

***Note:** Instructions are written for size Small; changes for sizes Medium and Large are in parentheses. When worn, garment stretches in both width and length.*

Materials

Worsted weight yarn,
10½ (12¼, 15¾) oz black
Faux fur type yarn,
3 oz black for all sizes.
***Note:** Photographed model made with Lion Brand® Glitterspun #153 Onyx and Lion Brand® Festive Fur #153 Black*
Stitch markers or contrast yarn
Size I (5.5 mm) crochet hook
(or size required for gauge)
Size K (6.5 mm) crochet hook

Gauge

14 sc = 4" with smaller hook and worsted weight yarn

Stitch Guide

Double Triple Crochet (dtr): YO 3 times; insert hook in specified st and draw up a lp; (YO and draw through 2 lps on hook) 4 times: dtr made

Cluster (Cl): YO, insert hook in specified st and draw up a lp; YO and draw through 2 lps on hook; (YO, insert hook in same st, YO and draw up a loop; YO and draw through 2 lps on hook) 2 times; YO and draw through all 4 lps on hook: Cl made

Beginning Cluster (begCl): Ch 2, (YO, insert hook in beg st and draw up a lp; YO and draw through 2 lps on hook) twice; YO and draw through all 3 lps on hook: begCl made.

INSTRUCTIONS

***Note:** Garment begins at neckline and has increases at 4 corners to create raglan-type shoulders. It is worked in rnds, which are joined and turned.*

YOKE

With smaller hook and worsted weight yarn, ch 64; join with sl st to form a circle, being careful not to twist ch.

Foundation Rnd: Ch 1, sc in same st as joining and in each rem sc: 64 sc; join in beg sc, turn.

***Note:** On all following rnds, mark each corner ch-3 sp or corner 3 sc group for ease in following pattern.*

Rnd 1 (right side): BegCl; (ch 3, skip next sc, sc in next 5 sc; ch 3, skip next sc, Cl in next sc) 2 times; [ch 3, skip next sc; sc in next 5 sc; ch 3, skip next sc; (Cl, ch 3, Cl, mark for corner) in next sc,] 2 times; (ch 3, skip next sc, sc in next 5 sc; ch 3, skip next sc, Cl in next sc) 2 times; ch 3, skip next sc. sc in next 5 sc; ch 3, skip next sc; (Cl, ch 3, Cl, mark for corner) in next sc; ch 3, skip next sc, sc in next 5 sc; ch 3, skip next sc, Cl in same sc as begCl, ch 2 (mark for corner), sc in top of begCl; ch 1, turn: 4 corner (Cl, ch 3, Cl) groups, 4 Cls and 40 sc.

Rnd 2: 3 sc in first ch-3 sp for corner, sc in next Cl; *(sc in next ch-3 sp, ch 3, skip next sc, sc in next 3 sc; ch 3, skip next sc, sc in next ch-3 sp, sc in next Cl) to next corner ch-3 sp, 5 sc in corner ch-3 sp, sc in next Cl; rep from * 3 more times, end last rep 2 sc in beg corner ch-3 sp, sl st in center sc of beg 3-sc corner group, turn.

Rnd 3: BegCl in center sc of corner, ch 3, *sc in next 4 sc, work (sc in next ch-3 sp, ch 3, skip next sc; Cl in next sc, ch 3, skip next sc, sc in next ch-3 sp, sc in next 3 sc) across next edge to corner, ending last rep with sc in next 4 sc; work (ch 3, Cl, ch 3) in corner sc; rep from * 3 times more, ending last rep (ch 3, sl st) in beg Cl; ch 1, turn.

Rnd 4: Sc in first Cl; *sc in next ch-3 sp, ch 3, skip next sc, sc in next 3 sc; ch 3, skip next sc, sc in next ch-3 sp, sc in next Cl; rep from * to last 11 sts, sc in next ch-3 sp, ch 3, skip next sc, sc in next 3 sc; ch 3, skip next sc, sc in next ch-3 sp, sl st in beg sc; ch 1, turn.

Rnd 5: Sc in center sc of corner, sc in next sc; *sc in next ch-3 sp, ch 3, skip next sc, Cl in next sc; ch 3, skip next sc, sc in next ch-3 sp, sc in next 3 sc; rep from * to last 10 sts, sc in next ch-3 sp; ch 3, skip next sc, Cl in next sc; ch 3, skip next sc, sc in next ch-3 sp, sc in next sc, sl st in beg sc; ch 1, turn.

Rnd 6: Sc in center sc of corner, sc in next sc; *ch 3, skip next sc, sc in next ch-3 sp, sc in next Cl; sc in next ch-3 sp, ch 3, skip next sc, sc in next 3 sc; rep from * to last 10 sts, ch 3, skip next sc, sc in next ch-3 sp, sc in next Cl; sc in next ch-3 sp, ch 3, skip next sc, sc in next sc, sl st in beg sc; turn.

Rnd 7: BegCl in center sc of corner; *ch 3, skip next sc, sc in next ch-3 sp; ch 3, skip next sc, work (Cl in next sc, ch 3, skip next sc, sc in next ch-3 sp; sc in next 3 sc, sc in next ch-3 sp, ch 3, skip next sc) to next corner; (Cl, ch 3, Cl) in center sc of corner; rep from * 3 more times, ending last rep with Cl in same sc as begCl, ch 3, sc in top of begCl, ch 1, turn.

Rnd 8: Rep Rnd 2.

Rnd 9: Rep Rnd 3.

Rnd 10: Rep Rnd 4.

Rnd 11: Rep Rnd 5.

Rnd 12: Rep Rnd 6.

For Size Small Only:

Rnd 13: BegCl in center sc of corner; *ch 3, skip next sc, sc in next ch-3 sp; sc in next 3 sc, sc in next ch-3 sp, ch 3, skip next sc, Cl in next sc; rep from * to last 11 sts, ch 3, skip next sc, sc in next ch-3 sp, sc in next 3 sc; sc in next ch-3 sp, ch 3, skip next sc, sl st in begCl; ch 1, turn.

Rnd 14: Rep Rnd 4.

Rnd 15: Rep Rnd 5; yoke is now completed for Size Small; proceed to Body for size Small.

For Sizes Medium and Large Only:

Rnd 13: Rep Rnd 7.

Rnd 14: Rep Rnd 2.

Rnd 15: Rep Rnd 3.

Rnd 16: Rep Rnd 4.

Rnd 17: Rep Rnd 5; yoke is now completed for size Medium; proceed to Body for size Medium.

For Size Large Only:

Rnd 18: Rep Rnd 6.

Rnd 19: Rep Rnd 7.

Rnd 20: Rep Rnd 2.

Rnd 21: Rep Rnd 3; yoke is now completed for size Large; proceed to Body for size Large.

BODY

***Note:** Body is formed by folding yoke rectangle so that the 2 long sides form the body Front and Back, and the two shorts sides form the armholes. The body is then worked in rounds from yoke to hemline.*

For Sizes Small and Medium Only:

Rnd 1 (wrong side): Sc in center sc of corner; *sc in next sc, (ch 3, skip next sc, sc in next ch-3 sp, sc in next Cl; sc in next ch-3 sp, ch 3, skip next sc, sc in next 3 sc) 5 (6) times, ending last rep with sc in next sc;* insert hook in next sc (corner sc) and draw up a lp, skip one short side of yoke (this will be sleeve opening), insert hook in next marked corner sc and draw up a lp, YO and draw through all 3 lps on hook; repeat from * to *; insert hook in corner sc and draw up a lp, skip next short side of yoke (this will be opposite sleeve opening), insert hook in beg sc, YO and draw through all lps on hook; turn: 120 (144) sts including 20 (24) ch-3 sps.

Rnd 2: BegCl in first sc; *ch 3, skip next sc, sc in next ch-3 sp; sc in next 3 sc, sc in next ch-3 sp, ch 3, skip next sc, Cl in next sc; rep from * to last 11 sts, ch 3, skip next sc, sc in next ch-3 sp; sc in next 3 sc, sc in next ch-3 sp, ch 3, skip next sc, sl st in begCl; ch 1, turn.

Rnd 3: Sc in first Cl; *sc in next ch-3 sp, ch 3, skip next sc, sc in next 3 sc; ch 3, skip next sc, sc in next ch-3 sp, sc in next Cl; rep from * to last 11 sts, sc in next ch-3 sp, ch 3, skip next sc, sc in next 3 sc; ch 3, skip next sc, sc in next ch-3 sp, sl st in beg sc; ch 1, turn.

Rnd 4: Sc in first 2 sc; *sc in next ch-3 sp, ch 3, skip next sc, Cl in next sc; ch 3, skip next sc, sc in next ch-3 sp, sc in next 3 sc; rep from * to last 10 sts, sc in next ch-3 sp, ch 3, skip next sc; Cl in next sc, ch 3, skip next sc, sc in next ch-3 sp, sc in next sc, sl st in beg sc; ch 1, turn.

Rnd 5: Sc in first 2 sc; *ch 3, skip next sc, sc in next ch-3 sp, sc in next Cl; sc in next ch-3 sp, ch 3, skip next sc, sc in next 3 sc; rep from * to last 10 sts, ch 3, skip next sc, sc in next ch-3 sp, sc in next Cl; sc in next ch-3 sp, ch 3, skip next sc, sc in next sc, sl st in beg sc; turn.

Rep Rnds 2 through 5, nine times more, or to desired length minus 4". End by working a wrong-side row. Finish off; weave in ends.

For Size Large Only:

Rnd 1 (wrong side): Sc in center sc of corner; *[sc in next ch-3 sp, ch 3, skip next sc, sc in next 3 sc; ch 3, skip next sc, sc in next ch-3 sp, sc in next Cl] 7 times, ending last rep at sc in ch-3 sp before corner Cl*; insert hook in next st (corner Cl) and draw up a lp, skip one short side of yoke (for sleeve opening), insert hook in next marked corner Cl and draw up a lp, YO and draw through all 3 lps on hook; repeat from * to *; insert hook in corner Cl and draw up a lp, skip next short side of yoke (for opposite sleeve opening), insert hook in beg sc, YO and draw through all lps on hook, turn: 168 sts including 28 ch-3 sps.

Rnd 2: Sc in first 2 sc; *sc in next ch-3 sp, ch 3, skip next sc, Cl in next sc; ch 3, skip next sc, sc in next ch-3 sp, sc in next 3 sc; rep from * to last 10 sts, sc in next ch-3 sp, ch 3, skip next sc; Cl in next sc, ch 3, skip next sc, sc in next ch-3 sp, sc in next sc, sl st in beg sc; ch 1, turn.

Rnd 3: Sc in first 2 sc; *ch 3, skip next sc; sc in next ch-3 sp, sc in next Cl; sc in next ch-3 sp, ch 3, skip next sc, sc in next 3 sc; rep from * to last 10 sts, ch 3, skip next sc, sc in next ch-3 sp; sc in next Cl, sc in next ch-3 sp, ch 3, skip next sc, sc in next sc, sl st in beg sc; turn.

Rnd 4: BegCl in first sc; *ch 3, skip next sc, sc in next ch-3 sp, sc in next 3 sc; sc in next ch-3 sp, ch 3, skip next sc, Cl in next sc; rep from * to last 11 sts. ch 3, skip next sc, sc in next ch-3 sp; sc in next 3 sc. sc in next ch-3 sp, ch 3, skip next sc, sl st in begCl; ch 1, turn.

Rnd 5: Sc in first Cl; *sc in next ch-3 sp, ch 3, skip next sc, sc in next 3 sc, ch 3; skip next sc, sc in next ch-3 sp, sc in next Cl; rep from * to last 11 sts, sc in next ch-3 sp, ch 3, skip next sc, sc in next 3 sc, ch 3, skip next sc, sc in next ch-3 sp, sl st in beg sc; ch 1, turn.

Rnd 6: Rep Rnd 2.

Rnd 7: Rep Rnd 3.

Rep Rnds 4 through 7, eight times more, or to desired length, minus 4". End by working a wrong-side row. Finish off; weave in ends.

SLEEVES (make 2)

Note: *Sleeves are attached directly to yoke and worked from armhole to wrist.*

With wrong side facing, at one underarm locate and mark the corner sc previously joined for the Body.

For Sizes Small and Medium Only

Rnd 1 (wrong side): With smaller hook, join worsted weight yarn with sl st in sc just marked; ch 1, sc in same st, sc in next sc of armhole; [ch 3, skip next sc. sc in next ch-3 sp, sc in next Cl; sc in next ch-3 sp, ch 3, skip next sc, sc in next 3 sc] 2 (3) times; ch 3, skip next sc, sc in next ch-3 sp, sc in next Cl; sc in next ch-3 sp, ch 3, skip next sc, sc in next sc, sl st in beg sc, turn.

Rnd 2: BegCl in first sc; *ch 3, skip next sc, sc in next ch-3 sp, sc in next 3 sc; sc in next ch-3 sp, ch 3, skip next sc, Cl in next sc; rep from * to last 11 sts, ch 3, skip next sc, sc in next ch-3 sp; sc in next 3 sc, sc in next ch-3 sp, ch 3, skip next sc, sl st in begCl; ch 1, turn.

Rnd 3: Sc in first Cl; *sc in next ch-3 sp, ch 3, skip next sc; sc in next 3 sc, ch 3, skip next sc, sc in next ch-3 sp, sc in next Cl; rep from * to last 11 sts, sc in next ch-3 sp, ch 3, skip next sc; sc in next 3 sc, ch 3, skip next sc, sc in next ch-3 sp, sl st in beg sc; ch 1, turn.

Rnd 4: Sc in first 2 sc; *sc in next ch-3 sp, ch 3, skip next sc; Cl in next sc, ch 3, skip next sc; sc in next ch-3 sp, sc in next 3 sc; rep from * to last 10 sts, sc in next ch-3 sp, ch 3, skip next sc; Cl in next sc, ch 3, skip next sc, sc in next ch-3 sp, sc in next sc, sl st in beg sc; ch 1, turn.

Rnd 5: Sc in first 2 sc; *ch 3, skip next sc, sc in next ch-3 sp, sc in next Cl; sc in next ch-3 sp, ch 3, skip next sc, sc in next 3 sc; rep from * to last 10 sts, ch 3, skip next sc, sc in next ch-3 sp; sc in next Cl, sc in next ch-3 sp, ch 3, skip next sc, sc in next sc, sl st in beg sc; turn.

Rep Rnds 2 through 5 five times more, or to desired length; end by working a wrong-side row. Leave yarn attached after last row and work Sleeve Edging.

For Size Large Only

Rnd 1 (wrong side): With smaller hook, join worsted weight yarn with sl st in corner sc previously joined for body; ch 1, sc in same st; [sc in next ch-3 sp; ch 3, skip next sc sc in next 3 sc; ch 3, skip next sc, sc in next ch-3 sp, sc in next cl] 4 times across armhole; sc in next ch-3 sp, ch 3, skip next sc, sc in next 3 sc; ch 3, skip next sc; sc in next ch-3 sp, sl st in beg sc; ch 1, turn.

Rnd 2: Sc in first 2 sc; *sc in next ch-3 sp, ch 3, skip next sc, Cl in next sc; ch 3, skip next sc, sc in next ch-3 sp, sc in next 3 sc; rep from * to last 10 sts, sc in next ch-3 sp, ch 3, skip next sc, Cl in next sc; ch 3, skip next sc, sc in next ch-3 sp, sc in next sc, sl st in beg sc; ch 1, turn.

Rnd 3: Sc in first2 sc; *ch 3, skip next sc, sc in next ch-3 sp, sc in next Cl; sc in next ch-3 sp, ch 3, skip next sc, sc in next 3 sc; rep from * to last 10 sts; ch 3, skip next sc, sc in next ch-3 sp; sc in next Cl, sc in next ch-3 sp; ch 3, skip next sc, sc in next sc, sl st in beg sc; turn.

Rnd 4: BegCl in first sc; *ch 3, skip next sc, sc in next ch-3 sp, sc in next 3 sc; sc in next ch-3 sp; ch 3, skip next sc, Cl in next sc; rep from * to last 11 sts, ch 3, skip next sc, sc in next ch-3 sp; sc in next 3 sc, sc in next ch-3 sp, ch 3, skip next sc, sl st in begCl; ch 1, turn.

Rnd 5: Sc in first Cl; *sc in next ch-3 sp, ch 3, skip next sc, sc in next 3 sc; ch 3, skip next sc, sc in next ch-3 sp; sc in next Cl; rep from * to last 11 sts, sc in next ch-3 sp, ch 3, skip next sc, sc in next 3 sc; ch 3, skip next sc, sc in next ch-3 sp, sl st in beg sc; ch 1, turn.

Rnd 6: Rep Rnd 2.

Rnd 7: Rep Rnd 3.

Rep Rnds 4 through 7, five times more or to desired length, end by working a wrong-side row. Leave yarn attached after last row and work Sleeve Edging.

SLEEVE EDGING (for all sizes)

Rnd 1: Ch 1, sc in each sc and in each ch-3 sp around, sl st in beg sc; ch 1, turn.

Rnd 2: Skip first st; *sc in next sc, ch 1, skip next sc; rep from * around, sl st in beg sc; ch 1, turn.

Rnd 3: *Sc in next ch-1 sp, sc in next sc; rep from * around, sl st in beg sc. Finish off; weave in ends.

NECK EDGING (for all sizes)

With the right side facing, with smaller hook, join worsted weight yarn with sl st in joining st of beg ch.

Rnd 1: Ch 1; working in unused lps of beg ch, sc in each ch around, sl st in beg sc; ch 1, turn: 64 sc.

Rnds 2 and 3: Work same as Sleeve Edging Rnds 2 and 3.

SKIRT TRIM

Note: *Dress is finished with slightly ruffled trim, about 4" deep, crocheted in joined rounds in faux fur yarn.*

Holding dress with the wrong side of garment facing and hem at top; with larger hook, join faux fur yarn with sl st in last sc of Body.

Rnd 1: Ch 5, (tr, ch 1, tr) in same sc; [ch 1, skip (sc, ch-3 sp, sc), sc in next sc, skip (sc, ch-3 sp, sc); (ch 1, tr) 5 times in next sc] 9 (11, 13) times; ch 1, skip (sc, ch-3 sp, sc), sc in next sc, ch 1; (tr, ch 1) 2 times in same sc as beg; sl st in 4th ch of beg ch; ch 1, do not turn.

Rnd 2: Sc in same st; [ch 2, (dtr, ch 2) 4 times in next sc; skip next 2 tr, sc in next tr] 9 (11, 13) times; ch 2, (dtr, ch 2) 4 times in next sc; skip next 2 tr, sl st in beg sc; ch 1, do not turn.

Rnd 3: Sc in same st; [ch 4; sk next dtr; (Cl in next ch-2 sp, ch 3) 2 times; Cl in next ch-2 sp; ch 4; sc in next sc] 9 (11, 13) times; ch 4; sk next dtr; (Cl in next ch-2 sp, ch 3) 2 times; Cl in next ch-2 sp; ch 4, sl st in beg sc. Finish off; weave in all ends.

BUGSY'S DATE

Designed by Nancy Nehring

Step back to the days of Prohibition when Bugsy Siegal ruled Las Vegas, and this glamorous outfit would certainly have been worn by Bugsy's lady. Once again in style today, it is the perfect choice for a date with today's high roller. Crystal beads accent the form-fitting dress, and a whimsical faux fur fox stole and a flapper hat complete the outfit.

BUGSY'S DATE

SIZES	X-Small	Small	Medium	Large	X-Large
Chest above Bust	34"	36"	38"	40"	42"

Note: *Instructions are written for size Extra Small; changes for sizes Small, Medium, Large and Extra Large are in parentheses.*

DRESS

Materials

Fingering weight yarn, 17½ (19, 20, 22, 22) oz rose
Note: *Photographed model made with Cotton Clouds Mina Dina*
Size 6/0 seed beads, silver lined pink, 3½ (3½, 4, 4, 4) oz
14" hidden zipper
Sewing thread, rose
Sewing needle
Sewing pins
Tapestry needle with narrow eye to fit through beads
Hook and eye
1" wide grosgrain ribbon, 2½ yds
¼" wide grosgrain ribbon, 12"
Optional: 1 yd lightweight knit lining fabric, 44" or 60" wide
Size 3 (2.1mm) steel crochet hook (or size required for gauge)

Gauge

4 diagonal sts = 2⅜"
28 sc = 4"

Pattern Stitches

Front bead double crochet (fbdc): YO, slide bead up to front of YO, insert hook in specified st, YO and draw up a lp, (YO and draw through 2 lps on hook) twice, making sure bead is on the front side of work: fbdc made.

Back bead double crochet (bbdc): YO, insert hook in specified st, YO and draw up a lp, slide bead up to back of work, (YO and draw through 2 lps on hook) twice, making sure bead is on the back side of work: bbdc made.

Diagonal Stitch (Dst): Sc in specified st or sp, ch 2, 3 dc in same st or sp: Dst made.

INSTRUCTIONS

BODY

Starting at top of front, ch 152 (164, 176, 188, 200).

Row 1 (right side): (Skip first 2 chs, dc in next 3 chs, skip 2 chs, sc in next ch); *(ch 2, dc in next 3 chs, skip 2 chs, sc in next ch): Dst made; rep from * 23 (25, 27, 29, 31) times more: 25 (27, 29, 31, 33) Dsts; ch 5, turn.

Row 2: (Skip 2 chs, dc in next 3 chs, sc in next ch-2 sp); *(ch 2, 3 dc in same ch-2 sp, sc in next ch-2 sp); rep from * 23 (25, 27, 29, 31) times more; (ch 2, 3 dc in same ch-2 sp): last Dst made: 26 (28, 30, 32, 34) Dsts; ch 5, turn.

Rows 3 through 5: Rep Row 2 three times more, increasing underlined number by one in each row: one more Dst in each row than in previous row. At end of Row 5: 29 (31, 33, 35, 37) Dsts; ch 5, turn.

Row 6: Rep Row 2, increasing by one more Dst: 30 (32, 34, 36, 38) Dsts; do not ch 5 at end of row; place marker or safety pin in last st, remove hook, turn; do not finish off.

Join new skein with sl st in 3rd ch of turning ch-5 at beg of row, ch 81 (87, 87, 93, 99); finish off; turn. Insert hook back in last st and remove stitch marker or safety pin, ch 82 (88, 94, 94, 100); turn.

Row 7: (Skip first 3 chs, 2 dc in next ch, skip 2 chs, sc in next ch); *(ch 2, dc in next 3 chs, skip 2 chs, sc in next ch); rep from * 11 (12, 13, 13, 14) times more; (ch 2, dc in next 3 chs, sc in next ch-2 sp) ; **(ch 2, 3 dc in same ch-2 sp, sc in next ch-2 sp; rep from ** 28 (30, 32, 34, 36) times more; (ch 2, 3 dc in same ch-2 sp, skip 2 chs, sc in next ch); ***(ch 2, dc in next 3 chs, skip 2 chs, sc in next ch) ; rep from *** 12 (13, 13, 14, 15) times more: 57 (61, 64, 67, 71) Dsts; ch 3, turn.

Row 8: (Work 2 dc in last sc made, sc in next ch-2 sp); *(ch 2, 3 dc in same ch-2 sp, sc in next ch-2 sp); rep from * 55 (59, 62, 65, 69) times more: 57 (61, 64, 67, 71) Dst; ch 3, turn.

Rep Row 8 until dress measures about 35" (or to desired length less 2"). At end of last row, do not ch 3. Finish off; weave in ends.

BEAD EDGING

Note: *With tapestry needle, string 3 feet of beads onto yarn. When beads run out, cut yarn and add 3 feet more beads. Tie ends of yarn together and continue.*

With right side facing, join with sl st in last sc, ch 3.

Row 1: (Work 2 fbdc in last sc, sc in next ch-2 sp); *(ch 2, 3 fbdc in same ch-2 sp, sc in next ch-2 sp); rep from * across: 57 (61, 64, 67, 71) Dst with beads; ch 3, turn.

Row 2: (Work 2 bbdc in last sc, sc in next ch-2 sp); *(ch 2, 3 bbdc in same ch-2 sp, sc in next ch-2 sp); rep from * across; ch 3, turn.

Rows 3 through 8: Rep Rows 1 and 2 of Bead Edging 3 times more. At end of Row 8, do not ch 3. Finish off; weave in ends.

TOP FRONT EDGING

Holding piece with right side facing and beg ch at top, working in unused lps of beg ch, join with sc in 4th ch (same ch as last dc on Row 1 of Body) of foundation ch (counts as first st on next row).

Row 1 (right side): Hdc in next ch, dc in next ch, tr in next ch; *skip next 2 chs, sc in next ch, hdc in next ch, dc in next ch, tr in next ch; rep from * 22 (24, 26, 28, 30) times more; skip next 2 chs, sc in next ch: 97 (105, 113, 121, 129) sts; ch 1, turn.

Row 2: Skip first st, sc in each st across to last 2 sts, skip next st, sc in last st: 95 (103, 111, 119, 127) sc; ch 1, turn.

Rows 3 through 7: Rep Row 2 five times more: 2 fewer sc in each row than in previous row. At end of Row 7: 85 (93, 101, 109, 117) sc; do not ch 1. Finish off; weave in ends.

TOP BACK RIGHT EDGING

Holding piece with right side facing and beg ch at top, working in unused lps of ch at end of Row 6 of Body, join with sc in first ch after last Dst on Row 6 (counts as first st on next row).

Row 1: Hdc in next ch, dc in next ch, tr in next ch; *skip next 2 chs, sc in next ch, hdc in next ch, dc in next ch, tr in next ch; rep from * 11 (12, 13, 13, 14) times more; skip next 2 chs, sc in next ch: 53 (57, 61, 61, 65) sts; ch 1, turn.

Row 2: Sc in each st across, 2 sc around post of last dc on Row 6 of Body: 55 (59, 63, 63, 67) sc; ch 1, turn.

Row 3: 2 sc in first sc, sc in each rem sc across: 56 (60, 64, 64, 68) sc; ch 1, turn.

Row 4: Sc in each sc across, sc in next 2 chs at base of first Dst on Row 5 of Body: 58 (62, 66, 66, 70) sc; ch 1, turn.

Row 5: Rep Row 3: 59 (63, 67, 67, 71) sc.

Row 6: Sc in each sc across, sc in next ch at base of first Dst on Row 5 of Body and around post of last dc on Row 4 of Body: 61 (65, 69, 69, 73) sc; ch 1, turn.

Row 7: Rep Row 3: 62 (66, 70, 70, 74) sc; do not ch 1. Finish off; weave in ends.

TOP BACK LEFT EDGING

Holding piece with right side facing and beg ch at top, working in unused lps of ch joined at beg of Row 6 of Body, join with sl st in last ch at center back.

Row 1: Sl st in next 2 chs, sc in next ch, hdc in next ch, dc in next ch, tr in next ch; *skip next 2 chs, sc in next ch, hdc in next ch, dc in next ch, tr in next ch; rep from * 11 (12, 12, 13, 14) times more; skip next 2 chs, sc in next ch (same ch as ch joining at beg of Row 6 of Body), sc in next 2 chs at base of last Dst on Row 6 of Body: 55 (59, 59, 63, 67) sts; ch 1, turn.

Row 2: 2 sc in first st, sc in each rem st across, leaving beg sl sts unworked: 56 (60, 60, 64, 68) sc; ch 1, turn.

Row 3: Sc in each sc across, 2 sc around post of last dc on Row 5 of Body: 58 (62, 62, 66, 70) sc; ch 1, turn.

Row 4: 2 sc in first sc, sc in each rem st across: 59 (63, 63, 67, 71) sc; ch 1, turn.

Row 5: Sc in each sc across, sc in next 2 chs at base of first Dst on Row 4 of Body: 61 (65, 65, 69, 73) sc; ch 1, turn.

Row 6: Rep Row 4: 62 (66, 66, 70, 74) sc; ch 1, turn.

Row 7: Sc in each sc across; do not ch 1. Finish off; weave in ends.

RIGHT UNDERARM EDGING

Holding piece with right side facing and beg ch at top, join with sl st in same ch as last sc on Row 1 of Top Front Edging.

Row 1: Sc in next 2 chs, 2 sc around post (vertical bar) of next last dc on Row 2 of Body, sc in next 3 chs at beg of Row 3 of Body, sc around post of last dc on Row 4 of Body, sl

st in next 2 sc on Row 7 of Top Back Right Edging: 8 sc; ch 1, turn.

Row 2: 2 sc in first sc, sc in each rem sc across underarm to last sc, 2 sc in last sc, sl st in edge of first sc on Row 2 of Top Front Edging: 10 sc. Finish off; weave in ends.

LEFT UNDERARM EDGING

Hold piece with right side facing and beg ch at top; join yarn with sl st in last sc on Row 7 of Top Back Left Edging.

Row 1: Sc in first ch at base of first Dst on Row 4 of Body, 2 sc around post of last dc on Row 3 of Body, sc in next 3 chs at beg of Row 2 of Body, skip first ch on foundation ch of Body, sc in next 2 chs, sl st in same ch as beg sc on Row 1 of Top Front Edging, sl st in edge of last sc on Row 2 of Top Front Edging: 8 sc; ch 1, turn.

Row 2: 2 sc in first sc, sc in each rem sc across underarm to last sc, 2 sc in last sc, sl st in next sc on Row 7 of Top Back Left Edging: 10 sc. Finish off; weave in ends.

FINAL EDGING

Hold piece with right side facing and beg ch at top; join yarn with sc in first sc of Top Back Left Edging, sc in each sc across Top Back Left Edging to last sc, skip last sc on Top Back Left Edging, sc in each sc on Left Underarm Edging, sc in edge of Rows 3 through 6 on Top Front Edging, 3 sc in first sc on Row 7 of Top Front Edging, sc in each sc across Row 7 of Top Front Edging, 3 sc in last sc on Row 7 of Top Front Edging, sc in edge of Rows 6 through 3 on Top Front Edging, sc in each sc across Right Underarm Edging, skip first sc on Top Back Right Edging, sc in each rem sc on Top Back Right Edging. Finish off; weave in ends.

SHOULDER STRAP (make 2)

Ch 8.

Row 1: Sc in 2nd ch from hook and in each ch across: 7 sc; ch 1, turn.

Row 2: Sc in each sc across; ch 1, turn.

Rep Row 2 until strap measures 16" (17", 18", 19", 20") or desired length plus 2". At end of last row, do not ch 1. Finish off; weave in ends.

Cut 1" wide grosgrain ribbon to length of strap. With sewing thread and needle, sew ribbon to back of strap along both long edges using running stitch.

Position straps on inside of edgings 1" from top corners of Top Front Edging and 2" from top center edge of Top Back Edging, overlapping edgings by about 3/4". With needle and thread, sew straps to Row 1 and Row 7 of Top Edgings.

String 39 beads onto yarn. Join with sl st in Final Edging on front in 4th st from one edge of strap (between strap and corner of Front Edging), ch 15, pulling up a bead in each ch; join with sl st in edge of strap about 2 1/2" up from Final Edging so it does not droop or pull; finish off. Join with sl st in Final Edging in 7th st from same edge of strap (in corner of Front Edging), ch 24, pulling up a bead in each ch; join with sl st in edge of strap about 4" from Final Edging so it does not droop or pull; finish off. Rep on other side of same strap and on both sides of other strap.

INSERT ZIPPER

Pin zipper into place on wrong side of dress along both edges of center back with top of zipper teeth at bottom of Top Edging. Edges of crochet should touch and completely hide zipper, with rows matching on each side of zipper. With sewing needle and sewing thread, sew zipper in place with back stitch. With tapestry needle and yarn, match rows and sew remainder of center back seam below zipper, stopping just above beaded rows to provide a walking slit.

OPTIONAL LINING

Cut lining fabric 36" (38", 40", 42", 44") wide by length of dress (top of Top Front Edging to top of Bead Edging). Trim or dart top of lining to conform to shape of top of dress. Serge or hem bottom edge of lining, stretching fabric a little. Sew lining tog at center back below zipper, using 1" seam allowance. Pin lining into place on wrong side of dress along top edge and along zipper, turning under 1" along each edge of zipper 1/4" away from zipper teeth. Blind stitch lining into place along zipper. Baste top edge of lining with long running stitch.

FACING

Cut 1/4" wide ribbon into two 6" lengths. Center and pin on inside of Underarm Edgings. Cut 1" wide grosgrain ribbon into two 12" and one 20" length. Center and pin 12" lengths on inside of Top Back Right and Left Edgings and 20" length on inside of Top Front Edging, covering bottom edges of straps. ***Note:*** *Ribbons should cover edges of lining fabric.* If possible, have person try on dress and adjust length of ribbon facings as necessary, stretching or gathering dress to fit. Trim ends of ribbon as necessary. Turn under ends of front and back ribbons with underarm ribbons beneath them, mitering corners to align with underarm ribbons. With needle and sewing thread, use running stitch to sew outer edges of ribbons to top and bottom edges of edgings. Sew hook and eye to top edge of back ribbon facings at center back.

CLOCHE

Size

Fits up to 23" head

Materials

Cotton crochet thread, size 3
300 yds tan

Note: *Photographed model made with J&P Coats® Royale™ Fashion Crochet Thread, size 3, #377 Tan*

Size 1 (3mm) steel crochet hook (or size required for gauge)
1/2" loop edge edge satin ribbon, wine color, 2 feet long
1 5/8" diameter button of choice
Three 4" long brown feathers
Sewing thread, wine color
Sewing needle

Gauge

24 sc = 4"

INSTRUCTIONS

Ch 4, join with sl st to form a ring.

Rnd 1 (right side): Ch 1, 6 sc in ring: 6 sc; join with sl st in first sc. Place marker in first sc and move up with each rnd.

Rnd 2: Ch 1, 2 sc in first sc and in each sc around: 12 sc; join as before.

Rnd 3: Ch 1; *sc in first sc, 2 sc in next sc; rep from * around: 18 sc; join.

Rnd 4: Working in back lps only for this rnd, ch 1, sc in first 2 sc, 2 sc in next sc; *sc in next 2 sc, 2 sc in next sc; rep from * around: 24 sc; join.

Rnd 5: Ch 1, sc in first **3** sc, 2 sc in next sc; *sc in next **3** sc, 2 sc in next sc; rep from * around: 30 sc; join.

Rnds 6 through 22: Rep Rnd 5 seventeen times more, increasing bold numbers by one sc in each rnd and working Rnds 8, 12, 16 and 20 in back lp of each sc: 6 more sc in each rnd than in previous rnd. At end of Rnd 22: 132 sc.

Rnd 23: Ch 1, sc in first sc and in each sc; join.

Rnd 24: Working in back lps only for this rnd, ch 1, sc in each sc; join.

Rnds 25 through 27: Rep Rnd 23 three times more.

Rnd 28: Rep Rnd 24.

Rnds 29 through 31: Rep Rnd 23 three times more.

Rnd 32: Rep Rnd 24.

Rnds 33 and 34: Rep Rnd 23 twice more.

Rnd 35: Ch 1, 2 sc in first sc, sc in next 43 sc; *2 sc in next sc, sc in next 43 sc; rep from * once: 135 sc; join.

Rnd 36: Rep Rnd 24.

Rnds 37 and 38: Rep Rnd 23 twice more.

Rnd 39: Ch 1, 2 sc in first sc, sc in next 44 sc; *2 sc in next sc, sc in next 44 sc; rep from * once: 138 sc; join.

Rnd 40: Rep Rnd 24.

Rnds 41 and 42: Rep Rnd 23 twice more.

Rnd 43: Ch 1, 2 sc in first sc, sc in next 34 sc; *2 sc in next sc, sc in next 33 sc; rep from * once; 2 sc in next sc, sc in next 34 sc: 142 sc; join.

Rnd 44: Rep Rnd 24.

Rnds 45 through 47: Rep Rnd 23 three times more.

Rnd 48: Rep Rnd 24.

Rnds 49 through 51: Rep Rnd 23 three times more.

BRIM

Rnd 52: Working in front lps only for this rnd, ch 1, 2 sc in first sc, sc in next 5 sc; *2 sc in next sc, sc in next 7 sc; rep from * 16 times more: 160 sc; join.

Rnd 53: Rep Rnd 23. Finish off; weave in ends.

Now work 3 rows of brim shaping, after which continue with Rnd 54 of hat.

BRIM SHAPING

Row 1: With right side facing, skip 68 sc after last sc on Rnd 53, join with sl st in next sc, ch 1, sc in same sc, sc in next 23 sc: 24 sc. Finish off; weave in ends.

Row 2: With right side facing, skip 56 sc after last sc on Rnd 53, join with sl st in next sc, ch 1, sc in same sc, sc in next 11 sc on Rnd 53, sc in next 24 sc on Row 1 of Brim Shaping, sc in next 12 sc on Rnd 53: 48 sc. Finish off; weave in ends.

Row 3: With right side facing, skip

44 sc after last sc on Rnd 53, join with sl st in next sc, ch 1, sc in same sc, sc in next 11 sc on Rnd 53, sc in next 48 sc on Row 2 of Brim Shaping, sc in next 12 sc on Rnd 53: 72 sc. Finish off; weave in ends.

BRIM (continued)

Rnd 54: With right side facing, join with sl st in back lp of first sc on Rnd 53, ch 1, sc in back lp of same sc and in back lp of each sc around: 160 sc; join.

Rnds 55 through 58: Rep Rnd 23 four times more. At end of Rnd 58, finish off; weave in ends.

Sew top edge of ribbon to Rnd 48, folding ribbon ends beneath ribbon and seaming ends together. Sew feathers and button to hat with bottom edge of button aligned with bottom edge of ribbon and positioned above beg of Row 3 of Brim Shaping.

FAUX FOX FUR

Size

8" wide x 40" long body
Head: 7" long
Tail: 16" long

Materials

Size 5 pearl cotton,
135 yds, white
135 yds, red/brown
2 yds, brown
Nylon microfiber eyelash yarn,
100g red/brown
50 g white, white
Note: *Photographed model made with DMC Pearl Cotton, Size 5, White, #221 Red/Brown and #801 Brown and Muench Apart, #8 Red/Brown and #19 White*
One Darice animal nose, 15 mm
Two Darice animal eyes, 12 mm
Knee-hi nylon stocking
Polyester fiberfill
Duchess satin, dark brown, 10" x 44"
Black polar fleece, 8" x 40"
1/2" diameter (size 1) black snap with 4 holes
Two round wood beads, 14 mm
Brown sewing thread
Sewing needle
Sewing pins
Tailor's chalk
Ruler
Size 7 (1.65 mm) steel crochet hook (or size required for gauge)
Size K (6.5 mm) crochet hook (or size required for gauge)

GAUGE

With size 7 hook and pearl cotton: 15 sc = 2"
With size K hook and eyelash yarn: 10 sc = 2"

Pattern Stitches

Bullion stitch (bullion st): YO 10 times, insert hook in specified st, YO and draw up a lp, YO and draw through 11 lps on hook, YO and draw through 2 lps on hook: bullion made.

To change color: Work st until 2 lps rem on hook, drop old color, pick up new color and draw through both lps on hook, cut dropped color.

INSTRUCTIONS

HEAD

With white pearl cotton and size 7 hook, ch 4, join with sl st to form a ring.

Rnd 1: Ch 1, 8 sc in ring: 8 sc; do not join. Place marker in last sc and move up as you work.

Rnd 2: 2 sc in each sc around: 16 sc.

Rnd 3: Sc in each sc around.

Rnds 4 through 5: Rep Rnd 3.

Rnd 6: 2 sc in first sc, sc in next **6** sc, 2 sc in next sc (top jaw formed), sc in next **8** sc (bottom jaw formed): 18 sc.

Rnd 7: Rep Rnd 3.

Rnds 8 through 23: Rep Rnds 6 and 7 eight times more, increasing bold numbers in Rnd 6 by one more than in previous rep of Rnd 6: for a total of 2 more sc in each rnd than in previous rnd. At end of Rnd 23: 34 sc.

Rnd 24: 2 sc in first sc, sc in next 15 sc, 2 sc in next sc, sc in next 17 sc: 36 sc.

Rnd 25: 2 sc in first sc; *sc in next sc, 2 sc in next sc; rep from * 6 times more; sc in next 2 sc, 2 sc in next sc, sc in next 18 sc: 45 sc.

Rnd 26: 2 sc in first sc, sc in next 4 sc; *2 sc in next sc, sc in next 3 sc; rep from *4 times more; 2 sc in next sc, sc in next 19 sc: 52 sc.

Rnd 27: 2 sc in first sc, sc in next **30** sc, 2 sc in next sc, sc in next **20** sc: 54 sc.

Rnds 28 through 39: Rep Rnd 27 twelve times more, increasing bold numbers by one more than in previous rnd: 2 more sc in each rnd than in previous rnd. At end of Rnd 39: 78 sc.

Rnd 40: Sc in each sc around. Finish off; weave in ends.

Attach nose to Rnd 3 on top jaw. Attach eyes to Rnd 27 on top jaw.

Rnd 41: Join red/brown eyelash yarn under chin. Ch 1, sc loosely in same sc as joining; *skip next sc, sc loosely in next sc; rep from * around, skipping last sc: 39 sc; do not join. Place marker in last sc and move up in each rnd to mark last sc in each rnd.

Rnds 42 through 48: Switch to K hook, sc in first sc and in each sc around; do not join.

Rnd 49: *Sc in next 2 sc, skip next sc; rep from * around: 26 sc.

Rnd 50: *Sc in next 2 sc, skip next sc; rep from * 7 times more; sc in next 2 sc: 18 sc.

Rnd 51: *Sc in next 2 sc, skip next sc; rep from * around: 12 sc.

Rnd 52: *Sc in next 2 sc, skip next sc; rep from * around: 8 sc. Finish off; weave in ends.

Stuff head with fiberfill. Pinch opening in half and sew opening closed with brown sewing thread.

EARS (make 2)

Front

With white pearl cotton and size 7 hook, ch 15.

Row 1: Sc in 2nd ch from hook and in each ch across: 14 sc; ch 1, turn.

Row 2: Sc in each sc across: 14 sc; ch 1, turn.

Rows 3 and 4: Rep Row 2.

Rows 5 through 16: Skip first sc, sc in each rem sc across: one less sc in each row than in previous row. At end of Row 16: 2 sc. Finish off; weave in ends.

Back

Row 1: With size 7 hook, join red/brown eyelash yarn with sl st in edge of last sc on Row 1 of front of ear, ch 7 with K hook; join with sl st in edge of first sc in Row 1 with size 7 hook; turn.

Row 2: Sl st in edge of first sc on Row 3 with size 7 hook, sc in each ch across with K hook: 7 sc; join with sl st in edge of last sc on Row 3 with size 7 hook; turn.

Row 3: Sl st in edge of last sc on Row 5 with size 7 hook, skip first sc, sc in each rem sc across with K hook: 6 sc; join with sl st in edge of first sc on Row 5 with size 7 hook; turn.

Rows 4 through 8: Rep Row 3 five times more, joining with sl st in edge of odd numbered rows of ear front: one less sc in each row than in previous row. At end of Row 8: 1 sc. Finish off. Sew tip closed if necessary. Weave in ends.

Sew Row 1 of front and back of ears onto face with white pearl cotton so that ears touch in center of face, inner/outer ends are on Row 36, and center is on Row 39. Tack center of Row 3 of ears with pearl cotton to Row 40 of face to help ears stand up.

FEET (make 4)

With white pearl cotton and size 7 hook, ch 9.

Rnd 1: 2 sc in 2nd ch from hook, sc in next 6 chs, 3 sc in last ch, working along other side of chs, sc in next 6 chs, sc in same ch as first 2 sc: 18 sc; do not join. Place marker in last sc and move up in each rnd to mark last sc in each rnd.

Rnd 2: Sc in each sc around; do not join.

Rnds 3 through 6: Rep Rnd 2 four times more.

Rnd 7: Sc in first 17 sc, turn, sc in next 7 sc, turn, sc in next 7 sc, sc in last sc (ball of foot made); do not join.

Rnds 8 through 16: Rep Rnd 2 nine times more. At end of Rnd 16, change to red/brown pearl cotton in last sc. Finish off white; weave in ends.

Rnds 17 through 65: Rep Rnd 2 forty-nine times more. At end of Rnd 65, finish off; weave in ends.

Stuff feet with fiberfill. Fold top opening in half even with bottom of foot. Sew closed with red/brown pearl cotton. With brown pearl cotton and needle, sew three 3/8" stitches evenly spaced through beg white end to form toes.

SAFETY CHAIN (make 2)

First Ring

With red/brown pearl cotton and size 7 hook, ch 20, join with sl st in first ch to form a ring.

Rnd 1: Ch 1, work 40 sc in ring, join with sl st in first sc. Finish off; weave in ends.

Second and Third Rings

With red/brown pearl cotton and size 7 hook, ch 20, insert ch through previous ring, join with sl st in first ch to form a ring.

Rnd 1: Rep Rnd 1 on First Ring.

SAFETY SNAP (make 2)

Rnd 1: With middle of snap facing and size 7 hook, join red/brown pearl cotton with sc in any hole of snap, sc in same hole, ch 2; *2 sc in next hole, ch 2; rep from * twice more: 8 sc and 8 chs; join with sl st in first sc.

Rnd 2: Ch 3, work bullion st in same sc as joining, work bullion st in each sc and in each ch around: 16 bullion sts; join with sl st in top of first bullion st.

Rnd 3: Ch 1, sc in top of first bullion st and in top of each bullion st

around: 16 sc; do not join. Insert 14 mm wood bead into center of bullion sts.

Rnd 4: *Skip next sc, sc in next sc; rep from * around: 8 sc; do not join.

Rnds 5 through 7: Rep Rnd 4 three times more. At end of Rnd 7: 1 sc; ch 10, finish off, leaving 2' long thread end. Insert ch through third ring of safety chain, sl st in sc on Rnd 7 of safety snap to form ring, turn, work 20 sc in ring with end of thread, sl st in same st as last sl st. Finish off; weave in ends.

TAIL

Rnd 1: With white eyelash yarn and K hook, ch 4; join with sl st to form a ring.

Rnd 2: Ch 1, 8 sc in ring: 8 sc; do not join. Place marker in last sc and move up in each rnd .

Rnd 3: 2 sc in each sc around: 16 sc.

Rnd 4: Rep Rnd 3: 32 sc.

Rnd 5: Sc in each sc around.

Rnds 6 through 20: Rep Rnd 5 fifteen times more. At end of Rnd 20, change to red/brown eyelash yarn in last sc. Finish off white; weave in ends.

Rnds 21 through 50: Rep Rnd 5 thirty times more.

Rnd 51: Skip first sc, sc in each rem sc around.

Rnds 52 through 60: Rep Rnd 51 nine times more. At end of Rnd 60: 22 sc. Finish off; weave in ends.

Stuff knee-high nylon with fiberfill. Tie top closed. Insert into tail. Fold opening in half and sew shut with brown sewing thread. Sew 10 to 15 randomly spaced loose stab stitches all the way through the tail and stuffing, securing the stuffing in the tail so it does not shift and the yarn does not stretch.

BODY

With red/brown eyelash yarn and K hook, ch 41.

Row 1: Sc in 2nd ch from hook and in each ch across: 40 sc; ch 1, turn.

Rep Row 1 until piece is 40" (44", 48") long. Finish off; weave in ends.

QUILTED LINING/ ASSEMBLY

Fold edges to wrong side of satin and press so piece is 8" x 40". Turn under 1" at each corner and press. Lift corner and trim off excess fabric 1" away from edge. Trim corners of fleece to match pressed satin lining. Place fleece on wrong side of lining under edges. Center and pin head at one short end and tail at other short end, overlapping satin lining by 1/2" (bottom of head should be facing right side of satin lining). Pin legs between head/tail and corners, 1/2" from folded corners, overlapping satin lining by 1/2" (balls of feet should be facing right side of satin). With brown sewing thread and needle, sew head, tail and legs to folded-in edge of satin lining. Place body on fleece side of fleece/lining, matching edges. Pin every 1" to 2" around outside edge. With brown sewing thread and needle, sew edge of body and lining together around entire outer edge of lining, sewing through head, tail and legs at short ends.

Place fur on table with lining up. Mark every 2" along long outside edges of lining with tailor's chalk. Draw diagonal lines at 45 degree angles using the 2" marks as endpoints. With brown sewing thread, quilt with running stitches on all the marked lines through all layers, making sure to catch the eyelash yarn in the stitches.

Sew chains with safety snap halves to end of diagonal corners on one long side.

LIME COOLER

Designed by
Jenny King

Be prepared to be the center of attention when you appear at poolside in this over the top outfit. It's easy to make: just shells and loops. But, wear it only if you dare!

LIME COOLER

Size

One size fits body bust 30" to 34"
Note: *Garment stretches to fit.*

Materials

DK weight yarn,
$3\frac{1}{2}$ oz lime
Note: *Photographed model made with Sirdar Silky Look #912 Lime*
$3\frac{1}{2}$ yds 3mm round elastic
Sewing thread and sewing needle
Size 1 (2.75mm) steel crochet hook
Size E (3.5mm) aluminum crochet hook (or size required for gauge)

Gauge

4 shells = 4"

Stitch Guide

Shell: Work 4 dc in specified st or ch: shell made.

Beg shell: Ch 3, 3 dc in same st: beg shell made.

Beg inc: At beg of row, ch 3, 3 dc in first st: beg inc made.

End inc: At end of row, 4-dc shell into last st: end inc made.

Beg dec: At beg of row, ch 1, skip 1 dc, sc in next st; continue in pattern: beg dec made.

End dec: At end of row, sc in last shell, but do not work a shell in last sc, turn: end dec made.

Loop (lp): Ch 5, sc in next ch-5 lp or in 2nd dc of next shell: lp made.

Note: *When ending a row with sc, place it in the 3rd dc of shell to keep the side edge straight.*

INSTRUCTIONS

FRONT

Starting at crotch, ch 14.

Row 1 (right side): Sc in 2nd ch from hook, skip 2 chs, shell of 4 dc in next ch; skip 2 chs, sc in next ch, skip 2 chs, shell in next ch, skip 2 chs, sc in last ch: 2 shells made; turn.

Row 2: Ch 3 (counts as a dc), 3 dc in first sc (shell made); * sc in 2nd dc of next shell, shell in next sc; rep from * across: 3 shells made; turn.

Row 3: Ch 1, sc in 2nd dc of shell; * shell in sc, sc in 2nd dc of shell; rep from * across: 2 shells made; turn.
Note: *Remember to work last sc in 3rd dc of shell instead of 2nd; this will not be mentioned again.*

Row 4: Rep Row 2.

Row 5: Rep Row 3.

Row 6: Rep Row 2.

Row 7: Work beg inc, work in pattern across, work end inc: 4 shells made; turn.

Row 8: Rep Row 3: 3 shells.

Row 9: Rep Row 2: 4 shells.

Row 10: Rep Row 3: 3 shells.

Row 11: Rep Row 2: 4 shells.

Row 12 (shape dart): Beg inc, sc, shell, sc, sc in next sc; sc in shell, shell, sc, end inc; turn.

Row 13: Beg inc, sc, shell, sc, skip 1 sc, work shell in center sc; skip 1 sc, sc, shell, sc, end inc: 5 shells; turn.

Row 14: Beg inc, work in pattern across, end inc: 6 shells; turn.

Row 15 (shape dart): Beg inc,(sc, shell) twice; sc, sc in next sc, (sc, shell) twice, sc, end inc: 6 shells; turn.

Row 16: Beg inc; (sc, shell) twice, sc, skip 1 sc, and work shell into center sc; skip 1 sc, (sc, shell) twice, sc, end inc: 7 shells; turn.

Row 17: Beg inc, work in pattern across, end inc: 8 shells; turn.

Row 18 (shape dart): Beg inc, (sc, shell) 3 times, sc, sc in next sc; (sc, shell) 3 times, sc, end inc: 8 shells; turn.

Row 19: Beg inc, (sc, shell) 3 times, sc, skip 1 sc, work shell in center sc; skip 1 sc, (sc, shell) 3 times, sc inc: 9 shells; turn.

Row 20: Beg inc, work in pattern across, end inc: 10 shells; turn.

Row 21 (shape dart): Beg inc, (sc, shell) 4 times, sc, sc in next sc; (sc, shell) 4 times, sc, end inc: 10 shells; do not turn; ch 30 for top of leg; finish off. Join yarn at beg of Row 21; ch 30 for top of opposite leg. Finish off.

Row 22: Turn work. Join yarn in the 11th ch closest to the front leg on beg ch at the end of Row 21. sc in next st, skip 2 ch, shell, skip 2 ch, sc; skip 2 ch, shell; sc in 2nd dc of next shell, (sc, shell) 4 times, sc, shell in the center sc; (shell, sc) 4 times, sc, skip 1 ch, shell, skip 2 ch, sc, skip 2 ch, shell, skip 2 ch, sc: 13 shells; turn.

Row 23: Beg dec, work in patt until 6 shells have been worked, sc; *ch 5, sc in 2nd dc of next shell; rep from * 4 times more, shell, end dec: 7 shells and 5 ch-5 lps; turn.

Row 24: Beg dec, shell, sc in lp; *ch 5, sc in next lp; rep from * 3 times more; ch 5, sc in next shell; work in pattern until 5 shells have been worked, end dec: 6 shells and 5 lps; turn.

Note: *Remember to work in pattern, with sc between shells.*

Row 25: Beg dec, 4 shells, 5 lps, 1 shell, end dec, turn.

Row 26: Beg dec, 1 shell, 5 lps, 3 shells, end dec, turn.

Row 27: Shell in first sc, 2 shells, 5 lps, 2 shells, ch 1, turn.

Row 28: Sc in first shell, 2 shells, 5 lps, 2 shells, dc in last shell, turn.

Row 29: Shell in first sc, shell, 5 lps, 3 shells; ch 1, turn.

Row 30: Sc in first shell, 3 shells, 5 lps, 1 shell, turn.

Row 31: Shell in first sc, 5 lps, 4 shells; ch 1, turn.

Row 32: Sc in shell, 1 lp, 3 shells, 5 lps, turn.

Row 33: Shell in first sc, 4 lps, 3 shells, 1 lp, 1 shell, turn.

Row 34: Beg inc, 2 lps, 3 shells, 4 lps, end inc, turn.

Row 35: Beg inc, 4 lps, 3 shells, 3 lps, end inc, turn.

Row 36: Beg inc, 4 lps, 3 shells, 4 lps, end inc, turn.

Row 37: Beg inc, 4 lps, 3 shells, 5 lps, end inc, turn.

Row 38: Beg inc, 6 lps, 3 shells, 4 lps, end inc, turn.

Row 39: Beg inc, 4 lps, 3 shells, 7 lps, end inc, turn.

Row 40: Beg inc, 8 lps, 3 shells, 4 lps, end inc, turn.

Row 41: Beg inc, 4 lps, 4 shells, 8 lps, end inc, turn.

Row 42: Beg inc, 8 lps, 5 shells, 4 lps, end inc, turn.

Row 43: Beg inc, 4 lps, 6 shells, 8 lps, end inc; do not turn, ch 70 for back strap; join with sl st in beg of Row 43. Finish off.

SHAPE BUST

Row 1: Join yarn with sc in 2nd dc of last shell worked in Row 43, work 19 shells across, sc in last shell; turn.

Rows 2 through 7: Beg dec, work in pattern to last shell, end dec; turn. At end of Row 7, finish off.

Row 8: Join yarn in last dc of Row 43, (sc, shell) 3 times; sc evenly along side edge of the last 7 rows, shell in last sc of Row 8, 11 shells along the top edge, work (sc, shell) 3 times, sc along other side of the last 7 rows, sc in the first dc of Row 43; turn.

Rows 9 and 10: Beg dec, shell to end, end dec, turn.

Row 11: Beg dec, 7 shells, 2 lps, 5 shells, end dec, turn.

Row 12: Beg dec, 5 shells, 2 lps, 6 shells, end dec, turn.

Row 13: Beg dec, 5 shells, 2 lps, 5 shells, end dec, turn.

Row 14: Beg dec, 5 shells, 2 lps, 4 shells, end dec. Finish off.

BOTTOM BACK

Row 1: Hold piece with right side facing and front crotch at top; join yarn with sc in first unused lp at right of beg ch; working in unused lps of ch (shell, sc) twice, shell: 3 shells made; turn.

Row 2: Beg inc, 2 shells, end inc, turn.

Row 3: 3 shells, turn.

Row 4: 3 shells, turn.

Row 5: Beg inc, 3 shells, end inc: 5 shells; turn.

Row 6: 4 shells, turn.

Row 7: Rep Row 5.

Row 8: Beg inc, 4 shells, end inc: 6 shells; turn.

Row 9: Beg inc, 5 shells, end inc: 7 shells; turn.

Row 10: Beg inc, 6 shells, end inc: 8 shells; turn.

Rows 11 and 12: Work even in pattern.

Row 13: Beg inc, 7 shells, end inc: 9 shells.

Rows 14 through 20: Work even in pattern.

Row 21: Beg inc, 8 shells, end inc: 10 shells. Finish off; weave in all ends.

FINISHING

Cut elastic into 4 pieces, each 21½" long; and one piece 34" long; sew ends of each piece into a circle. Smaller circles are used for legs and arm openings; large circle is used for back of pants.

Join yarn at crotch and sc over one smaller elastic circle all around one leg, join in beg sc; finish off. Rep for other leg.

Join yarn at underarm and sc over another smaller elastic circle around top of the swimsuit and strap, join in beg sc. Do not finish off; ch 1, sc over the 2nd smaller circle of elastic over the stitches just worked. Join with a sl st in beg ch of rnd. Finish off.

Join yarn at pants center back. Sc over the larger elastic circle, along back top of pants, top of leg, along side edge, bottom of back strap, down other side, along top of other leg to beg of rnd, join with sl st. Finish off; weave all ends in securely.

GLITTER TIME

Designed by Margaret Hubert

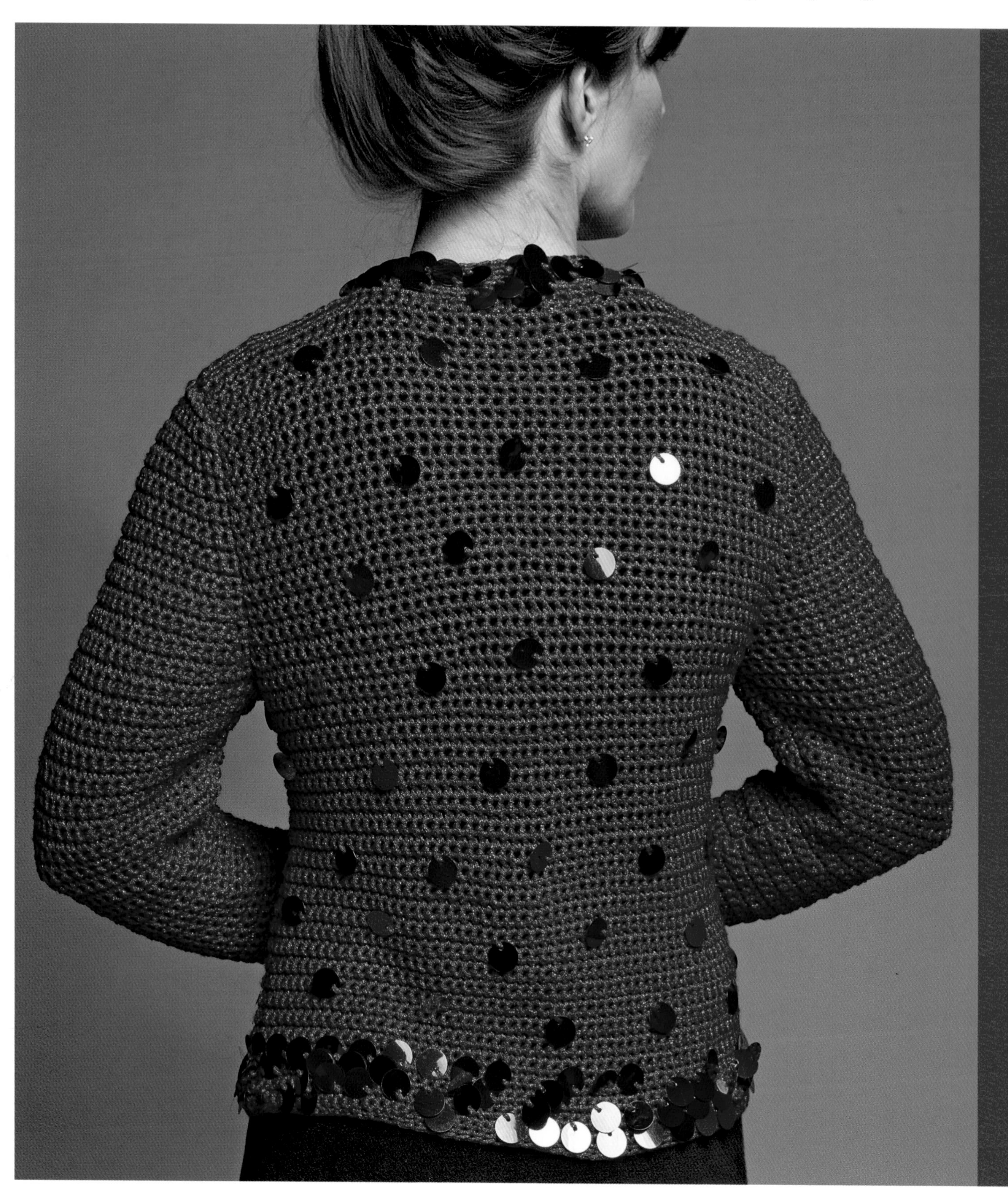

You'll be the glittering star of a festive evening in this sparkly Chanel-type glamour jacket! The metallic yarn is accented with paillettes, those wonderful shiny discs which catch and reflect the light. The pailettes are worked in as you crochet. What a way to make an entrance!

GLITTER TIME

SIZES Small	Medium	Large
Body Bust Measurements 32"	34"	36"
Finished Bust Measurements 35"	37"	39"

Note: *Instructions are written for size Small; changes for sizes Medium and Large are in parentheses.*

Materials

Metallic ribbon yarn, 16 (16, 18) oz

Note: *Photographed model was made with Lion Brand® Glitterspun* #113 Ruby

500 large-hole 20 mm red metallic paillettes

Size 20 tapestry needle (for stringing paillettes)

Size K (6.5mm) crochet hook (or size required for gauge)

Size I (5.5mm) crochet hook

Gauge

14 sc = 4" with larger hook

8 sc rows = 4"

Working With Paillettes

Before beginning each garment section, string paillettes onto yarn, using a tapestry needle, as follows:

For Back: 75 on first ball, 25 on second ball

For Each Front: 80 on first ball, 60 on second ball

For Each Sleeve: 30 on first ball

For Neckband: 60 on first ball

Paillettes are always worked on a wrong-side row.

Special Abbreviation:

PP (pull up a paillette): When instructions say PP, pull a paillette up close to work, then complete the next st; paillette falls between 2 sts and will appear on right side of work.

BACK

With larger hook, ch 60 (63, 66).

Foundation Row: Sc in 2nd ch from hook and in each rem ch: 59 (62, 65) sc; ch 1, turn.

Row 1 (right side): Skip first sc (ch 1 counts as the first st, here and throughout), sc in each rem sc; ch 1, turn.

Row 2: *PP, sc in next 3 sts; rep from * across row, ending PP, sc in last st, ch 1, turn.

Row 3: Sc across, ch 1, turn.

Row 4: Skip first sc; *sc in next 3 sc, PP; rep from * across, ending sc in each of last 4 sc; ch 1 turn.

Row 5: Rep Row 3.

Row 6: Rep Row 2.

Rows 7 through 13: Rep Row 3.

Row 14: Skip first sc, sc in next 9 (10, 12) sc, PP; *sc in next 10 sc, PP; rep from * across ending sc in last 9 (11, 12) sc; ch 1, turn.

Rows 15 through 21: Rep Row 3.

Row 22: Skip first sc, sc in next 4 (5,

7) sc, PP; * sc in next 10 sc, PP; rep from * across, end PP, sc in last 4 (6, 7) sts; ch 1, turn.

Rep Rows 7 through 22 for pattern until piece measures 11 1/2" (12", 12 1/2") from beg ch.

SHAPE ARMHOLES

Row 1: Continuing in established patt, sl st across 3 (3, 4) sts, work to within 3 (3, 4) sts of opposite side, ch 1, turn, leaving rem sts unworked.

Continue in patt, dec 1 st each arm edge every other row 2 times: 49 (52, 53) sts. Work even until armhole measures 7 1/2" (8", 8 1/2"), end by working a wrong-side row.

SHAPE NECK

Row 1: Sc across 12 (12, 13) sc, ch 1 turn.

Row 2: Sc across 12, (12, 13) sts, finish off.

With wrong side facing, join yarn at opposite arm edge and rep Rows 1 and 2. Center 25 (28, 27) sts are left unworked. Finish off; weave in ends.

LEFT FRONT

With larger hook, ch 33, (36, 39).

Foundation Row: Sc in 2nd ch from hook and in each rem ch: 32 (35, 39) sc; ch 1, turn.

Rep Rows 1 through 13 of Back. Continuing on 7 sts at front edge in the Paillette Pattern, begin paillette placement as for back. Work in pattern to start of armhole.

ARMHOLE SHAPING

Shape armhole edge same as back; continue in pattern until armhole measures 6½" (7", 7½") ending at neck front edge. Sl st over 10 (12, 14) sc, then dec 1 st at neck edge every row 5 (6, 5) times. Work even on rem 12 (12, 13) sts until armhole measures same as back to shoulder; finish off; weave in ends.

RIGHT FRONT

Work same as Left Front, reversing shaping.

SLEEVE (make 2)

With smaller hook, ch 33.

Foundation Row: Sc in 2nd ch from hook and in each rem ch: 32 sc; ch 1, turn.

Work first 6 rows same as back. Work even in sc with no paillettes until piece measures 2" from beg ch; on next row, inc one st at each side. Change to larger hook.

Work in sc, increasing one st each side every 2", 6 (7, 8) times more: 46 (48, 50) sc. Work even in sc until piece measures 16" (16½", 17") from beg ch.

SHAPE SLEEVE CAP

Sl st across first 3 sc, sc to within 3 sc of opposite side, ch 1 turn, leaving rem sts unworked.

Continuing to work in sc, dec one st each side every other row for 7" (7½", 8"); finish off; weave in ends.

NECKBAND

Sew shoulder seams.

Foundation Row: Hold garment with right side facing. With smaller hook, join yarn at Right Front neck edge, sc along neck edge picking up 18 sts from neck edge to shoulder seam, 26 sts across back of neck, and 18 sts from shoulder to Left Front neck edge: 62 sc; ch 1 turn.

Rows 1 through 6: Rep Rows 1 through 6 of Back, then work one more row of sc with no paillettes, end at left front neck edge, work 3 sc in last st for corner.

EDGING

Sc evenly down left front edge, work 3 sc in corner, sc across botton edge of left front, back and right front, work 3 sc in corner, sc up right front edge, work 2 sc in last st, join with sl st to neck border. Finish off, weave in ends.

FINISHING

Sew fronts to back at side edges.

Sew sleeves in armholes.

Sew sleeve seams.

GOLD FURRY TANK TOP

Designed by Tammy C. Hildebrand

Soft and glittery, this form-fitting tank makes a fashion statement! It's easy to make and fun to wear.

GOLD FURRY TANK TOP

SIZES	Small	Medium	Large
Body Bust Measurements	32"	36"	40"
Finished Bust Measurements	29"	33"	37"

Note: *Instructions are written for size Small; changes for sizes Medium and Large are in parentheses. Tank stretches to fit.*

Materials

Worsted weight metallic yarn, 3 1/2 (5, 6 1/2) oz gold

Novelty eyelash yarn, 2 1/2 (2 3/4, 3) oz lt. beige

Note: *Photographed model made with Lion Brand® Glitterspun #170 Gold and Fun Fur, #124 Champagne*

Gold metal craft ring, 2" diameter

Size I (5.5 mm) crochet hook (or size required for gauge)

Gauge

16 sc = 4" with eyelash yarn

13 sc rows = 4" with eyelash yarn

5 shells = 4" with metallic yarn in pattern

10 pattern rows = 4" with metallic yarn

INSTRUCTIONS

BRA

First Side

Row 1 (right side): Starting at center front with eyelash yarn, work 15 sc over craft ring; ch 1, turn.

Row 2: 2 sc in first sc, sc in each sc to last sc, 2 sc in last sc: 17 sc; ch 1, turn.

Row 3: Rep Row 2: 19 sc.

Rows 4 through 44 (51, 57): Sc in each sc across; ch 1, turn. At end of last row, do not ch 1. Finish off.

Second Side

With right side facing, rep first side in opposite side of ring. Whip stitch last row of each side tog.

MIDRIFF

Rnd 1: With right side facing, join metallic yarn with sc in edge of last

sc on Row 4 of first side, work 72 (86, 98) more sc evenly spaced in edge of rows, ending in Row 4 on second side; 5 tr in ring; join in first sc: 73 (87, 99) sc and 5 tr.

Rnd 2: Ch 4 (counts as a dc and ch-1 sp), dc in same st: beg V-st made; *skip next st; in next st work (dc, ch 1, dc): V-st made; rep from * around; join in 3rd ch of beg ch-4: 39 (46, 52) V-sts.

Rnd 3: Sl st in next ch-1 sp; ch 3, 2 dc in same sp: beg shell made; *3 dc in ch-1 sp of next V-st: shell made; rep from * around; join in 3rd ch of beg ch-3: 39 (46, 52) shells.

Rnd 4: Ch 1, sc around joining sl st; *ch 3, sc in sp between next 2 shells; rep from * around; ch 3, join in beg sc: 39 (46, 52) ch-3 sps.

Rnd 5: Sl st in next ch-3 sp, ch 3, 2 dc in same sp; *shell in next ch-3 sp; rep from * around; join in 3rd ch of beg ch-3.

Rnd 6: Sl st in next st, ch 4, dc in same st, V-st in center st of each shell around; join in 3rd ch of beg ch-4.

Rep Rnds 3 through 6 to 2" less than desired length, ending with Row 6.

Rep Rnds 3 and 4 once more. At end of last rnd, finish off; weave in ends.

BOTTOM EDGING

With right side facing, join eyelash yarn with sl st in any ch-3 sp on last rnd, ch 3, 2 dc in same sp, 3 dc in each ch-3 sp around; join in 3rd ch of beg ch-3. Finish off; weave in ends.

STRAP (make 2)

With metallic yarn, ch 47 (51, 55); dc in 4th ch from hook and in each rem ch. Finish off. Pin straps to top edge of bra, one end of each strap to Row 8 (9, 10) and the other end to Row 36 (42, 47). Try on garment, adjust length and placement of straps as desired.

Sew straps in place.

THREE EASY PIECES

Designed by Vashti Braha

Straight from a designer runway comes this elegant outfit with trendy detached sleeves. Worked in a stretchy ribbon yarn with metallic highlights, the skirt and tube top skim the body, creating a flattering silhouette. Glistening beads accenting the fringe reflect candlelight beautifully.

SIZES	X-Small	Small	Medium	Large
Body Bust Measurements	32”	34”	36”	38”
Finished Bust Measurements	30”	32”	34”	36”
Body Hip Measurements	34”	36”	38”	40”
Finished Hip Measurements	32”	34”	36”	38”

Note: *Instructions are written for size Extra Small; changes for sizes Small, Medium, and Large are in parentheses.*

Note: *Both skirt and tube top will stretch in width when worn.*

Materials

Worsted weight stretchy yarn,
- For Top, 10½ (10½, 14, 14) oz black
- For Skirt, 14 (14, 17½ oz, 17½) oz black

Super bulky weight yarn,
- 1.75 oz black

Note: *Photographed model made with Patons® Katrina #10040 Noir and Patons® Allure #04040 Ebony*

Selection of beads of varying sizes and shapes

Size G (4.25mm) crochet hook (or size required for gauge)

Gauge

17 sc = 4” in sc worked in front lp only

Stitch Guide

Double triple crochet (Dtr): YO hook 3 times; *insert hook in specified st and draw up a lp; (YO and draw through first 2 lps on hook) 4 times: Dtr made.

SKIRT

INSTRUCTIONS

With worsted weight stretchy yarn, ch 136 (145, 153, 162)

Row 1: Sc in 2nd ch from hook and in each rem ch; 135 (144, 152, 161) sc; ch 1, turn.

Row 2: Working in front lp only of each st here and throughout pattern, sc in each sc; ch 1, turn.

Rep Row 2 until piece measures 16”, or desired length. Finish off; weave in ends.

FINISHING

Fold piece in half vertically and sew side seam.

SKIRT BORDER

Hold skirt with right side facing and last row worked at top.

Rnd 1: Join bulky yarn with sl st in seam; ch 3; *skip 1 st, hdc in both lps of next stitch, ch 1; rep from * around; join with sl st in 2nd chain of beg ch-3. Finish off.

Rnd 2: Join worsted weight stretchy yarn with sl st in joining of Row 1; ch 3; *skip 1 st, hdc in both lps of next st, ch 1; rep from * around, join with sl st in 2nd ch of beg ch-3; ch 4 (counts as a dc and ch-1 sp), turn.

Rnd 3: *Skip 1 st, dc in both lps of next st, ch 1; rep from * across, join in 3rd ch of ch-4; ch 5 (counts as a tr and ch-1 sp), turn.

Rnd 4: *Skip 1 st, tr in both lps of next st, ch 1; rep from * across, join in 4th ch of ch-5; ch 6 (counts as a dtr and ch-1 sp), turn.

Rnd 5: *Skip 1 st, dtr in both lps of next st, ch 1; rep from * across, join in 5th ch of ch-5. Finish off; weave in all ends.

FRINGE

Cut both yarns into random lengths measuring between 12" and 24". Following Fringe instructions on page 190, knot yarn into ch-1sps of Row 5 of Border, placing as desired. Thread beads on some or all of the yarn strands, and tie a large enough knot under each bead to secure.

TOP

INSTRUCTIONS

With worsted weight stretchy yarn, ch 128 (136, 145, 153).

Row 1: Sc in 2nd ch from hook and in each rem ch: 127 (135, 144, 153) sc; ch 1, turn.

Row 2: Working in front lp only of each st here and throughout, sc in each sc; ch 1, turn.

Rep Row 2 until piece measures 15" from beg ch. Finish off; weave in ends.

Fold piece in half vertically and sew side seam.

BORDER AND FRINGE

Work same as Skirt Border and Skirt Fringe.

DETACHED SLEEVES (make 2)

With worsted weight stretchy yarn, ch 36.

Row 1: Sc in 2nd ch from hook and in each rem ch: 35 sc; ch 1, turn.

Rows 2 through 8: Sc in front lp only of each sc; ch 1, turn. At end of last row, do not ch or turn. Finish off, leaving a long yarn end for sewing. Sew side seam.

BORDER

Join yarn at top of seam with sl st.

Rnd 1: Ch 3; *hdc in next st, ch 1; rep from * around, join with sl st in 2nd ch of beg ch-3; ch 4, turn.

Rnd 2: *Skip next st, dc in next st, ch 1; rep from * around, join in 3rd ch of ch-4; ch 4, turn.

Rnd 3: Rep Rnd 2. Finish off; weave in ends.

FRINGE

Work fringe as for skirt and top, cutting strands from 8" to 18" long, and knotting in ch sps of Rnd 3 of Border.

Skirt is hip-hugging and can be worn with fringe as bottom edge, or as top edge folded over.

BOBBLE BOLERO

designed by Penny O'Neill for Cleckheaton Yarns

This fun and flirty bolero has an unusual construction. Pair it with jeans or a skirt, and watch the bobbles dance around as you move. It's fun and easy to make in pretty stripes. Choose a color combination of brights, pastels or earthtones — they will all look terrific!

BOBBLE BOLERO

Size:

Fits 32" to 36" bust

Materials

DK weight yarn,
 1 3/4 oz each of your choice of 4 solid colors and 5 1/4 oz variegated

Note: *Photographed model made with 4 solid colors of Cleckheaton Country 8 ply and one variegated color Cleckheaton Tapestry 8 ply.*

Size I (5.5 mm) crochet hook, or size required for gauge

Gauge

14 dc = 4"
15 dc rows = 7"

PATTERN STITCHES:

Dc decrease (dc dec): (YO, insert hook in next st and draw up a lp, YO and draw through 2 lps on hook) twice, YO and draw through all 3 lps on hook: dc dec made.

To change color: Work st until 2 lps rem on hook, drop old color, pick up new color and draw through both lps on hook, cut dropped color.

INSTRUCTIONS:

Note: *Bolero is worked in stripes of alternating colors. Work 1 row in each color, changing color as desired in last st of each row.*

FRONTS AND YOKE (see Diagram 1 on page 57)

With desired color, loosely ch 142; chain should measure about 40" long. Change to another hook size if needed to achieve length

Row 1 (right side): Dc in 4th ch from hook and in each rem ch: 140 dc (3 skipped chs count as dc); ch 1, turn. Place markers in 56th dc (16") from each end to indicate position of shoulders. All shaping is worked in back yoke center section. Front sections are straight.

Row 2 (wrong side): Sc in first dc, ch 1, dc in next 55 sts; *2 dc in next st, dc in next 4 sts; rep from * 4 times more; 2 dc in next st, dc in next 57 sts, dc in first skipped ch at beg of Row 1: 146 dc (beg sc and ch-1 count as first dc); ch 1, turn.

Row 3 (right side): Sc in first dc, ch 1, dc in next 55 sts; *2 dc in next st, dc in next **5** sts; rep from * 4 times more; 2 dc in next st, dc in next **58** sts, dc in beg ch-1: 152 dc (beg sc and ch-1 count as first dc); ch 1, turn.

Rows 4 through 15: Rep Row 3, increasing bold numbers by one more in each row than in previous row: 224 dc at end of Row 15 (6 more dc in each row than in previous row). Turn at end of each row except Row 15. At end of Row 15, finish off; weave in ends.

GUSSETS (see Diagram 2 on page 57):

Along curved outer edge of back yoke, place markers in Row 15 in 70th dc (20") and 86th dc (24¾") from each end (4" away from shoulders and 7½" away on each side of center back). Gussets are worked between markers. Change color as desired in last st of each row.

FIRST GUSSET

With wrong side facing, join desired color with sl st in 71st dc on right side of back and work toward 86th dc.

Row 1: Ch 1, sc in next 3 sts, hdc in next 3 sts, dc in next 10 sts: 16 sts; ch 1, turn.

Row 2: Sc in first st, ch 1, dc in next 5 sts, dc dec in next 2 sts: 7 dc (sc and ch-1 count as dc; dc dec counts as dc); ch 1, turn.

Row 3: Sc in first st, dc in next 5 sts, dc in beg ch-1: 7 sts; ch 1, turn.

Row 4: Sc in first st, ch 1, dc in next 3 sts, dc dec in next 2 sts: 5 dc (sc and ch-1 count as dc; dc dec counts as dc); ch 1, turn.

Row 5: Sc in first st, (dc dec in next 2 sts) twice: 3 sts. Finish off; weave in ends.

SECOND GUSSET

Note: *Use same colors as in first gusset, changing color in last st of each row.*

With wrong side facing, join with sc in 86th dc on left side of back and work toward 71st dc.

Row 1: Ch 1, dc in next 9 sts, hdc in next 3 sts, sc in next 3 sts: 16 sts (sc and ch-1 count as dc). Finish off; turn.

Row 2: Join with sc in 9th st, dc in next 6 sts, dc in beg ch-1: 7 dc (sc and first dc count as dc dec, which counts as dc); ch 1, turn.

Row 3: Sc in first st, ch 1, dc in next 5 sts, sc in next st: 7 sts; turn.

Row 4: Sl st in sc, sc in next dc, dc in next 4 sts, dc in beg ch-1: 5 dc (sc and first dc count as dc dec, which counts as dc); ch 1, turn.

Row 5: Sc in first st, dc in next st, dc dec in next 2 sts, sc in next st: 3 sts (sc and first dc count as dc dec, which counts as dc). Finish off; weave in ends.

BACK (see Diagram 3 on page 57):

Note: *Use same colors on Rows 1 through 5 as in gussets, changing color in last st of each row.*

With wrong side facing, join with sl st in same st as last dc made at corner of yoke and first gusset.

Row 1: Ch 3, sl st in top of last dc on Row 1 on side of first gusset, **turn**, dc in next 8 sts on yoke; *2 dc in next st, dc in next 13 sts; rep from * 2 times more; dc in next 2 sts, dc in same st as joining st at corner of yoke and second gusset, sl st in beg ch-1 on Row 1 on side of second gusset: 56 dc; turn.

Row 2: Ch 3, sl st in top of last dc on Row 2 on side of second gusset, **turn**, dc in next 8 sts; *2 dc in next st, dc in next 14 sts; rep from * 2 times more; dc in next 3 sts, dc in same st as first st on Row 2 of first gusset, sl st in beg ch-1 on Row 2 on side of first gusset: 60 dc; turn.

Row 3: Ch 3, sl st in top of last dc on Row 3 on side of first gusset, **turn**, dc in next 8 sts; *2 dc in next st, dc in next 15 sts; rep from * 2 times more; dc in next 4 sts, dc in same st as first st on Row 3 of second gusset, sl st in beg ch-1 on Row 3 on side of second gusset: 64 dc; turn.

Row 4: Ch 3, sl st in top of last dc on Row 4 on side of second gusset, **turn**, dc in next 8 sts; *2 dc in next st, dc in next 16 sts; rep from * 2 times more; dc in next 5 sts, dc in same st as first st on Row 4 of first gusset, sl st in beg ch-1 on Row 4 on side of first gusset: 68 dc; turn.

Row 5: Ch 3, sl st in top of last dc dec on Row 5 on side of first gusset, **turn**, dc in next 8 sts; *2 dc in next st, dc in next 17 sts; rep from * 2 times more; dc in next 6 sts, dc in same st as first st on Row 5 of second gusset, sl st in first dc on Row 5 on side of second gusset: 72 dc; turn.

Row 6: Sc in first dc, ch 1, dc in next 2 sts; *2 dc in next st, dc in next **18** sts; rep from * 2 times more; dc in next **12** sts: 75 dc (sc and ch-1 count as dc); turn.

Rows 7 through 19: Rep Row 6, increasing bold numbers by one more in each row than in previous row: 114 dc at end of Row 19 (3 more dc in each row than in previous row). Turn at end of each row except Row 19. At end of Row 19, finish off; weave in ends.

BOBBLE BOLERO

BOBBLES (make 20 in a variety of colors and lengths):

Ch 11 to 20, sl st in 4th ch from hook to form a ring.

Rnd 1: (Sc, hdc, 3 dc, 3 tr, 3 dc, hdc, sc) in ring, hdc in each rem ch. Finish off, leaving 12" end.

TIES (make 2 in desired colors):

Ch 30, sl st in 4th ch from hook to form a ring, being careful not to twist chain.

Rnd 1: (Sc, hdc, 3 dc, 3 tr, 3 dc, hdc, sc) in ring, hdc in each rem ch. Finish off, leaving 12" end.

JOINING (see Diagram 4 on page 57):

Fold fronts over at shoulder line. Place markers at side of fronts 7" from lower edge to indicate position of armholes. Sew side seams, matching markers with bottom points of gussets. If back neck is too wide, work 2 rows dc along front edges and back neck, evenly decreasing 6 dc in each row across back neck. Finish off; weave in ends. Attach bobbles randomly along lower edge. Attach ties to front edge of bolero as desired to fasten vest.

1 – Fronts and Yoke

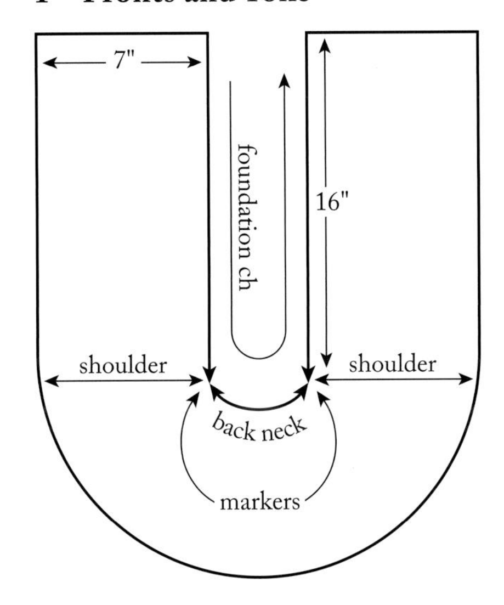

2 – Add Gussets

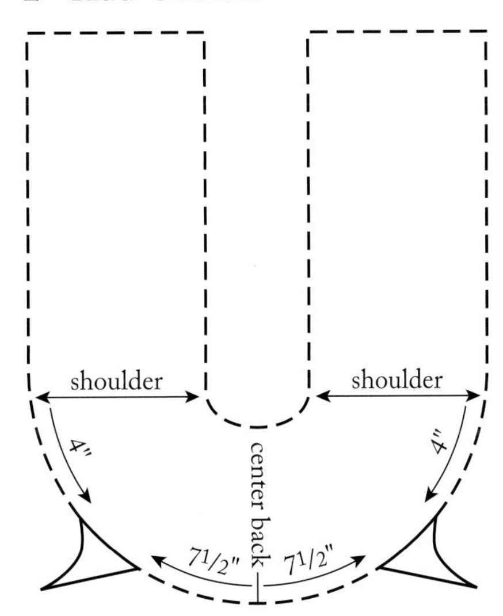

2 – Add Back

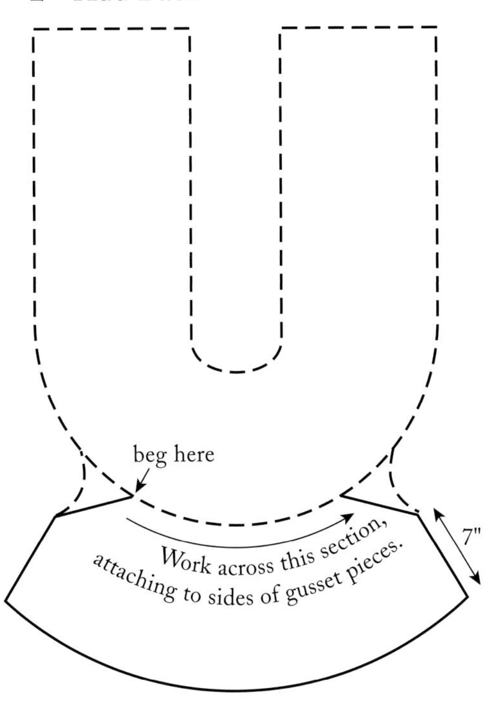

4 – Fold at shoulders, then sew side seams.

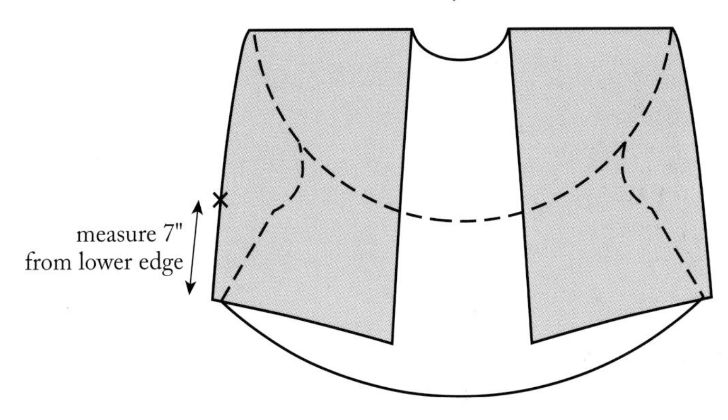

BOBBLE

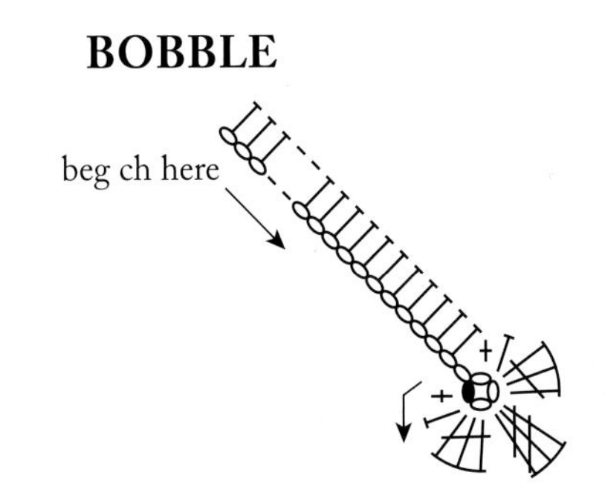

Key

- ○ = ch
- + = sc
- ⊗ = 3 ch joined with a sl st to form a ring
- = hdc
- = dc
- = tr

LIGHT UP THE NIGHT

designed by Judith Solomon

Ribbon yarn and faux fur yarns combine to create this elegant evening shawl. Be prepared for "oohs" and "ahs" when you wear it.

LIGHT UP THE NIGHT

Size

72" long by 26" deep at center back

Materials

Eyelash yarn,
 420 yds black (A)
Eyelash yarn with slubs
 82 yds multicolor (B)
Ribbon yarn,
 100 yds multicolor (C)
Fur yarn
 71 yds, black (D)

Note: *Photographed model made with Lion Brand® Fun Fur #153 Black (A); Muench Yarns Fee #5 Multi (B); Lion Brand® Incredible #201 Rainbow (C) and Bernat® Boa #81040 Raven (D).*

Yarn needle
Large safety pins or contrast yarn (to keep track of rows worked)
Straight pins
Sewing thread to match Color C
Sewing needle
Size K (6.5mm) crochet hook (or size required for gauge)

Gauge

7 sc = 3"
Rows 1 through 9 = 3"

Notes:

1. Shawl is worked loosely; use a larger hook if needed to achieve gauge.

2. For pattern, work in spaces, not stitches, except for end stitches.

3. With textured yarns, it is sometimes difficult to find the stitches or spaces.

Try inserting the index finger of your non-hook hand through from the back as you work. If it goes through, it's a space, and if it resists, it's a stitch.

4. Use safety pins or markers every 5 rows to keep count.

5. To avoid finishing off the main color (A) frequently, carry it along the edge when rows of A are separated by only one row of a contrast color.

6. Work over the yarn ends as you go whenever possible to save finishing time.

Pattern Stitch

Odd rows: (Sc in first sp, ch 1, skip next sp) across, end with sc in last st.

Even rows: Sc in first st, (sc in next sp, ch 1, skip next sp) across, end with sc in last sp, sc in last sc.

INSTRUCTIONS

BODY

Starting at long top edge with A, loosely ch 150.

Row 1 (right side): Sc in 2nd ch from hook, ch 1, skip next ch; *sc in next ch, ch 1, skip next ch; rep from * across, ending with sc in last ch: 75 sc and 74 sps; ch 1, turn.

Row 2: Sc in first sc; *sc in next sp, ch 1, skip next sp; rep from * across, ending sc in last 2 sts; ch 1, turn.

Row 3: Sc in first sc; *ch 1, skip next sp, sc in next sp; rep from * across, ending with sc in last sc; drop A, do not turn.

Row 4: Join B, work Even Row of patt, turn; finish off B.

Row 5: With A, ch 1, work Odd Row of patt; turn.

Row 6: Work Even Row, at end of row drop A, do not turn.

Row 7: With C, work Odd Row, turn; finish off C.

Row 8: With A, work Even Row, turn.

Row 9: Rep Row 3. Drop A.

Row 10: With C, rep Row 4; finish off C.

Rows 11 and 12: With A, rep Rows 5 and 6; drop A.

Row 13: With B, rep Row 7; finish off B.

Rows 14 through 19: Work in pattern with A, alternating even and odd rows; at end of last row, finish off A; do not turn.

Row 20: With D, work as for Row 4; do not turn, drop A.

Row 21: With B, rep Row 7, turn.

Row 22: With D, work as for Row 4; finish off D, turn.

Rows 23 and 24: With A, work 2 rows in pattern; finish off A, do not turn.

Row 25: With D, rep Row 7; do not turn.

Row 26: With C, rep Row 4; turn.

Row 27: With D, rep Row 7; finish off, turn.

Row 28 and 29: With A, work 2

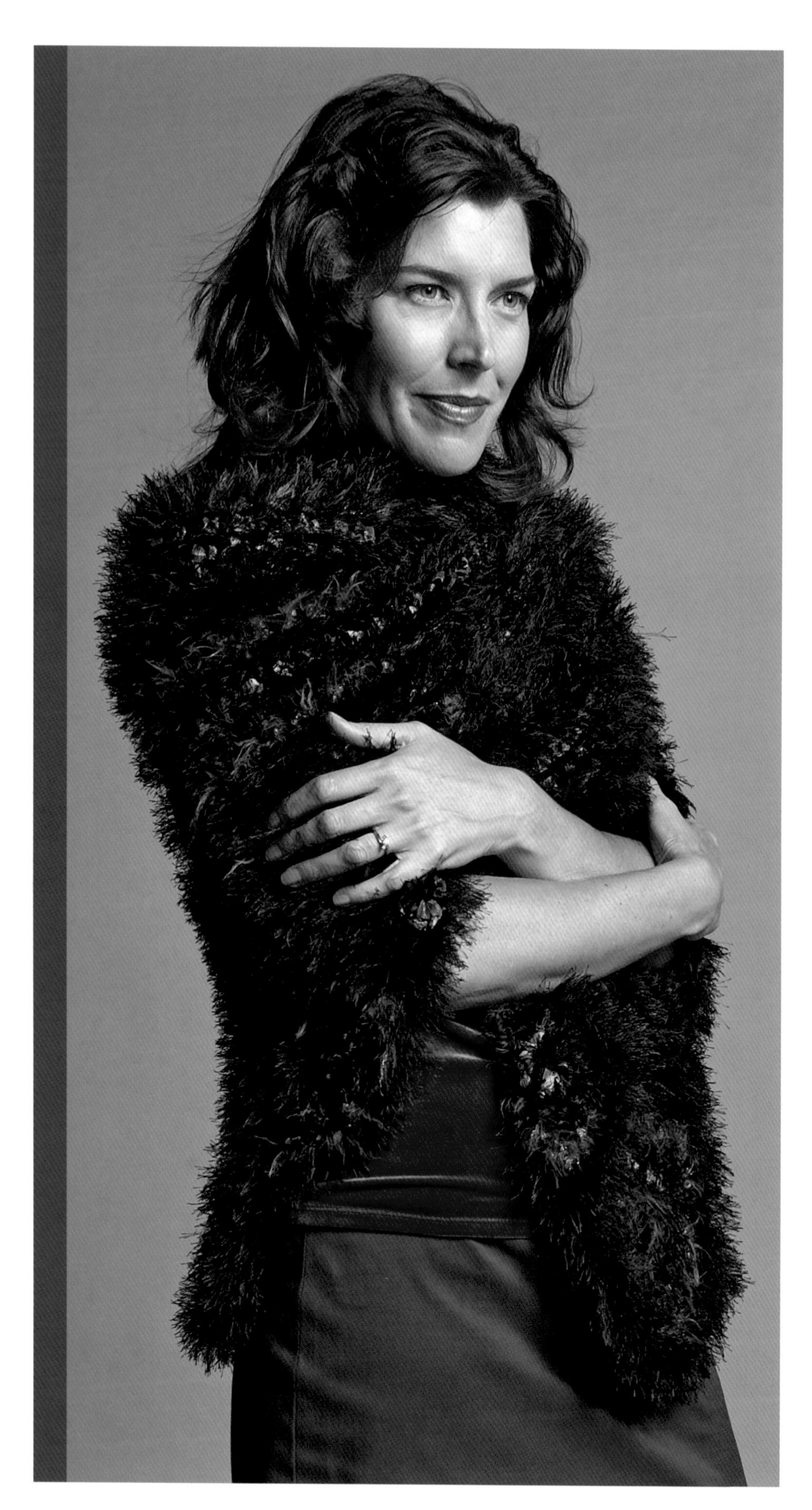

rows in pattern; finish off A, do not turn.

Row 30 through 32: Rep Rows 20 through 22.

Rows 33 through 38: Work in pattern with A, alternating odd and even rows; at the end of last row do not finish off or turn.

Rows 39 through 48: Rep Rows 4 through 13; turn.

Rows 49 through 51: With A, work in pattern, do not finish off. At end of Row 51, work 2 sc in the last st, then work sc across the short side. Finish off.

Join A at top of opposite short side, and work sc along short side. Finish off; weave in all ends.

SQUARES

Note: *When 2 rnds are done in the same yarn, do not finish off after first rnd, ch 1 and continue working around. At end of square, place a marker on side facing you to indicate right side.*

BASIC SQUARE

Rnd 1: Ch 2, in 2nd ch from hook work (sc, ch 1) 4 times, join with sl st. Finish off.

Rnd 2: Join yarn in any ch-1 sp, ch 1; *(sc, ch 1, sc) in sp, ch 1, skip 1 sc; rep from * around, join with sl st. Finish off.

Rnd 3: Join yarn in any corner sp, ch1; *work (sc, ch 1, sc) in corner sp, ch 1, skip 1 sc, sc in next sp, ch 1, skip 1 sc; rep from * around, join.

Rnds 4 through 10: Join yarn in any corner sp, ch 1; *(sc, ch 2, sc) in corner sp, ch 1, work (skip 1 sc, ch 1, sc in next sp) to next corner, ch 1; rep from * around; join with sl st. Finish off, leaving a long yarn end for sewing squares tog.

Following Basic Square instructions, make squares in following color sequences:

8" Square (make 3)
Rnd 1: D.
Rnd 2: B.
Rnds 3 and 4: A
Rnd 5: C.
Rnds 6 and 7: D.
Rnd 8: B.
Rnds 9 and 10: A

5" Square (make 6)
Rnd 1: A.
Rnd 2: C.
Rnds 3 and 4: D.
Rnd 5: B.
Rnds 6 and 7: A.

4" Square (make 2)
Rnds 1and 2: D.
Rnd 3: B.
Rnds 4 and 5: A.

3"Square (make 2)
Rnd 1: D.
Rnd 2: B.
Rnd 3: A.

2" Square (make 2)
Rnd 1: D.
Rnd 2: A.

JOINING

Fold Shawl Body in half lengthwise; longer edge will be the bottom edge of the shawl.

Line up one 5", one 8", and one 5" square, with the marked side up, and sew tog, keeping one long edge straight.

When joined, with straight edge on the bottom, join A in lower right corner and sc around the sides and tops of the squares, working 3 sc in each outer corner, and dec 2 sts at inner corners. Do not sc along the long edge. Finish off, leaving a 36" yarn end for joining.

Place straight edge of piece beside one short end of Shawl Body and sew, easing to fit.

Rep with three more squares of same sizes, and sew to opposite short end of Shawl Body.

Line up remaining squares with largest in the center and smallest at the ends, with marked sides up. Sew, keeping one long edge straight. With the straight edge on the bottom, sc around the sides and tops of the strip of squares, leaving straight edge unworked. Center straight edge on lower edge of the shawl body; pin edges tog, matching stitch to stitch, and sew tog.

Weave in all ends.

Note: *Color C sometimes works itself loose, so it may be necessary to tack the ends with a needle and thread.*

PEEK-A-BOO DRESS

Designed by Tammy Hildebrand

Sensual yet demure, this dress will be the center of attention wherever it is worn. Crocheted in a stretchy yarn, it will hug a beautiful body. Trimmed with eyelash yarn, the dress will be an outstanding addition to anyone's wardrobe.

PEEK-A-BOO DRESS

SIZES	X-Small	Small	Medium	Large
Body Chest Measurements	28"-30"	32"-34"	36"-38"	40"-42"
Finished Chest Measurements	29"	33"	37"	41"

Note: *Instructions are written for size Extra Small; changes for sizes Small, Medium, and Large are in parentheses.*

Note: *Garment is tight fitting and made with a stretchy yarn.*

Materials

Worsted weight stretchy yarn, 21 (22½, 24, 25½) oz blue
Super bulky eyelash yarn, 1 oz blue
Bulky weight novelty yarn, 1 oz shaded blue/green
Note: *Photographed model made with Patons® Katrina #10742 Lagoon; Bernat® Eyelash #35237 Diva and Bernat® Boa #81205 Peacock.*
3 craft rings, 2" diameter
Size I (5.50 mm) crochet hook
Size F (3.75 mm) crochet hook (or size required for gauge)

Gauge

16 sc = 4" with F hook and worsted yarn

Stitch Guide

V-stitch (V-st): (Dc, ch 1, dc) in specified st: V-st made.

Single Crochet Decrease (sc dec): (Draw up a lp in next stt) twice; YO and draw through all 3 lps on hook: sc dec made.

INSTRUCTIONS

Note: *Use worsted yarn and smaller hook unless otherwise stated.*

FRONT AND BACK

Top ring

Rnd 1: Work 42 sc over one craft ring; join in first sc: 42 sc.

Rnd 2: Ch 1, sc in same sc as joining, ch 3, skip next 2 sc; *sc in next sc, ch 3, skip next 2 sc; rep from * around; join as before: 14 ch-3 sps and 14 sc. Finish off; weave in ends.

Middle Ring

Rnd 1: With 2nd craft ring, rep Rnd 1 on top ring.

Rnd 2: Ch 1, sc in same sc as joining; *ch 1, drop lp from hook, insert hook in center ch of any ch-3 sp on top ring, pick up dropped lp and pull through ch; ch 1, skip next 2 sc, sc in next sc; rep from * 2 times more; ch 3, skip next 2 sc; **sc in next sc, ch 3, skip next 2 sc; rep from ** around; join: 3 joined ch sps, 11 ch-3 sps and 14 sc. Finish off; weave in ends.

Bottom Ring

Rnd 1: With 3rd craft ring, rep Rnd 1 on top ring.

Rnd 2: Ch 1, sc in same sc as joining, skip next 6 ch-3 sps on middle ring; *ch 1, drop lp from hook, insert hook in center ch of next ch-3 sp on middle ring, pick up dropped lp and pull through ch; ch 1, skip next 2 sc, sc in next sc; rep from * 2 times more; ch 3, skip next 2 sc; **sc in next sc, ch 3, skip next 2 sc; rep from ** around; join: 3 joined ch sps, 11 ch-3 sps and 14 sc. Finish off; weave in ends.

LEFT HALF

Row 1 (right side): Join with sl st in 4th ch-3 sp on bottom ring before joined ch sps, ch 3 (counts as dc), 2 dc in same sp; *3 dc in next ch-3 sp on same ring; rep from * 2 times more; tr around first ch sp joining on same ring, 3 dc in next ch-3 sp on next ring; rep from * once; 3 dc in each of next 3 ch-3 sps on same ring: 36 dc and 2 tr; ch 1, turn.

Row 2: Sc in first 9 dc; *hdc in next 3 dc, dc in next tr, hdc in next 3 dc, sc in next 6 dc; rep from * once; sc in last 3 dc: 24 sc, 12 hdc and 2 dc; ch 1, turn.

Row 3: Sc in first 11 sts; *skip next st, 3 dc in next st, skip next st, sc in next 10 sts; rep from * once; sc in last st: 32 sc and 6 dc; ch 1, turn.

Row 4: Sc in each st across: 38 sc; ch 1, turn.

Rep Row 4 until piece measures about 13" (15", 17", 19") from Row 1 to end. At end of last row, finish off; weave in ends.

RIGHT HALF

Row 1 (right side): Join yarn with sl st in 4th ch-3 sp on top ring before joined ch sps, ch 3 (counts as dc), 2 dc in same sp; *3 dc in next ch-3 sp

on same ring; rep from * 2 times more; tr around 3rd ch sp joining on next ring, 3 dc in next ch-3 sp on next ring; rep from * once; 3 dc in each of next 3 ch-3 sps on same ring: 36 dc and 2 tr; ch 1, turn.

Rows 2 through 4: Rep Rows 2 through 4 on Left Side.

Rep Row 4 until piece measures about 13" (15", 17", 19") from Row 1 to end, making sure number of rows is same as on Left Half. At end of last row, finish off; weave in ends.

Sew back seam.

TOP EDGING

With right side facing, join yarn with sc in 2nd unworked ch-3 sp on top ring, 2 sc in next unworked ch-3 sp, 2 sc around beg ch-3 on Row 1 on Right Half, sc in edge of each row to last row, 2 sc around post (vertical bar) of last dc on Row 1 on Left Half, 2 sc in first unworked ch-3 sp on top ring, sc in same ch-3 sp as first sc; join with sl st in beg sc. Finish off; weave in ends.

RIGHT SHOULDER STRAP

Row 1: With right side facing, measure 3" (3 3/4", 4 1/2", 5 1/4") to left of first sc on Top Edging, join with sc in next st, sc in next 14 sts: 15 sc; ch 1, turn, leaving rem sts unworked.

Rows 2 through 4: Skip first st, sc in next st and in each st across to last st, leaving last st unworked: 2 fewer sts in each row than in previous row; ch 1, turn. At end of Row 4: 9 sc.

Row 5: Sc in each st across: 9 sc; ch 1, turn.

Rep Row 5 until strap measures about 14" long, or desired length to top edge of back, having an odd number of rows. At end of last row, finish off, leaving a long length for sewing.

LEFT SHOULDER STRAP

Row 1: With right side facing, measure 3" (3 3/4", 4 1/2", 5 1/4") to right of first sc on Top Edging, join with sc in 15th st to right of measurement, sc in next 14 sts: 15 sc; ch 1, turn, leaving rem sts unworked.

Note: *Make sure there is an even number of sts between shoulder straps on Front.*

Rows 2 through 5: Rep Rows 2 through 5 on Right Shoulder Strap.

Rep Row 5 until strap measures about 14" long, or desired length to top edge of back, making sure number of rows is same as on Right Shoulder Strap. At end of last row, finish off, leaving long yarn length for sewing.

Sew end of straps to top edge of back, leaving 2" (2 1/2", 3", 3 1/2") between front and back of each strap along Top Edging for armhole openings and 4" (4 3/4", 5 1/2", 6 1/4") from center of back to edge of straps, or as desired.

Note: *Make sure there is an even number of sts between shoulder straps on Back and number of sts for each armhole opening is the same.*

NECK

Rnd 1: With right side facing and working around neck opening, join with sc in neck edge of last row of Left Shoulder Strap on back, sc in edge of each row on Left Shoulder Strap, sc in each st across front between straps, sc in edge of each row on Right Shoulder Strap; *sc dec in next 2 sts on top edge of back; rep from * across top of back between straps; join with sl st in beg sc.

Rnd 2: Ch 1, sc in same st as joining; *ch 1, skip next st, sc in next st; rep from * across edge of Left Shoulder Strap; sc in each st across front between straps, sc in next st on Right Shoulder Strap; **ch 1, skip next st, sc in next st; rep from ** across edge of Right Shoulder Strap; sc in each st across back between straps; join with sl st in beg sc. Finish off; weave in ends.

NECK FUR TRIM

Rnd 1: With right side facing and larger hook, holding one strand of eyelash yarn and one strand of novelty yarn together, join with sc in ch-1 sp after first sc on Rnd 2 of Neck, sc in each ch-1 sp on Left Shoulder Strap, sc in each st along front between straps, sc in each ch-1 sp of Right Shoulder Strap, sc in each st across back between straps; join with sl st in beg sc. Finish off; weave in ends.

ARMHOLES

Rnd 1: With right side facing, join worsted weight yarn with sc in first unworked st of armhole opening on Top Edging, sc in next st and in each st of armhole opening, sc in edge of each row on strap; join with sl st in beg sc.

Rnd 2: Ch 1, sc in same sp as joining, ch 1, skip next st; *sc in next st, ch 1, skip next st; rep from * around; join with sl st in beg sc. Finish off; weave in ends.

Rep Rnds 1 and 2 on second armhole.

SKIRTING

Rnd 1: With right side facing and holding top upside down, with smaller hook join worsted weight yarn with sl st in first unworked ch-3 sp on bottom ring, ch 3, (2 dc, ch 1, 2 dc) in next ch-3 sp, dc in next ch-3 sp, sc around beg ch-3 on Row 1 on Left Half, sc in edge of each row to last row, sc around post of last dc on Row 1 on Right Half; join with sl st in 3rd ch of beg ch-3.

Rnd 2: Ch 1, sc in same st as joining, sc in next 2 dc, sc in ch-1 sp, sc in next 2 dc, sc in each st around; do not join. Place marker in last st and move up in each rnd to mark last st of rnd.

Rnds 3 and 4: Sc in each st around; do not join.

Rnd 5: Ch 1, sc in same st as joining, sc in each st around, increasing one or two sc evenly spaced as necessary to achieve total number of sts evenly divisible by 3; join with sl st in beg sc.

Rnd 6: Ch 4, dc in same st as joining; *skip next 2 sts, V-st in next st; rep from * around; join with sl st in 3rd ch of beg ch-4.

Rnd 7: Sl st in ch-1 sp of next V-st, ch 1, (sc, ch 3, sc) in same ch-1 sp; *(sc, ch 3, sc) in ch-1 sp of next V-st; rep from * around; join with sl st in beg sc.

Rnd 8: Sl st in next ch-3 sp, ch 1, 3 sc in same sp; *3 sc in next ch-3 sp; rep from * around; join with sl st in beg sc.

Rnd 9: Ch 1, sc in same st as joining, sc in each st around; do not join. Place marker in last st and move up in each rnd to mark last st of rnd.

Rnd 10: Sc in each st around; do not join.

Rep Rnd 10 until skirting measures 16", or to desired length. At end of last rnd, finish off; weave in ends.

BOTTOM FUR TRIM

With right side facing and larger hook, holding one strand of eyelash yarn and one strand of novelty yarn together, join with sl st in any st on last rnd of skirting, ch 3, dc in same st as joining, skip next 2 sts; *2 dc in next st, skip next 2 sts; rep from * around; join with sl st in 3rd ch of beg ch-3. Finish off; weave in ends.

JEWELED COPPER SPIRAL

Designed by Judith Solomon

Is this really crocheted? Yes! Real copper wire accented with sparkling beads is crocheted into an exciting piece of jewelry.

Note: *Instructions are written for average neck size; changes for larger size are in parentheses.*

Materials

32-gauge copper wire, 1 spool (30 yds)
240 glass beads, # 11, turquoise
8mm round turquoise glass bead
Size B (2.25mm) aluminum crochet hook or Size 2 (2.25mm) steel crochet hook (or size required for gauge)
Wire cutters or heavy scissors

Gauge

12 ch = 1⅝"

Stitch Guide

Bead sc: Insert hook in back lp of next st, YO and draw a lp through; push bead up against work, YO and draw wire through 2 lps on hook: bead sc made.

INSTRUCTIONS

Ch 153 (173).

Row 1: Sc in 2nd ch from hook; 3 sc in each of next 30 (34) chs; 3 dc in each of next 30 (34) chs; 3 tr in each of next 30 (34) chs; 3 dc in each of next 30 (34) chs; 3 sc in each of next 30 (34) chs; sc in last ch; cut wire, leaving a 6" wire end, finish off.

Set piece aside, marking this side as right side.

Row 2 (beaded edging): String beads on rem wire. Leaving 12" of wire free at beg, hold Row 1 with right side facing and sl st into back lp of first sc. *Bead sc in back lp next st, sc in back lp of next st; rep from * to last st, sc in last st; cut wire, leaving a 6" end; finish off.

FASTENING

Loop: Insert hook into turning ch at end of foundation ch, pull lp from 12" wire end through, ch 7. Be sure the ch will fit around the 8 mm bead. Cut wire. Finish off and weave loose wire securely into the end of necklace and trim excess.

Bead: Even off the wire at ends of Rows 1 and 2, and string both ends through the 8 mm bead and one size 11 bead. Return wire ends through the 8 mm bead and into the end of the necklace. Weave ends in securely and trim excess. Place lp over 8mm bead to close.

BRIDAL TUNIC

Designed by
Margaret Hubert

for the advanced crocheter

True elegance is the theme of the gorgeous tunic, perfect in white for the bride or in a pastel shade for summer parties. Pearl beads accent the delicate lace neckline border, and a row of pearl buttons dances down the back. Our version is made in a cool cotton yarn.

BRIDAL TUNIC

SIZES	Small	Medium	Large
Body Bust Measurements	38”	39”	40”
Finished Bust Measurements	41”	42”	43”

***Note:** Instructions are written for size Small; changes for sizes Medium and Large are in parentheses.*

Materials

DK or Sport weight cotton yarn, 23 (23, 25) oz white

***Note:** Photographed model made with Patons® Grace #6005 Snow*

9 round 3/8” diameter shank pearl buttons

1 package 8mm pearl beads (about 40 beads)

Sewing needle and white sewing thread for attaching beads

Straight pins

Sizes F (3.75 mm) crochet hook (or size required for gauge)

H (5mm) crochet hook

***Note:** Larger hook is used only at beginning of sleeves.*

Gauge

16 dc = 4” with smaller hook

8 dc rows = 3”

Stitch Guide

Double Crochet Decrease (dc dec): (YO, insert hook in next st and draw up a lp, YO and draw through first 2 lps on hook) twice; YO and draw through all 3 lps on hook: dc dec made.

Double Crochet Increase (dc inc): Work 2 dc in the same st: dc inc made.

INSTRUCTIONS

***Note:** Turning ch-3 counts as a dc throughout pattern.*

FRONT

***Note:** The two side points are worked separately, then joined with a center section to complete the Front. Each point has a seam edge, which is straight, and a center edge, which is shaped with increases.*

Front Points (make 2)

Foundation Row: With smaller hook, starting at bottom of right point, ch 3 (counts as a dc), 2 dc in 3rd ch from hook: 3 dc; ch 3, turn.

Row 1: Dc in next dc, 2 dc in last st (inc made): 4 dc; ch 3, turn.

Row 2: Dc in first st (last dc of prev row): inc made; dc in next 3 dc: 5 dc; ch 3, turn.

Row 3: Dc in each dc to last st, 2 dc in last st: 6 dc; ch 3, turn.

Row 4: Dc in first st as before, dc across: 7 dc; ch 3, turn.

Rows 5 thru 14: Rep Rows 3 and 4 five times more, increasing 1 st at center edge on each row: 17 dc at end of Row 14.

Row 15: Dc in each dc, ch 7, turn.

Row 16: 4 dc in 3rd ch from hook, skip next 4 chs, dc in each of 17 established dc: 22 dc; ch 3, turn.

Row 17: Dc in 21 dc, dc in top of turning ch, ch 7, turn.

Row 18: 4 dc in 3rd ch from hook, skip 4 chs, dc in next 22 established sts: 27 dc; ch 3, turn.

Row 19: Dc in 26 dc and in top of turning ch: 27 dc; ch 14 (15, 16); finish off, leaving last 14 (15, 16) chs unworked.

Joining Row

Hold one point piece with straight seam edge at your right and unworked ch at your left; join yarn with sl st in first st at right; ch 3, dc in each dc and in each unworked ch of this piece; pick up second point piece and hold with straight seam edge at your left and unworked ch at your right; continue working dc across each ch st and in each dc: 82 (84, 86) dc; ch 3, turn.

Work even in dc until piece measures 7" (7½", 8") from joining row.

Shaping

Row 1: Dc in first dc, dc dec over next 2 dc (see Stitch Guide) dc to last 3 sts, dc dec over next 2 sts, dc in last st; ch 3 turn.

Rows 2 and 3: Rep Row 1; at end of Row 3: 76 (78, 80) dc.

Row 4: 2 dc in next dc (inc made), dc to last 2 sts, 2 dc in next st, dc in last st; ch 3, turn.

Rows 5 and 6: Rep Row 4: 82 (84, 86) sts.

Work even in dc until piece measures 15" (15½", 16") from joining row; end last row with ch 1, turn.

Armhole Shaping

Row 1: Sl st across 6 sts, ch 3, dc to last 6 sts, ch 3, turn, leaving last 6 sts unworked.

Rows 2 through 6: Dc dec over next 2 sts, dc to last 2 sts, dc dec over last 2 sts: 60 (62, 64) dc; ch 3, turn.

Left Neck Shaping

Row 1 (right side): Dc across 16 (17, 18) sts, ch 3 turn, leaving rem sts unworked.

Working on these sts only, dc dec at neck edge every row till 4 (5, 6) sts rem. Work even (if necessary) until piece measures 7½" (8", 8½") from start of armhole shaping. Finish off; weave in ends.

Right Neck Shaping

Row 1: Hold piece with wrong side facing. Join yarn in first st at right edge, ch 3 (counts as a dc), dc across 15 (16, 17) sts, ch 3, turn, leaving center 28 sts unworked. Complete as for Left Neck Shaping.

BACK

Note: *Back is worked in two pieces.*

Back Points (make 2)

Work as for Front Points through Row 18.

Row 19: Dc across, finish off. Back is now worked in 2 separate sections.

Right Back

Row 1 (right side): Hold one point piece with straight seam edge at your right; join yarn in first st at right, ch 3, dc across, ch 16 (17, 18), turn.

Row 2: Dc in 4th ch (first 3 ch count as first dc), dc in each rem ch, dc in each dc across: 41 (42, 43) dc; ch 3, turn.

Continue to work in dc rows, shaping arm (seam) edge same as front until 4 rows after last armhole dec is completed, ending at neck edge: 30 (31, 32) dc; at end of last row, ch 1, turn.

Shape Neck

Sl st over 23 sts, ch 3, work dc on rem 7 (8, 9) sts. Dec 1 st at neck edge every row until 4 (5, 6) sts rem. Work even until piece measures same as front from start of armhole shaping. Finish off; weave in ends.

Left Back

Row 1 (right side): Hold other point piece with straight seam edge at your left; join yarn in first st at right, ch 3, dc across, ch 3, turn.

Continue to work in dc rows, shaping arm (seam) edge same as front until 4 rows after last armhole dec is completed, ending at neck edge: 30 (31, 32) dc; at end of last row, ch 3, turn.

Shape Neck

Dc in next 7 (8, 9) dc; continue working in dc rows, dec 1 st at neck edge every row until 4 (5, 6) sts rem. Work even until piece measures same as front from start of armhole shaping; finish off, weave in ends.

SLEEVES (make 2)

With larger hook, ch 43 (47, 51).

Foundation Row: Dc in 3rd ch from hook and in each rem ch: 40 (44, 48) dc; ch 3, turn.

Rows 1 through 5: Dc across, ch 3, turn.

Change to smaller hook and continue to work in dc rows until piece measures 5" from beg ch.

Increase Row: 2 dc in next dc, dc to last 2 sts, 2 dc in next st, dc in last st; ch 3, turn.

Continue to work in dc rows, repeating Increase Row every 2½" for 3 (3, 4) times more: 48 (52, 58) dc.

Work even in dc until sleeve measures 14" (14½", 15")" from cast-on row, or until 2" less than desired finished length; at end of last row, ch 1, turn.

SHAPE SLEEVE CAP

Row 1: Sl st across first 6 dc, ch 3, dc to within 6 dc of opposite side, ch 3 turn, leaving last 6 dc unworked.

Rows 2 through 4 (4, 5): Dc across, ch 3, turn.

Row 5 (5, 6): Dc dec over first 2 dc, dc to last 2 sts, dc dec; ch 3, turn.

Continue to work in dc rows, working a dc dec at each side every other row 4 (4, 5) times more: 26 (30, 34 sts). Then dec 1 st each side every row 3 times: 20 (24, 28) sts. Work 0 (0, 1) row even. Next row, dc dec across row: 10 (12, 14) sts rem. Finish off; weave in ends.

LACE BORDERS

Note: *The lace borders are composed of three motifs, the third of which is repeated until the border is the desired length. Following is the border pattern, which you may want to try with scrap yarn first. Instructions for length of borders for neckline, sleeves and bottom follow that.*

BORDER INSTRUCTIONS

First Motif

Ch 6, join with sl st to form a ring.

Row 1: Ch 3 (counts as a dc), 13 dc in ring: 14 dc; ch 1 turn.

Row 2: Sc in first dc (mark this stitch), sc in next dc; (ch 4, sc in each of next 2 dc) 6 times (last sc will be in top of turning ch); ch 6, turn.

Second Motif

Row 1: Sl st in the first free ch 4 lp of First Motif, ch 3. turn.

Row 2: 13 dc in ch-6 lp, sl st in the first (marked) sc of first motif, ch 1, turn.

Row 3: Sc in first 2 dc, (ch 4, sc in each of next 2 dc) 6 times, sl st in next free ch-4 lp of adjoining motif, ch 6, turn.

Third Motif

Row 1: Sl st in first free ch-4 lp of adjoining motif, ch 3, turn.

Row 2: 13 dc in ch-6 lp, sl st in next free ch-4 lp of adjoining motif, ch 1, turn.

Row 3: Sc in first 2 dc, (ch 4, sc in each of next 2 dc) 6 times, sl st in next free ch-4 lp of adjoining motif, ch 6. turn.

Rep Third Motif for pattern until desired length; on last rep, omit last ch 6. Finish off; weave in ends.

Note: *When working borders, be sure each piece is the correct length before finishing off.*

SLEEVE BORDERS (make 2)

Work first 3 motifs, then rep 3rd motif only 11 (11, 12) times more Finish off; weave in ends.

BOTTOM BORDERS (make 2)

Work first 3 motifs, then rep 3rd motif only 30 (30, 31) times more. Finish off; weave in ends.

NECKLINE BORDER (make 1)

Work first 3 motifs, then rep 3rd motif only 34 (34, 35) times more. Finish off; weave in ends

FINISHING

Neckline Border

Sew shoulder seams. Mark center front of garment. Fold Neckline Border in half to find center. Place border over garment, with bottom ch-4 lps of Border just overlapping garment, and pin around neckline, easing to fit. Border should end exactly at back edge of each back piece. Sew in place.

Right Back Button Band

Row 1: With right side of garment facing you, and starting at neck edge, join yarn in top st of Border and work sc along lace border, down back to bottom, ch 1 turn.

Rows 2 through 5: Sc in each sc, ch 1, turn.

At end of Row 5, finish off; weave in ends.

Measuring carefully, place 9 pins evenly spaced on center row of button band to mark button placement. First button should be placed about 3 sts from top edge, and last button about 6 sts up from bottom edge. Sew buttons in place.

Left Back Buttonhole Band

Row 1: With wrong side of garment facing you, and starting at neck edge, join yarn in top st of Border and work sc along lace border, down back to bottom, ch 1, turn.

Row 2: Sc in each sc, ch 1, turn.

On the next row you will make buttonholes opposite the buttons. Place two back pieces side by side with button edge beside buttonhole edge, and carefully mark placement for buttonholes.

Note: *After working first buttonhole on next row, check to be sure the size is correct for the button you are using.*

Row 3: Sc across, working buttonholes at markers as follows: ch 2, skip 2 sc; ch 1, turn at end of row.

Row 4: Sc in each sc, working 2 sc in each ch-2 sp; ch 1, turn.

Row 5: Sc in each sc. Finish off; weave in ends.

Lap Buttonhole Band over Button Band at bottom of garment, and sew in place.

Garment now becomes a pullover.

Sleeves

Mark center point of sleeve cap, matching center point with shoulder seam. Pin in place, easing to fit, and sew. Sew sleeve and garment side seams.

At bottom of sleeves, fit cuff borders around and pin in place, easing to fit and placing ch-4 lps of border top just above bottom of last row of sleeve. Sew in place.

Front Bottom Border

Hold front of garment with right side facing you and bottom edge of garment at top.

Take one of the bottom borders, fold to find center; find center of front. Matching centers, pin border to garment, having ch-4 lps of edge of border just overlapping bottom of sts of last row of front. Carefully pin border in place, ending at side seams on each side, easing to fit. Sew in place.

Back Bottom Border

Hold back of garment with right side facing you and bottom edge of garment at top.

Finish as for Front Bottom Border.

Pearl Bead Accents

Sew pearl beads randomly spaced across top border, as shown in photo on page 73.

MARTINIQUE SUNSET

Designed by Nancy Nehring for DMC®

A beautiful tropical sunset with colors moving from yellow through red to purple is reflected in this sleeveless tank top where the color gradations are created by swapping out one of the three strands of thread at a time for another color. The classic pineapple trim around the bottom is another reminder of the tropics. The outfit is completed with a mini skirt and is accented with a long skinny scarf capped by its own pineapples.

MARTINIQUE SUNSET

SIZES	Small	Medium	Large	X-Large
TOP				
Body Bust Measurements	32"-34"	36"-38"	40"-42"	44"-46"
Finished Bust Measurements	36"	40"	43"	47"
SKIRT				
Body Hip Measurements	34"	37"	40"	43"
Finished Hip Measurements	36"	39"	42"	45"

Note: *Instructions are written for size Small; changes for sizes Medium and Large are in parentheses; garments stretch to fit.*

SCARF

6' 8" long x 1 3/4" wide (3" wide pineapple at each end)

Materials

Cotton thread,
- Yellow, 9 (10, 10, 11) 165-yd skeins
- Red, 37 (40, 43, 46) 165-yd skeins
- Purple, 12 (13, 14, 15) 165-yd skeins

Note: *Photographed model made with DMC® Floche, #744 Yellow, #321 Red and #208 Purple*

Sizes 7 (1.65mm) steel crochet hook (or size required for gauge)

Size 11 (1.1mm) steel crochet hook (or sizes required for gauge)

3/4" wide elastic, 25" long (or waist measurement plus 1")

Sewing needle and thread

Spray Starch (optional)

Gauge

11 ch-3 sps = 4" in patt

(ch 1, sc) 16 times = 3" in patt

Pattern Stitches

Beg decrease (beg dec): (Insert hook in next ch-1 sp, YO and draw up a lp) twice, YO and draw through all 3 lps on hook: beg dec made.

End decrease (end dec): Insert hook in next ch-1 sp, YO and draw up a lp, insert hook in next ch-1 sp or turning ch-1, YO and draw up a lp, YO and draw through all 3 lps on hook: end dec made.

To change color: Work st until 2 lps rem on hook, drop one strand of old color, pick up one strand of new color and draw all 3 strands through both lps on hook, cut dropped strand of old color.

TOP

INSTRUCTIONS

Wind skeins into balls. Starting at bottom with 3 strands of yellow held together, ch 300 (330, 360, 390), join with sl st in first ch to form a circle, being careful not to twist ch.

Rnd 1 (right side): Ch 3, skip next 2 chs, sc in next ch; *ch 3, skip next 2 chs, sc in next ch; rep from * around to last 2 chs; ch 5, sc in first ch-3 sp: 100 (110, 120, 130) ch sps. Place marker in ch-5 sp to mark one side seam. Move marker up with each rnd to indicate end of rnd and side seam.

Rnd 2: *Ch 3, sc in next ch sp; rep from * around: 100 (110, 120, 130) ch sps; do not join.

Continue to rep Rnd 2, changing colors and working number of rnds of each color as follows:

8 rnds with 2 strands yellow and 1 strand red
1 rnd with 1 strand yellow and 2 strands red
1 rnd with 2 strands yellow and 1 strand red
1 rnd with 1 strand yellow and 2 strands red
1 rnd with 2 strands yellow and 1 strand red
8 rnds with 1 strand yellow and 2 strands red
1 rnd with 3 strands red
1 rnd with 1 strand yellow and 2 strands red
1 rnd with 3 strands red
1 rnd with 1 strand yellow and 2 strands red
3 rnds with 3 strands red

Continue with 3 strands red for Rnds 30 and 31.

Rnd 30: *(Ch 1, sc) twice in next ch-3 sp; rep from * 18 (20, 22, 24) times more; ch 1, sc in next ch-3 sp**; rep from * to ** four times more: 390 (430, 470, 510) sts [195 (215, 235, 255) sc and 195 (215, 235, 255) ch-1 sps]. Place marker in last sc and move up with each rnd worked to mark end of each rnd and side seam.

Rnd 31: *Ch 1, sc in next ch-1 sp; rep from * around.

Continue working in rnds same as Rnd 31, changing color and working number of rnds of each color as follows:.

11 rnds with 3 strands red
1 rnd with 2 strands red and 1 strand purple
1 rnd with 3 strands red
1 rnd with 2 strands red and 1 strand purple
1 rnd with 3 strands red
13 rnds with 2 strands red and 1 strand purple
1 rnd with 1 strand red and 2 strands purple
1 rnd with 2 strands red and 1 strand purple
1 rnd with 1 strand red and 2 strands purple
1 rnd with 2 strands red and 1 strand purple
13 rnds with 1 strand red and 2 strands purple

On last rnd, work last 4 sts with (ch 1, sl st in next ch-1 sp) twice: 76 rnds completed. Finish off.

Place marker 195 (215, 235, 255) stitches away from first marker to mark second side seam.

FRONT

Row 1 (right side): With right side facing, skip 18 (24, 28, 34) sts from first side marker, join 3 strands purple with sl st in next ch-1 sp (sl st does not count as st); *ch 1, sc in next ch-1 sp; rep from * 76 (80, 86, 90) times more: 154 (162, 174, 182) sts; ch 1 (counts as st on next row now and throughout), turn.

Row 2: With 1 strand red and 2 strands purple, work beg dec; *ch 1, sc in next ch-1 sp; rep from * across to last 4 sts; ch 1, work end dec: 150 (158, 170, 178) sts; ch 1, turn.

Row 3: With 3 strands purple, rep Row 2: 146 (154, 166, 174) sts.

Row 4: With 1 strand red and 2 strands purple, rep Row 2: 142 (150, 162, 170) sts.

Rows 5 and 6: With 3 strands purple, rep Row 2. At end of Row 6: 134 (142, 154, 162) sts.

Row 7: With 3 strands purple, sc in first ch-1 sp; *ch 1, sc in next ch-1 sp; rep from * across, ending with ch 1, sc in turning ch-1; ch 1, turn.

Row 8: With 3 strands purple, rep Row 2: 130 (138, 150, 158) sts.

Rows 9 through 17: Rep Row 7 nine times more.

RIGHT FRONT

Row 18 (wrong side): Sc in first ch-1 sp; *ch 1, sc in next ch-1 sp; rep from * 20 times more; ch 1, work end dec: 46 sts; ch 1, turn.

Row 19: Sc in first ch-1 sp; *ch 1, sc in next ch-1 sp; rep from * across; ch 1, turn.

Row 20: Sc in first ch-1 sp; *ch 1, sc in next ch-1 sp; rep from * across to last 4 sts; ch 1, work end dec: 44 sts; ch 1, turn.

Row 21: Work beg dec; *ch 1, sc in next ch-1 sp; rep from * across: 42 sts; ch 1, turn.

Row 22: Rep Row 20: 40 sts.

Rows 23 through 26: Rep Rows 19 and 20 two times more. At end of Row 26: 36 sts.

Rows 27 and 28: Rep Rows 21 and 22. At end of Row 28: 32 sts.

Rows 29 through 32: Rep Rows 19 and 20 two times more. At end of Row 32: 28 sts.

Rows 33 and 34: Rep Rows 21 and 22. At end of Row 34: 24 sts.

Rows 35 through 68: Rep Row 19 thirty-four times more. At end of Row 68, finish off; weave in ends.

LEFT FRONT

Row 18: With wrong side facing, skip 33 (41, 53, 61) sts on Row 17, join 3 strands purple with sl st in next ch-1 sp (sl st does not count as st), ch 1, work beg dec; *ch 1, sc in next ch-1 sp; rep from * 21 times more: 46 sts; ch 1, turn.

Row 19: Rep Row 19 for Right Front.

Row 20: Work beg dec; *ch 1, sc in next ch-1 sp; rep from * across: 44

sts; ch 1, turn.

Row 21: Rep Row 20 for Right Front: 42 sts; ch 1, turn.

Row 22: Rep Row 20 for Left Front: 40 sts.

Rows 23 through 26: Rep Rows 19 and 20 for Left Front 2 times more. At end of Row 26: 36 sts.

Rows 27 and 28: Rep Rows 21 and 22 for Left Front. At end of Row 28: 32 sts.

Rows 29 through 32: Rep Rows 19 and 20 for Left Front 2 times more. At end of Row 32: 28 sts.

Rows 33 and 34: Rep Rows 21 and 22 for Left Front. At end of Row 34: 24 sts.

Rows 35 through 68: Rep Row 19 for Left Front 34 times more. At end of Row 68, finish off; weave in ends.

BACK

Row 1: With right side facing, skip 13 (19, 23, 27) sts from second side marker, join 3 strands purple with sl st in next ch-1 sp (sl st does not count as st); *ch 1, sc in next ch-1 sp; rep from * 81 (85, 91, 97) times more: 164 (172, 184, 196) sts; ch 1 (counts as st on next row now and throughout), turn.

Rows 2 through 4: With appropriate colors, rep Rows 2 through 4 for Front: At end of Row 4: 152 (160, 172, 184) sts.

Rows 5 and 6: With 3 strands purple, rep Row 2 for Front 2 times more. At end of Row 6: 144 (152, 164, 176) sts.

Row 7: Rep Row 7 for Front.

Row 8: With 3 strands purple, rep Row 2 for Front: 140 (148, 160, 172) sts.

Rows 9 and 10: Rep Rows 7 and 8 for Back. At end of Row 10: 136 (144, 156, 168) sts.

Rows 11 through 46: Rep Row 7 for Front 36 times more.

RIGHT BACK

Row 47 (right side): Rep Row 18 for Right Front: 46 sts; ch 1, turn.

Rows 48 through 63: Rep Rows 19 through 34 for Right Front. At end of Row 63: 24 sts.

Rows 64 through 68: Rep Row 19 for Right Front 5 times more. At end of Row 68, finish off; weave in ends.

LEFT BACK

Row 47: With right side facing, skip 39 (47, 59, 71) sts on Row 46, join 3 strands purple with sl st in next ch-1 sp (sl st does not count as st), ch 1, work beg dec; *ch 1, sc in next ch-1 sp; rep from * 21 times more: 46 sts; ch 1, turn.

Rows 48 through 63: Rep Rows 19 through 34 for Left Front. At end of Row 63: 24 sts.

Rows 64 through 68: Rep Row 19 for Right Front 5 times more. At end of Row 68, finish off; weave in ends.

With 3 strands purple, sew shoulder seams.

NECKLINE EDGING

With right side facing and 3 strands purple, sc in each st and in edge of each row around; join with sl st in first sc. Finish off; weave in ends.

ARMHOLE EDGING

With right side facing and 3 strands purple, sc in edge of each row and in each ch-1 sp; at underarms, sc in each ch-1 sp; join with sl st in first sc. Finish off; weave in ends. Note: underarms will be slightly gathered.

BOTTOM PINEAPPLES

Hold piece with right side facing and beg ch at top; working in skipped ch-2 sps of beg ch, join 3 strands yellow with sl st in 5th ch-2 sp on right of last ch-2 sp on Rnd 1 of Top (for Small and Large sizes) or in last ch-2 sp on Rnd 1 of Top (for Medium and X-Large sizes).

Row 1 (right side): *Ch 16, sc in same ch-2 sp; rep from * 8 times more; ch 8, skip 2 ch-2 sps of beg ch, sc in next ch-2 sp: 9 ch-16 sps; ch 5, turn.

Row 2: Sc in first ch-16 sp, *ch 5, sc in next ch-16 sp; rep from * 7 times more; skip 2 ch-2 sps of beg ch, sc in next ch-2 sp: 9 ch-5 sps; ch 5, turn.

Row 3: Sc in first ch-5 sp, *ch 5, sc in next ch-5 sp; rep from * across to last ch-5 sp; ch 3, tr in 3rd ch of last ch-5 sp: 8 ch-5 sps; ch 5, turn.

Rows 4 through 10: Rep Row 3 seven times more. At end of Row 10: 2 ch-5 sps.

Row 11: Sl st in next ch-5 sp. Finish off; weave in ends.

*Skip 6 ch-2 sps after last sc on Rnd 2, join 3 strands yellow with sl st in next ch-2 sp; rep Rows 1 through 11 of Pineapple; rep from * until 10 (11, 12, 13) pineapples are worked.

PINEAPPLE EDGING

With right side facing, join 3 strands yellow with sl st in first ch-5 sp on Row 3 of pineapple, work 5 sc in same ch-5 sp and in each of rem 17 ch sps around edge of pineapple, *work 3 sc in each of next 3 ch-2 sps of beg ch between pineapples, work 5 sc in each of first 2 ch sps on next pineapple, work 4 sc in next ch sp on same pineapple, sl st in corresponding sc on edging of previous pineapple, sc in same ch sp and in next ch sp on current pineapple, sl st in corresponding sc on edging of previous pineapple, work 4 more sc in same ch sp on current pineapple**, work 5 sc in each of rem 14 ch sps around edge of current pineapple; rep from * around to last pineapple; rep from * to ** once; work 5 sc in each of next 10 ch sps on current pineapple, work 4 sc in next ch sp on same pineapple, sl st in corresponding sc on edging of first pineapple, sc in same ch sp and in next ch sp on current pineapple, sl st in corresponding sc on edging of first pineapple, work 4 more sc in same ch sp on current pineapple, work 5 sc in each of rem 2 ch sps on current pineapple, work 3 sc in each of next 3 ch-2 sps of beg ch between last and first pineapples, sl st in first sc. Finish off; weave in ends.

Block and steam press Top, easing in gathered edging under arms. Apply light coat of spray starch to pineapples only.

SKIRT

INSTRUCTIONS

Wind skeins into balls. With 3 strands red thread held tog and larger hook, ch 380 (410, 440, 470), join with sc in back bar of first ch to form a circle, being careful not to twist ch.

Rnd 1: Working in back bar of chs, ch 1; *skip next ch, sc in next ch, ch 1; rep from * around: 190 (205, 220, 235) sc and 190 (205, 220, 235) ch-1 sps; do not join. Place marker in last st and move marker up to indicate end of each rnd.

Rnd 2: *Sc in next ch, ch 1; rep from * around.

Rep Rnd 2 until piece measures 17" (or desired length). Finish off 2 strands thread.

WAISTBAND

Rnd 1: With 1 strand thread and smaller hook, working in front lps only, work 2 sc in each sc and 1 sc in each ch-1 sp around: 570 (615, 660, 705) sc; do not join.

Rnd 2: Sc in each st, do not join.

Rep Rnd 2 until waistband measures 1 1/2" wide.

Cut piece of elastic 25" long (or waist measurement plus 1"). Overlap 1" and sew ends together. Pin elastic to wrong side of waistband.

Joining Rnd: Working in back lp of last rnd of skirt and encasing elastic, work 2 sc in each sc and 1 sc in each ch-1 sp around. Finish off; weave in ends.

Block and steam press to size.

SCARF

INSTRUCTIONS

Note: Wind skeins into balls.

With 3 strands yellow held together, ch 24.

Row 1: Sc in 6th ch from hook (5 skipped chs count as a ch-3 sp); *ch 3, skip next 2 chs, sc in next ch; rep from * 4 times more; ch 1, tr in last ch (counts as ch-3 sp): 7 ch-3 sps; ch 3, turn.

Row 2: Sc in next ch-3 sp; *ch 3, sc in next ch-3 sp; rep from * across: 6 ch-3 sps; ch 3, turn.

With 2 strands yellow and one strand red:

Row 3: Sc in first ch-3 sp; *ch 3, sc in next ch-3 sp; rep from * across, ending with ch 1, tr in top of tr 2 rows below (counts as ch-3 sp): 7 ch-3 sps; ch 3, turn.

Continue working in pattern of Rows 2 and 3 alternately, changing colors and working number of rows of each color as follows, to center of scarf. Reverse color sequence and work from center to other end of scarf, working 3 additional rows in same colors as Rows 3 through 1: 444 rows completed.

- 19 rows with 2 strands yellow and 1 strand red
- 1 row with 1 strand yellow and 2 strands red
- 1 row with 2 strands yellow and 1 strand red
- 1 row with 1 strand yellow and 2 strands red
- 1 row with 2 strands yellow and 1 strand red
- 20 rows with 1 strand yellow and 2 strands red
- 1 row with 3 strands red
- 1 row with 1 strand yellow and 2 strands red
- 1 row with 3 strands red
- 1 row with 1 strand yellow and 2 strands red
- 20 rows with 3 strands red
- 1 row with 2 strands red and 1 strand purple
- 1 row with 3 strands red
- 1 row with 2 strands red and 1 strand purple
- 1 row with 3 strands red
- 20 rows with 2 strands red and 1 strand purple
- 1 row with 1 strand red and 2 strands purple
- 1 row with 2 strands red and 1 strand purple
- 1 row with 1 strand red and 2 strands purple
- 1 row with 2 strands red and 1 strand purple
- 20 rows with 1 strand red and 2 strands purple
- 1 row with 3 strands purple
- 1 row with 1 strand red and 2 strands purple
- 1 row with 3 strands purple
- 1 row with 1 strand red and 2 strands purple
- 100 rows with 3 strands purple

PINEAPPLES (make 2)

Use 3 strands yellow for each pineapple.

Row 1 (right side): Join yellow with sl st in center ch-3 sp at one end of scarf, *ch 16, sc in same ch-3 sp; rep from * 8 times more; ch 8, sc in last ch-3 sp at end of scarf: 9 ch-16 sps; ch 5, turn.

Row 2: Sc in first ch-16 sp, *ch 5, sc in next ch-16 sp; rep from * 7 times more; ch 3, tr in first ch-3 sp at end of scarf: 10 ch-5 sps; ch 5, turn.

Row 3: Sc in next ch-5 sp; *ch 5, sc in next ch-5 sp; rep from * across to last ch-5 sp; ch 3, tr in 3rd ch of last ch-5 sp: 8 ch-5 sps; ch 5, turn.

Rows 4 through 10: Rep Row 3 seven times more. At end of Row 10: 1 ch-5 sp.

Row 11: Sl st in next ch-5 sp. Finish off; weave in ends.

PINEAPPLE EDGING

With right side facing, join yellow with sl st in last ch-5 sp on Row 2, ch 1, work 5 sc in same ch-5 sp and in each ch sp around edge of pineapple, includes sps formed by ch2 and tr. Finish off; weave in ends.

Work pineapple at other end of scarf in same manner.

FUN IN THE SUN

Designed by
Tammy Hildebrand

Show off a beautiful body in this barely there sun-time fashion. You'd better apply the sunblock liberally since lots of pretty skin is revealed!

FUN IN THE SUN

SIZES	Small	Medium	Large
Body Bust Measurements	32"	36"	40"
Body Hip Measurements	35"	40"	44"

Note: *Instructions are written for size Small; changes for sizes Medium and Large are in parentheses.*

Note: *Finished garment measurements are same as body for a close fit.*

Materials

Worsted weight stretchy yarn,
9 oz bright pink
Note: *Photographed model made with Patons® Katrina #10732 Blossom*
3 metal craft rings, 2" diameter
Size G (4mm) crochet hook
(or size required for gauge)

Gauge

7 sc and 6 tr = 3" in patt

INSTRUCTIONS

FIRST BRA CUP

Row 1: Working over craft ring, 15 sc in ring, ch 1, turn.

Row 2: Sc in first st, (tr in next st, sc in next st) across: 8 sc, 7 tr; ch 1, turn.

Row 3: 2 sc in first st, sc in each st to last st, 2 sc in last st: 17 sc; ch 1, turn.

Rows 4 through 7: Rep Rows 2 and 3 twice more: 21 sc.

Row 8: Sc in first st, (tr in next st, sc in next st) across: 11 sc, 10 tr; ch 1, turn.

Row 9: Sc in each st across, ch 1, turn.

Rows 10 through 19: Rep Rows 8 and 9, five more times.

Row 20: Rep Row 8.

Row 21: Skip first st, sc in each st to last st, ch 1, turn, leaving last st unworked: 19 sc; ch 1, turn.

Row 22: Rep Row 8.

Rows 23 through 30: Rep Rows 21 and 22, four more times: 6 sc, 5 tr.

Row 31: Sc in each st across: 11 sc; ch 1, turn.

Row 32: Sc in first st, (tr in next st, sc in next st) to end, ch 1, turn.

Rows 33 through 50: Rep Rows 31 and 32 ninteen, (twenty-one, twenty-three) more times.

Row 51: Rep Row 31. Finish off.

SECOND BRA CUP

Rows 1 through 19: Working over same craft ring, rep patt for first bra cup.

Row 20: Skip first st, sc in each st to last st, ch 1, turn, leaving last st unworked: 19 sc.

Row 21: Rep Row 8: 10 sc, 9 tr.

Row 22 through 29: Rep Rows 20 and 21 four more times: 6 sc, 5 tr.

Row 30: Sc in each st across, ch 1, turn.

Row 31: Sc in first st, (tr in next st, sc in next st) to across, ch 1, turn.

Rows 32 through 49: Rep Rows 30 and 31 ninteen, (twenty-one, twenty-three) more times. Finish off leaving a long yarn length for sewing. Lining up sts of Row 51 of first cup side and Row 49 of second cup, using tapestry needle, whipstitch tog.

TRIM

For top edge, sc in ring, working in row ends, (sl st, ch 1) in each row to end, sl st in ring. Finish off.

Work bottom edge the same way.

TUMMY PANEL

Row 1: Work 13 sc in ring between first and second cups (see photo), ch 1, turn.

Row 2: Sc in first st, (tr in next st, sc in next st) across: 7 sc, 6 tr; ch 1, turn.

Row 3: Sc in each st across, ch 1, turn.

Row 4 through 11: Rep Rows 2 and 3 four more times.

Row 12: Rep Row 2 once more.

Row 13: 2 sc in first st, sc in each st to last st, 2 sc in last st: 15 sc; ch 1, turn.

Row 14: Sc in first st, (tr in next st, sc in next st) across: 8 sc, 7 tr; ch 1, turn.

Row 15: Sc in each st across, ch 1, turn.

Rows 16 and 17: Rep Rows 14 and 15.

Row 18: Rep Row 14.

Row 19: Rep Row 13: 17 sc.

Rows 20 through 23: Rep Rows 14 and 15 twice.

Row 24: Rep Row 14.

Row 25: Rep row 13: 19 sc.

Rows 26 through 29: Rep Rows 14 and 15 twice.

Row 30: Rep Row 14.

Row 31: Rep Row 13: 21 sc.

Row 6: Rep Row 2. Finish off. Mark both ends of Row 6 for joining to metal rings later.

Row 7: With wrong side facing, skip first 10 sts, join with sc in next st; (tr in next st, sc in next st) to last 10 sts, ch 1, turn, leaving rem sts unworked: 20 (27, 34) sc, 19 (26, 33) tr; ch 1, turn.

Row 8: Skip first st, sc in each st to last st, ch 1, turn, leaving last st unworked: 37 (51, 65) sc.

Row 9: Sc in first st, (tr in next st, sc in next st) across: 19 (26, 33) sc, 18 (25, 32) tr; ch 1, turn.

Row 32: Sc in first st, (tr in next st, sc in next st) across, ch 19 (26, 33) for bottom side front. Finish off.

Ch 19 (26, 33) for other side front of bottom, join with sl st in first st of Row 32. Finish off; weave in ends

BOTTOM FRONT

Hold tummy panel with last row at top.

Row 1: Join yarn with sc in first ch at right, sc in each ch and across sts of tummy panel, then in each ch at opposide side: 59 (73, 87 sc); ch 1, turn.

Row 2: Sc in first st, (tr in next st, sc in next st) across: 30 (37, 44) sc, 29 (36, 43) tr); ch 1, turn.

Row 3: Sc in each st across: 59 (73, 87) sc; ch 1, turn.

Row 4: Rep Row 2.

Row 5: Sc in each sc across.

Rep Row 8 and 9 until 17 (23, 37) sts rem.

Work even in patt for 3 more rows. Finish off; weave in ends.

BOTTOM BACK

Row 1: Ch 60, (74, 88), sc in 2nd ch from hook and each ch to end; ch 1, turn.

Work same as Bottom Front until 17 (23, 37) sts rem. Finish off, leaving a long yarn length for sewing.

Carefully matching sts, sew last rows of Front and Bottom Backs tog at crotch.

RING JOININGS

Front

Hold piece with rows marked for joining (Rows 1 through 6); working over one craft ring and into ends of these rows, sc in each row end and over ring. Finish off; weave in ends.

Join a 2nd ring in same manner of opposite side of front.

Back

Join marked rows of back to same rings in same manner. Finish off; weave in ends.

LEG OPENING EDGING

Join yarn with sc in either ring; working in row ends around leg opening, (sl st, ch 1) in each row, end sc in ring. Finish off. Rep around opposite leg opening.

BACK BOTTOM EDGING

Join with sc over ring, working in bottom lps of starting ch, (sl st, ch 1) in each lp, sc in ring. Fasten off.

FRONT BOTTOM EDGING

Join with sc over ring, working in bottom lps of starting ch, (sl st, ch 1) in each lp up to tummy panel, working in row ends, (sc, ch 5, sc in 5th ch from hook) in first row; *skip next row, (sc, ch 5, sc in 5th ch from hook) in next row; rep from *up to bottom of bust. Finish off. Work opposite side to correspond.

NECK TIE

Holding piece with wrong side facing, join yarn with sc in center front ring, ch 81.

Row 1: Sc in ring; ch 1, turn.

Row 2: (Sc, ch 5, sc in 5th ch from hook) in next ch; *skip next ch, (sc, ch 5, sc in 5th ch from hook) in next ch; rep from * across, sc in ring. Finish off; weave in all ends.

SANTA FE EVENING

Designed by Belinda "Bendy" Carter

Dressed up or down,
this striking sweater goes
everywhere. Pair it with
jeans for an informal look.
Wear it with a lovely skirt,
and you are sure to feel
best-dressed all day long
and into your own
Santa Fe evening.

SANTA FE EVENING

SIZES	Small	Medium	Large	X-Large
Body Bust Measurements	32"-34"	36"-38"	40"-42"	44"-46"
Finished Bust Measurements	36"	40"	44"	48"

Note: *Instructions are written for size Small; changes for sizes Medium, Large and Extra Large are in parentheses.*

Materials

Worsted weight ribbon type yarn, 12 1/4 (14, 15 3/4 , 17 1/2) oz multicolor

Bulky weight fur type yarn, 3 1/2 (5 1/4, 5 1/4, 5 1/4) oz multicolor

Note: *Photographed model made with Berroco® Lullaby #4309 Kookaburra; and Berroco® Hush #6309 Kookaburra*

4 stitch markers

Size J (6mm) crochet hook (or size required for gauge)

Size K (6.5mm) crochet hook (or size required for gauge)

Gauge

15 sts = 5" with smaller hook and ribbon yarn

14 st = 6" with larger hook and fur type yarn

Stitch Guide

Front Bar sc (FBsc): Work sc in front horizontal bar (front loop) only of specified st instead of in the top two lps, inserting hook from bottom of bar to top of bar: Fbsc made.

Back Lp sc (BLsc): Work sc in back lp only (lp away from you) of specified st: Blsc made.

Sc decrease (sc dec): Draw up a lp in each of next 2 sts, YO and draw through all 3 lps on hook: one st decreased.

Pattern Stitch

Row 1: Sc in first st; *FBsc in next st, BLsc in next st; rep from * across to last st, sc in last st.

Rep Row 1 for Patt, always working FBsc in BLsc of prev row, and BLsc in FBsc of prev row.

INSTRUCTIONS

FRONT

With smaller hook and ribbon yarn, ch 55 (61, 67, 73).

Foundation Row: Sc in 2nd ch from hook and in each rem ch: 54 (60, 66, 72) sc; ch 1, turn.

Pattern Row: Sc in first st; * FBsc, in next st, BLsc in next st; rep from * across to last st, sc in last st; ch 1, turn.

Rep Patt Row until piece measures 13 1/2" (14", 14 1/2", 15") from beg ch.

SHAPE ARMHOLE

Row 1: Sl st across first 4 sts, ch 1, sc in same st as last sl st; work in patt across to last 4 st, sc in next st, leave rem sts unworked: 48 (54, 60, 66) sts; ch 1, turn.

Row 2: Work in pattern, scdec 1 (2, 2, 2) sts at each end of row, ch 1, turn.

Row 3: Work even in patt, ch 1, turn.

Row 4: Rep Row 2: 44 (48, 52, 58) sts.

Row 5: Work even in patt, ch 1, turn.

Row 6: Work in patt, dec 1 (1, 2, 2) sts at each end of row: 42 (44, 48, 54) sts; ch 1, turn.

Row 7: Rep Row 5.

For Size X-Large Only

Row 8: Work in patt, dec 2 sts at each end of row: 50 sts.

For All Sizes

Work even on 42 (44, 48, 50) sts until piece measures 2 1/2" (3", 3 1/4", 3 1/4") from beg of armhole shaping.

Finish off; weave in all ends.

BACK

Work same as Front.

SLEEVE (make 2)

With smaller hook and ribbon yarn, ch 25.

Row 1: Sc in 2nd ch from hook and in each rem ch: 24 sc; ch 1, turn.

Row 2: Work patt row.

Continue in patt, increasing 1 st at each end of next row; and then increasing 1 st at each end every 5th (4th, 3rd, 3rd) row, until there are 40 (42, 46, 48) sts. Work even until piece measures 17" (17", 17 1/2", 17 1/2") from beg ch.

SHAPE SLEEVE CAP

Row 1: Sl st across first 4 sts, ch 1, sc in same st as last sl st; work

across in patt to last 3 sts, ch 1, turn, leaving rem sts unworked: 34 (36, 40, 42) sts.

Continue in patt, decreasing 1 st at each end of next 5 rows; at end of last row: 24 (26, 30, 32) sts rem. Work even until piece measures 2½" (3", 3¼", 3¼") from beg of cap shaping. Finish off; weave in ends.

ASSEMBLY

Sew sleeves in armholes, leaving top of cap free, sew side and sleeve seams.

BOTTOM EDGING

Rnd 1: With wrong side facing, with larger hook join fur type yarn at bottom of one side seam; ch 1, sc in same st as joining; work 83 (91, 101, 109) sc evenly spaced around bottom edge: 84 (92, 102, 110) sc; join in beg sc, ch 1; do not turn.

Rnd 2: Sc in each st around; join in beg sc. Finish off.

SLEEVE EDGING

Rnd 1: With wrong side facing, using larger hook join fur type yarn at seam, ch 1, sc in same st as joining; work 19 sc evenly spaced around opening: 20 sc; join in beg sc, ch 1; do not turn.

Rnd 2: Sc in each st around; join in beg sc. Finish off.

NECK EDGING

Rnd 1: With wrong side facing, using larger hook join yarn fur type yarn at center back, ch 1, sc in same st as joining; work 16 (17, 18, 19) sc evenly spaced across back, place marker; work 19 (21, 23, 25) sc evenly spaced across sleeve, place marker; work 32 (34, 37, 39) sc evenly spaced across front, place marker; work 19 (21, 23, 25) sc evenly sp across sleeve, place marker; work 16 (17, 19, 20) sc evenly spaced across back: 102 (110, 120, 128) sc; join in beg sc; do not turn.

Note: *Move markers up as you work each rnd.*

Rnd 2: Ch 1, sc to marker; * sc in next st, sc dec over next 2 sts; sc to 3 sts before next marker, sc dec over next 2 sts, sc in next st; * sc to next marker, rep from * to * once, sc in rem sts: 98 (106, 116, 124) sc; join in beg sc; do not turn.

Rep Rnd 2, five more times. Last rnd will have 78 (86, 96, 104) sts. Finish off; weave in all ends.

STRAPS (make 2)

With smaller hook and ribbon yarn, make a sl knot on hook, leaving a long yarn end for attaching to garment; ch 4.

Row 1: Sc in 2nd ch from hook and in each rem ch: 3 sc; turn.

Row 2: Ch 1, sc across; turn.

Rep Row 2 till 10" from beg. Finish off, leaving a long yarn end for attaching to garment.

Mark center 7" (7½", 7½", 8") on front and back for neck opening. Sew straps to last ribbon row on front and back at markers.

PAINT THE TOWN RED

Designed by
Dora Ohrenstein

This glamorous coat is for special nights on the town! Details include an eye-catching stripe in a fur-look yarn, and a flared extra-long sleeve. Accessorize it with a fabulous brooch at the neck or bust and a wide belt. The coat is worked in vertical rows with longer stitches at the lower portion of the garment to add width for the hips. The wave pattern sculpts an attractive lapel edge.

PAINT THE TOWN RED

SIZES	Small	Medium	Large
Body Bust Measurements	32"-34"	36"-38"	40"-42"
Finished Bust Measurements	40"	44"	48"
Finished Hip Measurements	44"	48"	52"

Note: *Instructions are written for size Small; changes for sizes Medium and Large are in parentheses.*

Materials

Worsted weight yarn, 30 (35, 35) oz red

Fur-type yarn. 1 3/4 oz variegated

Note: *Photographed model made with TLC® Lustre™ #5915 Claret and Moda Dea™ Chichi™ #9946 Flamingo*

Size G (4 mm) crochet hook

Size H (5 mm) crochet hook (or size required for gauge)

Safety pins

Stitch markers

Gauge

12 sc or 12 dc = 4" with larger hook

5 rows of dc = 5" in wave pattern

Stitch Guide

2 Dc decrease (2-dc dec): *YO, insert hook in specified st, YO and draw up a lp, YO and draw through 2 lps on hook; rep from * once; YO and draw through all 3 lps on hook: 2-dc dec made.

3 Dc decrease (3-dc dec): *YO, insert hook in specified st, YO and draw up a lp, YO and draw through 2 lps on hook; rep from * 2 times more; YO and draw through all 4 lps on hook: 3-dc dec made.

2 Tr decrease (2-tr dec): *YO twice, insert hook in specified st, YO and draw up a lp, (YO and draw through 2 lps on hook) twice; rep from * once; YO and draw through all 3 lps on hook: 2-tr dec made.

3 Tr decrease (3-tr dec): *YO twice, insert hook in specified st, YO and draw up a lp, (YO and draw through 2 lps on hook) twice; rep from * 2 times more; YO and draw through all 4 lps on hook: 3-tr dec made.

2 Sc decrease (2-sc dec): *Insert hook in specified st and draw up a lp; rep from * once; YO and draw through all 3 lps on hook: 2-sc dec made.

Back Loop (BL): This is the lp away from you.

To change color: Work st until 2 lps rem on hook, drop old color, pick up new color and draw through all lps on hook, cut dropped strand of old color.

INSTRUCTIONS

RIGHT BACK

With larger hook and red, ch 101.

Row 1 (wrong side): 2 dc in 4th ch from hook (3 skipped chs count as dc); *dc in next 3 chs, (3-dc dec in next 3 chs) twice, dc in next 3 chs**,

(3 dc in next ch) twice; rep from * 5 times more; rep from * to ** once; 3 dc in last ch: 98 sts (7 waves); ch 3 (counts as dc on next row now and throughout), turn.

Row 2 (right side): 2 dc in first st; *dc in next 3 sts, (3-dc dec in next 3 sts) twice, dc in next 3 sts**, (3 dc in next st) twice; rep from * 5 times more; rep from * to ** once; 3 dc in next ch; ch 3, turn.

Row 3: 2 dc in first st, 2 dc in next st, dc in next 2 sts; *(3-dc dec in next 3 sts) twice, dc in next 3 sts**, (3 dc in next st) twice, dc in next 3 sts; rep from * 5 times more; rep from * to ** once; 3 dc in last ch of turning ch: 99 sts; ch 4 (counts as tr on next row now and throughout), turn.

Row 4: 2 tr in first st; *tr in next 3 sts, (3-tr dec in next 3 sts) twice, tr in next 3 sts**, (3 tr in next st) twice; rep from * once; rep from * to ** once; 3 tr in next st, 3 dc in next st, ***dc in next 3 sts, (3-dc dec in next 3 sts) twice****, dc in next 3 sts, (3 dc in next st) twice; rep from *** 2 times more; rep from *** to **** once; dc in next 4 sts, 3 dc in last ch of turning ch, changing to fur yarn in last dc; ch 1, turn.

Row 5: Sc in first st and in each st across, changing to red in last sc: 99 sc; ch 4, turn.

Row 6: 2 tr in BL of first sc; *tr in BL of next 3 sc, (3-tr dec in BL of next 3 sc) twice, tr in BL of next 3 sc**, (3 tr in BL of next sc) twice; rep from * once; rep from * to ** once; 3 tr in BL of next sc, 3 dc in BL of next sc, ***dc in BL of next 3 sc, (3-dc dec in BL of next 3 sc) twice****, dc in BL of next 3 sc, (3 dc in BL of next sc) twice; rep from *** 2 times more; rep from *** to **** once; dc in BL of next 2 sc, 2 dc dec in BL of next 2 sc, 3 dc in BL of last sc: 98 sts; ch 3, turn.

Row 7: Rep Row 2.

Row 8: 2 dc in first st; *dc in next 3 sts, (3-dc dec in next 3 sts) twice**, dc in next 3 sts, (3 dc in next st) twice; rep from * 5 times more; rep from * to ** once; dc in next st, 2-dc dec in next 2 sts, 3 dc in last ch of turning ch: 97 sts; ch 3, turn.

Row 9: 2 dc in first st, dc in next 2 sts; *(3-dc dec in next 3 sts) twice, dc in next 3 sts**, (3 dc in next st) twice, dc in next 3 sts; rep from * 2 times more; rep from * to ** once; 3 dc in next st, 3 tr in next st, ***tr in next 3 sts, (3-tr dec in next 3 sts) twice, tr in next 3 sts****, (3 tr in next st) twice; rep from *** once; rep from *** to **** once; 3 tr in last ch of turning ch; ch 3, turn.

Row 10: 2 dc in first st; *dc in next 3 sts, (3-dc dec in next 3 sts) twice**, dc in next 3 sts, (3 dc in next st) twice; rep from * 5 times more; rep from * to ** once; dc in next 2 sts, 3 dc in last ch of turning ch, changing to fur yarn in last dc; ch 1, turn.

Row 11: Rep Row 5, changing to red in last sc: 97 sc; ch 4, turn.

Row 12: 2 tr in BL of first sc; *tr in BL of next 3 sc, (3-tr dec in BL of next 3 sc) twice, tr in BL of next 3 sc**, (3 tr in BL of next sc) twice; rep from * once; rep from * to ** once; 3 tr in BL of next sc, 3 dc in BL of next sc, ***dc in BL of next 3 sc, (3-dc dec in BL of next 3 sc) twice****, dc in BL of next 3 sc, (3 dc in BL of next sc) twice; rep from *** 2 times more; rep from *** to **** once; 2-dc dec in BL of next 2 sc, 3 dc in BL of last sc: 96 sts; ch 1, turn.

For Size Small Only:

Row 13: Sl st in first 2 sts, sc in next st, hdc in next st, dc in next 3 sts; hdc in next 2 sts; sc in next st, sl st in next 4 sts, sc in next st, hdc in next 2 sts; dc in next 4 sts, hdc in next 2 sts; sc in next st, sl st in next 3 sts (place marker in last sl st to mark as armhole edge); ch 3, 2 dc in same st as last sl st; *dc in next 3 sts, (3-dc dec in next 3 sts) twice, dc in next 3 sts**, (3 dc in next st) twice; rep from * 3 times more; rep from * to ** once; 3 dc in last ch of turning ch: 96 sts; ch 1, turn.

Row 14: Sl st in first 2 sts; *sc in next st, hdc in next 2 sts, dc in next 4 sts, hdc in next 2 sts, sc in next st**, sl st in next 4 sts; rep from * 3 times more; rep from * to ** once; sl st in last st and in 3rd ch of ch-3 by marker: 69 sts. Finish off.

For Size Medium Only:

Row 13: Ch 2, 2 dc in first st, dc in next st; *(3-dc dec in next 3 sts) twice, dc in next 3 sts**, (3 dc in next st) twice, dc in next 3 sts; rep from * 5 times more; rep from * to ** once; 3 dc in last ch of turning ch: 96 sts; ch 3, turn.

Row 14: 2 dc in first st; *dc in next 3 sts, (3-dc dec in next 3 sts) twice, dc in next 3 sts**, (3 dc in next st) twice; rep from * 3 times more; rep from * to ** once; 2 dc in next st, ch 3, sl st in same st as last 2 dc, sl st in next 2 sts (place marker in first of 2 sl sts to mark as armhole edge); sc in next st, hdc in next 2 sts, dc in next 4 sts, hdc in next 2 sts; sc in next st, sl st in next 4 sts, sc in next st, hdc in next 2 sts; dc in next 3 sts, hdc in next st, sc in next st, sl st in next st and in last ch of turning ch. Finish off.

Row 15: With wrong side facing and larger hook, join red with sl st in 3rd ch of ch-3 by marker (does not count as st), sl st in next st; *sc in next st, hdc in next 2 sts, dc in next 4 sts, hdc in next 2 sts, sc in next st**, sl st in next 4 sts; rep from * 3 times more; rep from * to ** once; sl st in next st and in last ch of turning ch: 69 sts. Finish off.

For Size Large Only:

Row 13: Rep Row 13 of size Medium.

Row 14: 2 dc in first st; *dc in next 3 sts, (3-dc dec in next 3 sts) twice**, dc in next 3 sts, (3 dc in next st) twice; rep from * 5 times more; rep from * to ** once; dc in next st, 3 dc in last ch of turning ch; ch 1, turn.

Rows 15 and 16: Rep Rows 13 and 14 of size Small.

For All Sizes:

Final Row: Hold piece with right side facing and beg ch at top; working in unused lps of beg ch, join red with larger hook and sl st in same ch as first 2 dc on Row 1; ch 4, tr in next ch, 2-dc dec in next 2 chs, hdc in next ch; *sc in next 4 chs, hdc in next ch, 2-dc dec in next 2 chs**, (2-tr dec in next 2 chs) twice, 2-dc dec in next 2 chs, hdc in next ch; rep from * 5 times more; rep from * to ** once; tr in last 2 chs: 98 sts. Finish off; weave in all ends.

LEFT BACK

With larger hook and red, ch 101.

Rows 1 and 2: Rep Rows 1 and 2 of Right Back.

Row 3: 2 dc in first st; *dc in next 3 sts, (3-dc dec in next 3 sts) twice**, dc in next 3 sts, (3 dc in next st) twice; rep from * 5 times more; rep from * to ** once; dc in next 2 sts, 2 dc in next st, 3 dc in last ch of turning ch: 99 sts; ch 3, turn.

Row 4: 2 dc in first st, dc in next 4 sts; *(3-dc dec in next 3 sts) twice, dc in next 3 sts**, (3 dc in next st) twice, dc in next 3 sts; rep from * 2 times more; rep from * to ** once; 3 dc in next st, 3 tr in next st, ***tr in next 3 sts, (3-tr dec in next 3 sts) twice, tr in next 3 sts****, (3 tr in next 3 sts) twice; rep from *** once; rep from *** to **** once; 3 tr in last ch of turning ch, changing to fur yarn in last tr; ch 1, turn

Row 5: Rep Row 5 of Right Back, changing to red in last sc: 99 sc; ch 3, turn.

Row 6: 2 dc in BL of first sc, 2-dc dec in BL of next 2 sc, dc in BL of next 2 sc; *(3- dc dec in BL of next 3 sc) twice, dc in BL of next 3 sc**, (3-dc in BL of next sc) twice, dc in BL of next 3 sc; rep from * 2 times more; rep from * to ** once; 3 dc in BL of next sc, 3 tr in BL of next sc, ***tr in BL of next 3 sc, (3-tr dec in BL of next 3 sc) twice, tr in BL of next 3 sc****, (3 tr in BL of next sc) twice; rep from *** once; rep from *** to **** once; 3 tr in BL of last sc: 98 sts; ch 3, turn.

Row 7: Rep Row 2 of Right Back.

Row 8: 2 dc in first st, 2-dc dec in next 2 sts, dc in next st; *(3-dc dec in next 3 sts) twice, dc in next 3 sts**, (3 dc in next st) twice, dc in next 3 sts; rep from * 5 times more; rep from * to ** once; 3 dc in last ch of turning ch: 97 sts; ch 4, turn.

Row 9: 2 tr in first st; *tr in next 3 sts, (3-tr dec in next 3 sts) twice, tr in next 3 sts**, (3 tr in next st) twice; rep from * once; rep from * to **

once; 3 tr in next st, 3 dc in next st, ***dc in next 3 sts, (3-dc dec in next 3 sts) twice****, dc in next 3 sts, (3 dc in next st) twice; rep from *** 2 times more; rep from *** to **** once; dc in next 2 sts, 3 dc in last ch of turning ch; ch 3, turn.

Row 10: 2 dc in first st, dc in next 2 sts; *(3-dc dec in next 3 sts) twice, dc in next 3 sts**, (3 dc in next st) twice, dc in next 3 sts; rep from * 5 times more; rep from * to ** once; 3 dc in last ch of turning ch, changing to fur yarn in last dc; ch 1, turn.

Row 11: Rep Row 5 of Right Back, changing to red in last sc: 97 sc; ch 3, turn.

Row 12: 2 dc in BL of first sc, 2 dc dec in BL of next 2 sc; *(3 dc dec in BL of next 3 sc) twice, dc in BL of next 3 sc**, (3 dc in BL of next sc) twice, dc in BL of next 3 sc; rep from * 2 times more; rep from * to ** once; 3 dc in BL of next sc, 3 tr in BL of next sc, ***tr in BL of next 3 sc, (3-tr dec in BL of next 3 sc) twice, tr in BL of next 3 sc****, (3 tr in BL of next sc) twice; rep from *** once; rep from *** to **** once; 3 tr in BL of last sc: 96 sts; ch 3, turn.

For Size Small Only:

Rows 13 and 14: Rep Rows 14 and 15 of size Medium on Right Back.

For Size Medium Only:

Rows 13 through 15: Rep Rows 14 through 16 of size Large on Right Back.

For Size Large Only:

Row 13: Rep Row 14 of size Large on Right Back.

Rows 14 through 16: Rep Rows 13 through 15 of size Medium on Right Back.

For All Sizes:

Final Row: Rep Final Row on Right Back.

LEFT FRONT

With larger hook and red, ch 90.

Row 1 (wrong side): 2 dc in 4th ch from hook (3 skipped chs count as dc), 3 dc in next ch; *dc in next 3 chs, (3-dc dec in next 3 chs) twice, dc in next 3 chs**, (3 dc in next ch) twice; rep from * 4 times more; rep from * to ** once; 3 dc in last ch: 87 sts (6 waves); ch 3 (counts as dc on next row now and throughout), turn.

Row 2 (right side): 2 dc in first st; *dc in next 3 sts, (3-dc dec in next 3 sts) twice, dc in next 3 sts, (3 dc in next st) twice; rep from * 5 times more; dc in next st and in next ch: 89 sts; ch 3, turn.

Row 3: *Dc in next 3 sts; (3 dc in next st) twice, dc in next 3 sts, (3-dc dec in next 3 sts) twice; rep from * 5 times more; dc in next 3 sts, 3 dc in last ch of turning ch: 91 sts; ch 4 (counts as tr on next row now and throughout), turn.

Row 4: 2 tr in first st; *tr in next 3 sts, (3-tr dec in next 3 sts) twice, tr in next 3 sts**, (3 tr in next st) twice; rep from * once; rep from * to ** once; 3 tr in next st, 3 dc in next st, ***dc in next 3 sts, (3-dc dec in next 3 sts) twice, dc in next 3 sts, (3 dc in next st) twice; rep from *** 2 times more; dc in next 3 sts, 3-dc dec in last 3 sts, ch 7, changing to fur yarn in last ch: 98 sts; ch 1, turn.

Row 5: Sc in 2nd ch from hook and in next 6 chs, sc in each st across, changing to red in last sc: 98 sc; ch 4, turn.

Row 6: 2 tr in BL of first sc; *tr in BL of next 3 sc, (3-tr dec in BL of next 3 sc) twice, tr in BL of next 3 sc**, (3 tr in BL of next sc) twice; rep from * once; rep from * to ** once; 3 tr in BL of next sc, 3 dc in BL of next sc, ***dc in BL of next 3 sc, (3-dc dec in BL of next 3 sc) twice, dc in BL of next 3 sc****, (3 dc in BL of next sc) twice; rep from *** 2 times more; rep from *** to **** once; 3 dc in BL of last sc: 98 sts; ch 3, turn.

Rows 7 through 12: Rep Rows 7 through 12 on Right Back.

Rows 13 through 14 (15, 16): Rep Rows 13 through 14 (15, 16) on Right Back for appropriate size.

RIGHT FRONT

With larger hook and red, ch 90.

Row 1 (wrong side): 2 dc in 4th ch from hook (3 skipped chs count as dc); *dc in next 3 chs, (3-dc dec in next 3 chs) twice, dc in next 3 chs**, (3 dc in next ch) twice; rep from * 4 times more; rep from * to ** once; 3 dc in next ch, 3 dc in last ch: 87 sts; ch 3 (counts as dc on next row now and throughout), turn.

Row 2 (right side): Dc in next st; *(3 dc in next st) twice, dc in next 3 sts, (3-dc dec in next 3 sts) twice, dc in next 3 sts; rep from * 5 times more; 3 dc in next ch: 89 sts; ch 3, turn.

Row 3: 2 dc in first st; *dc in next 3 sts, (3-dc dec in next 3 sts) twice, dc in next 3 sts, (3 dc in next st) twice;

rep from * 5 times more; dc in next 3 sts, dc in last ch of turning ch: 91 sts; turn. Finish off.

Row 4: With larger hook and red, ch 7, 3-dc dec in first 3 sts on Row 3; *dc in next 3 sts, (3 dc in next st) twice, dc in next 3 sts, (3-dc dec in next 3 sts) twice; rep from * 2 times more; dc in next 3 sts, 3 dc in next st, 3 tr in next st, ***tr in next 3 sts, (3- tr dec in next 3 sts) twice, tr in next 3 sts****, (3 tr in next st) twice; rep from *** once; rep from *** to **** once; 3 tr in last ch of turning ch, changing to fur yarn in last tr: 98 sts; ch 1, turn.

Row 5: Sc in first st and in each st across, sc in each of 7 chs, changing to red in last sc: 98 sc; ch 3, turn.

Row 6: 2 dc in BL of first sc; *dc in BL of next 3 sc, (3-dc dec in BL of next 3 sc) twice, dc in BL of next 3 sc**, (3 dc in BL of next sc) twice; rep from * 2 times more; rep from * to ** once; 3 dc in BL of next sc, 3 tr in BL of next sc, ***tr in BL of next 3 sc, (3-tr dec in BL of next 3 sc) twice, tr in BL of next 3 sc****, (3 tr in BL of next sc) twice; rep from *** once; rep from *** to **** once; 3 tr in last sc: 98 sts; ch 3, turn.

Rows 7 through 12: Rep Rows 7 through 12 on Left Back.

Rows 13 through 14 (15, 16): Rep Rows 13 through 14 (15, 16) on Left Back for appropriate size.

SLEEVES (make 2)

Starting at top of sleeve, with larger hook and red, ch 19.

Row 1 (wrong side): 2 dc in 4th ch from hook (3 skipped chs count as dc), 3 dc in next ch, dc in next 3 chs, (3-dc dec in next 3 chs) twice; dc in next 3 chs, (3 dc in next ch) twice: 20 sts; ch 3 (counts as dc on next row now and throughout), turn.

Row 2 (right side): Dc in next st, (3 dc in next st) twice, dc in next 3 sts, (3-dc dec in next 3 sts) twice, dc in next 3 sts, (3 dc in next st) twice, dc in next st, dc in next ch: 24 sts; ch 4 (counts as tr on next row now and throughout), turn.

Row 3: *Tr in next 3 sts, (3 tr in next st) twice, tr in next 3 sts**, (3-tr dec in next 3 sts) twice; rep from * to ** once; tr in last ch of turning ch: 28 sts; ch 3, turn.

Row 4: 2-dc dec in next 2 sts; *dc in next 3 sts, (3 dc in next st) twice, dc in next 3 sts**, (3-dc dec in next 3 sts) twice; rep from * to ** once; 2-dc dec in next 2 sts, dc in last ch of turning ch: 30 sts; ch 3, turn.

Row 5: 2 dc in first st, 3-dc dec in next 3 sts; *dc in next 3 sts, (3 dc in next st) twice, dc in next 3 sts**, (3-dc dec in next 3 sts) twice; rep from * to ** once; 3-dc dec in next 3 sts, 3 dc in last ch of turning ch: 34 sts; ch 3, turn.

Row 6: 2 dc in first st, 3-dc dec in next 3 sts, 2-dc dec in next 2 sts; *dc in next 3 sts, (3 dc in next st) twice, dc in next 3 sts**, (3-dc dec in next 3 sts) twice; rep from * to ** once; 2-dc dec in next 2 sts, 3-dc dec in next 3 sts, 3 dc in last ch of turning ch: 36 sts; ch 4, turn.

Row 7: 2 tr in first st; *(3-tr dec in next 3 sts) twice, tr in next 3 sts, (3 tr in next st) twice, tr in next 3 sts; rep from * once; (3-tr dec in next 3 sts) twice, 3 tr in last ch of turning ch; ch 3, turn.

Row 8: 2 dc in first st, dc in next 3 sts, 3-dc dec in next 3 sts; *dc in next 3 sts, (3 dc in next st) twice, dc in next 3 sts**, (3-dc dec in next 3 sts) twice; rep from * to ** once; 3-dc dec in next 3 sts, dc in next 3 sts, 3 dc in last ch of turning ch: 40 sts; ch 3, turn.

For Size Large Only:

Row 9: 2 dc in first st, dc in next 3 sts, 2-dc dec in next 2 sts, 3-dc dec in next 3 sts; * dc in next 3 sts, (3 dc in next st) twice, dc in next 3 sts **, (3-dc dec in next 3 sts) twice; rep from * to ** once; 3-dc dec in next 3 sts, 2-dc dec in next 2 sts, dc in next 3 sts, 3 dc in last ch of turning ch: 40 sts. Ch 3, turn.

For All Sizes:

Row 9 (9, 10): 2 dc in first st, dc in next 3 sts; 2-dc dec in next 2 (2, 3) sts, 3-dc dec in next 3 sts; *dc in next 3 sts, (3 dc in next st) twice, dc in next 3 sts**, (3-dc dec in next 3 sts) twice; rep from * to ** once; 3-dc dec in next 3 sts, 2-dc dec in next 2 (2, 3) sts, dc in next 3 sts, 3 dc in last ch of turning ch: 42 sts; ch 3, turn. Mark this row as armhole edge.

Row 10 (10, 11): 2 dc in first st; *dc in next 3 sts, (3-dc dec in next 3 sts) twice, dc in next 3 sts**, (3 dc in next st) twice; rep from * once; rep from * to ** once; 3 dc in last ch of turning ch; ch 4, turn.

Row 11 (11, 12): 2 tr in first st; *tr in next 3 sts, (3-tr dec in next 3 sts) twice, tr in next 3 sts**, (3 tr in next st) twice; rep from * once; rep from * to ** once; 3 tr in last ch of turning ch; ch 3, turn.

Rows 12 (12, 13) and 13 (13, 14): Rep Row 10 (10, 11) two times more, ending ch 3, turn.

Rows 14 (14, 15) and 15 (15, 16): Rep Rows 10 (10, 11) and 11 (11, 12).

Rows 16 (16, 17) and 17 (17, 18): Rep Row 10 (10, 11) two times more, ending ch 3, turn.

Rows 18 (18, 19) and 19 (19, 20): Rep Rows 10 (10, 11) and 11 (11, 12).

Row 20 (21, 21): Dc in first st, 3 dc in next st, dc in next 2 sts; *(3-dc dec in next 3 sts) twice, dc in next 3 sts, (3 dc in next st) twice, dc in next 3 sts; rep from * once; (3-dc dec in next 3 sts) twice, dc in next 2 sts, 3 dc in next st, 2 dc in last ch of turning ch: 44 sts; ch 3, turn.

Row 21 (22, 22): 3 dc in next st; *dc in next st, 2 dc in next st, dc in next st, (3-dc dec in next 3 sts) twice, dc in next st, 2 dc in next st, dc in next st**, (3 dc in next st) twice; rep from * once; rep from * to ** once; 3 dc in next st, dc in last ch of turning ch: 50 sts; ch 3, turn.

Row 22 (22, 23): 4 dc in next st; *dc in next 4 sts, (3-dc dec in next 3 sts) twice, dc in next 4 sts**, (4 dc in next st) twice; rep from * once; rep from * to ** once; 4 dc in next st, dc in last ch of turning ch: 56 sts; ch 4, turn.

Row 23 (23, 24): 4 tr in next st; *tr in next 5 sts, (3-tr dec in next 3 sts) twice, tr in next 5 sts**, (4 tr in next st) twice; rep from * once; rep from * to ** once; 4 tr in next st, tr in last ch of turning ch: 62 sts; ch 3, turn.

Row 24 (24, 25): 3 dc in next st; *dc in next 6 sts, (3-dc dec in next 3 sts) twice, dc in next 6 sts**, (3 dc in next st) twice; rep from * once; rep from * to ** once; 3 dc in next st, dc in last ch of turning ch, changing to fur yarn; ch 1, turn.

Row 25 (25, 26): Sc in first st and in each st across, changing to red in last sc: 62 sc; ch 3, turn.

Row 26 (26, 27): 3 dc in BL of next sc; *dc in BL of next 6 sc, (3-dc dec in BL of next 3 sc) twice, dc in BL of next 6 sc**, (3 dc in BL of next sc) twice; rep from * once; rep from * to ** once; 3 dc in BL of next sc, dc in BL of last sc: 62 sts; ch 3, turn.

Row 27 (27, 28): Rep Row 24, ending dc in last ch of turning ch. Finish off. Weave in ends.

ASSEMBLY

Sew Back pieces together at center (final row). Sew Left and Right Front to Back at shoulder seams from Row 5 through Row 13 (14, 15). Sew sleeves into armholes, matching Row 9 (9, 10) of sleeve to stitch markers of armhole on Fronts and Back. Sew sleeve and side seams.

COLLAR

With right side facing and smaller hook, join red with sc in top of last dc worked on Row 1 on Right Front.

Row 1: Work sc along Right Front, Back and Left Front neckline as follows: work 1 sc in each ch or sc, 2 sc in edge of each dc or ch-3, and 3 sc in edge of each tr or ch-4, ending with 1 sc in last ch of foundation ch on Row 1 on Left Front: 54 sc; ch 1, turn.

Row 2: Sc in first 12 sc, 2-sc dec in next 2 sc, sc in next 26 sc, 2-sc dec in next 2 sc, sc in next 12 sc: 52 sc; ch 1, turn.

Row 3: Sc in first 11 sc; *2-sc dec in next 2 sc, sc in next 5 sc; rep from * 3 times more; 2-sc dec in next 2 sc, sc in next 11 sc: 47 sc; ch 1, turn.

Row 4: Sc in first 10 sc; *2-sc dec in next 2 sc, sc in next 4 sc; rep from * 3 times more; 2-sc dec in next 2 sc, sc in next 11 sc: 42 sc; ch 1, turn.

Row 5: Sc in first 5 sc, 2-sc dec in next 2 sc; *sc in next 5 sc, 2-sc dec in next 2 sc; rep from * once; **2-sc dec in next 2 sc, sc in next 5 sc; rep from ** 2 times more: 36 sc; ch 1, turn.

Row 6: Sc in first 11 sc, 2-sc dec in next 2 sc, sc in next 10 sc, 2-sc dec in next 2 sc, sc in next 11 sc: 34 sc; ch 1, turn.

Rows 7 through 9: Sc in first sc and in each sc across; ch 1, turn. At end of Row 9, do not ch 1. Finish off; weave in ends.

BOTTOM EDGING

With wrong side facing and larger hook, join red with sc in free lp of ch at base of first dc in Row 1 of Right Front.

Row 1: Work 1 sc in edge of each sc row, 2 sc in edge of each dc row, and 4 sc in edge of each tr row around bottom edge, ending with 1 sc in first ch on Row 1 of Left Front: 140 (148, 156) sc; ch 1, turn.

Rows 2 through 3 (4, 6): Sc in each sc across; ch 1, turn. At end of last row, do not ch 1. Finish off; weave in ends.

RING AROUND THE ROSES

Designed by Vashti Braha

Elegant full-blown roses create a feminine look on this fun-to-wear skirt and tube top. The outfit is crocheted with a yarn that has a lot of stretch, so if you choose to use a yarn without this quality, you will need to make a larger size.

SIZES	X-Small	Small	Medium	Large
Body Bust Measurements	28"	32"	36"	40"
Finished Bust Measurements (unstreched)	35"	37"	39"	41"
Body Hip Measurements	30"	34"	38"	42"
Finished Hip Measurements (unstreched)	35"	37"	39"	41"

Note: *Instructions are written for size Extra Small; changes for sizes Small, Medium, Large and Extra Large are in parentheses.*

Note: *Both skirt and tube top will stretch up to 6" in width when worn.*

Materials

Worsted weight stretchy yarn,
For Tube Top, 10 1/2 (14, 17 1/2, 20) oz peach
For Skirt, 21 (24 1/2, 28, 32) oz peach

Note: *Photographed model made with Patons® Katrina #10510 Peach*

3 (3, 5, 5 1/2) yds flat elastic, 1/8" wide
Sewing pins
Size H (5mm) crochet hook
Size G (4mm) crochet hook (or size required for gauge

Gauge

16 sc worked in front lp only = 4" with smaller hook

Stitch Guide

Sc Decrease (sc dec): Draw up a lp in each of next 2 sts, YO and draw through all 3 lps on hook: sc dec made.

Front Loop Only: Work st in front lp only (lp toward you) of stitch.

Clustered Crab Stitch Edging:

Note: *Edging is worked from left to right for right-handers; left handers should work from right to left.*

Row 1: *Insert hook in next stitch to the right (left) 2 rows below; YO and draw up a lp; insert hook in next stitch to right (left) 2 rows below; YO and draw up a lp; YO and draw through all lps on hook: crab cluster made; rep from * arcross Finish off; weave in ends.

INSTRUCTIONS

Note: *For entire pattern sc sts are worked in front lp only of each st.*

SKIRT

Front

With smaller hook, ch 53 (61, 69, 73).

Row 1 (right side): Sc in 2nd ch from hook and in each rem ch: 52 (60, 68, 72) sc; ch 1, turn.

Row 2: Working in front lp only of each st, sc in each sc across, ch 1, turn.

Rep Row 2 until piece measures 11½" (12", 12½", 13") from beg ch.

Waist Shaping

Row 1: Sc dec over first 2 sts, sc to last 2 sts, sc dec over last 2 sts; ch 1, turn: 50 (58, 66, 70) sc.

Rows 2 and 3: Sc in each sc, ch 1, turn.

Rep Rows 1 through 3, five times more: 40 (48, 56, 60) sc.

Rep Row 1 twice: 36 (44. 52, 56) sc. Rep Row 2 once more.

Finish off; weave in ends.

Back

Work same as front.

Finishing

Hold front and back with right sides tog and sew side seams.

Bottom Ruffle

Hold skirt with right side facing; with larger hook join yarn with sl st at bottom of one seam.

Rnd 1 (worked in both lps of each st): Ch 3, 2 dc in joining, 3 dc in next st; *3 tr in each of next 2 sts, 3 dc in each of next 2 sts; rep from * around; join in top of beg ch, Finish off; weave in ends.

Waistband

Cut 2 pieces of elastic each 4" longer than desired waist measurement.

Hold skirt with waist at top and right side facing; pin tied end of one elastic circle to one skirt seam. Working over elastic, work one row of hdc around, working in both lps of each st.

Work another row of hdc in same manner over 2nd piece of elastic.

Finish off; weave in ends. Adjust elastic for correct fit and re-knot firmly (or sew ends tog)) Cut off excess elastic

TUBE TOP

With smaller hook, ch 105 (121, 137, 153).

Row 1: Sc in 2nd ch from hook and in each rem ch: 104 (120, 136, 152) sc; ch 1, turn.

Row 2: Working on front lp only of each st, sc in each sc, ch 1, turn.

Rep Row 2 until piece measures 10" (10", 10½", 11") from starting ch. Finish off.

Fold piece in half with side edges tog and sew side seam.

Hold piece with right side facing, last row at top and seam inside and at your left; join yarn with sl st in side seam. Ch 1, work one row of Clustered Crab St Edging, working in both lps of each st. This edging row becomes bottom of piece and is on the right side.

SLEEVE (make 2)

With smaller hook, ch 34 (36, 38, 40).

Row 1: Sc in 2nd ch from hook and in each rem ch: 33 (35, 37, 39) sc.

Rows 2 through 14 (14, 16, 18): Working in front lp only of each st, sc in each sc, ch 1 turn. At end of last row, do not ch 1, finish off. Sew side seam

Hold piece with right side facing and seam inside and at your left. Join yarn at seam and work Clustered Crab Stitch, working in both lps of each st, around bottom of sleeve. Finish off; weave in ends.

INSERT SLEEVES

Right Sleeve: Pin top edge of a sleeve to top of bodice, with seams

tog. Starting 5 sts to right of bodice seam, and ending 2 sts to left of seam, sew sleeve to top. Finish off.

Left Sleeve: Pin top edge of 2nd sleeve to top of bodice at opposite side, centering sleeve seam on side of bodice. Sew sleeve in place as before, starting starting 2 sts to right of bodice side and ending 5 sts to left of bodice side. Finish off.

RUFFLE

Fold rem elastic in half and knot loosely.

Hold piece with right side facing and sleeves at top. With larger hook join yarn at center back.

Rnd 1: Working over elastic and in both lps of each st, ch 3, 2 dc in joining; *3 tr in each of next 2 sts, 3 dc in each of next 2 sts; rep from * around, including tops of sleeves; join in 3rd ch of beg ch-3; finish off. Adjust elastic to desired size and knot securely or sew ends tog. Cut excess. Weave in yarn ends.

ROSES

Note: Make all roses with larger hook.

Small Flower (Make 3 (3, 4, 5) for neckline and 2 for each sleeve).

Ch 16.

Row 1: Dc in 5th chain from hook (first ch sp made); *ch 1, dc in next ch; rep from * across: 12 ch sps made; ch 3, turn.

Row 2: 5 dc in first ch sp (one petal made); *sc in next ch sp, 6 dc in next ch sp; rep from * across, ending with sc in last st: 6 petals.

Finish off, leaving a yarn end of about 10" for assembly.

Medium Flower (Make 6 (6, 7, 8) for the neckline; 1 for each sleeve, and 18 (18, 20, 22) for skirt)

Ch 20.

Row 1: Dc in 5th ch from hook (first ch sp made); *ch 1, dc in next stitch; rep from * across: 16 ch sps made; ch 3, turn.

Row 2: 5 dc in first ch sp; *sc in next ch sp, 6 dc in next ch sp; rep from * across, ending with sc in last st: 8 petals.

Finish off, leaving a yarn end of about 10" for assembly.

Large Flower (Make 1 for the bodice)

Foundation Row: Chain 28.

Row 1: Dc in 5th ch from hook (first ch sp made); *ch 1, dc in next stitch; rep from * across: 24 ch sps made; ch 3, turn.

Row 2: 5 dc in first ch sp: petal made; *sc in next ch sp, 6 dc in next ch sp: petal made; rep from * across, ending sc in last st: 12 petals.

Finish off, leaving a long tail of about 10" for assembly.

Rose Assembly

For each flower: Thread yarn tail into a tapestry needle. Roll the first petal (nearest tail) tightly to form the rose center, and sew to secure. Roll rem strip around the center into a rose shape, sewing as you go. Do not cut yarn.

Assemble all roses before sewing to garments.

Attaching Roses

Skirt: Place skirt, right side facing, on a flat surface. Arrange half the Medium flowers for skirt around bottom of skirt front, as shown in photo, placed just above ruffle, and pin in place. Arrange roses so that seam is covered. Sew to skirt, using rem long yarn tail. Flip skirt over and rep on opposite side. Weave in ends.

Tube Top: *(Roses are attached to front of top only.)* Place top with right side facing on a flat surface. Arrange roses around neckline, just below ruffle, as shown in photo. Place one large rose a little to left of center front, and arrange medium and small roses at each side, placing 2 small roses and one medium rose at top of each sleeve. Place one small rose just below and to left of large rose on front. Pin in place, sew to garment.

LOVE LACE LINGERIE

Designed by
Tammy Hildebrand

The lingerie look uncovered! Why relegate such a charming garment only to the bedroom? Why hide this beautiful outfit when you can wear it as the perfect sundress?

LOVE LACE LINGERIE

SIZES	Small	Medium	Large
Body Bust Measurements	30"-32"	34"-36"	38"-40"
Finished Bust Measurements	30"	34"	38"

Note: *Instructions are written for size Small; changes for sizes Medium and Large are in parentheses.*

Materials

Sport weight ribbon yarn, 6 1/4 (7, 7 3/4) ozs lavender

Bulky weight fur-type yarn, 2 1/4 oz pastel variegated

Note: *Photographed model made with Patons® Brilliant #03314 Lilac Luster and Bernat® Boa # 81240 Love Bird*

Size G (4mm) crochet hook (or size required for gauge)

Gauge

8 cross sts = 4"

Stitch Guide

Cross Stitch (Cr St): Skip next st, dc in next st; working in front of st just made, dc in skipped st: Cr St made.

Sc around post: Insert hook from front to back to front around post (vertical bar) of next sc and draw up a lp; YO and draw through both lps on hook: sc around post made.

INSTRUCTIONS

BODICE

Starting at bottom of bodice with ribbon yarn, ch 108 (124, 140); join with sl st to form a ring, being careful not to twist ch.

Rnd 1: Ch 1, sc in each ch around, join with sl st in beg sc: 108 (124, 140) sc.

Note: *Do not turn rnds.*

Rnd 2: Sl st in first sc, ch 3, working in front of ch-3 just made, dc in sl st (beg cross stitch made), ch 2, (CrSt over next 2 sts) to end; join with sl st to top of beg ch: 53 (61, 69) CrSt plus beg CrSt.

Rnd 3: Ch 1, sc in same place, sc in each dc to end skipping ch 2; join with sl st in beg sc: 108 (124, 140) sc.

Rep Rnds 2 and 3 ten more times. Finish off.

MIDRIFF

Rnd 1: Working in unused lps of starting ch, join ribbon yarn with sc 2 lps to the right of center, sc in next lp, ch 2, skip next 2 lps, sc in each lp to end, join with sl st in beg sc: 106 (122, 138 sc).

Rnd 2: Ch 3, tr in ch-2 sp, skip next st; (dc in next st, ch 1, skip next st) to end, join with sl st in top of beg ch.

Rnd 3: Sl st in next tr, ch 1, (sc, ch 3, sc) in same st; sc in next ch-1 sp, (ch 3, sc in next ch-1 sp) to end, join with sl st in beg sc: 53 (61, 69) ch-3 sps.

Rnd 4: Sl st in ch-3 sp, ch 3, 4 dc in same sp; sc in next ch-3 sp, 2 dc in each ch-3 sp to last sp, sc in last sp, join with sl st in top of beg ch: 100 (116, 132) dc plus 4 dc at center front.

Rnd 5: Sl st in next st, ch 1, sc in same st, ch 3; CrSt over next 2 sts; rep from * to end, ch 3, join with sl st in beg sc: 50 (58, 66) cross sts.

Rnd 6: Ch 5, dc in same st, dc in next ch-3 sp, ch 1, dc in next st; (ch 1, skip next st, dc in next st) to next ch-3 sp, dc in sp, join with sl st in 3rd ch of beg ch-5: 54 (62, 70 dc).

Rnd 7: Sl st in next ch-2 sp, (sc, ch 3, sc) in same sp, ch 3; (sc in next ch-1 sp, ch 3) to end, join with sl st in beg sc: 52 (60, 68) sc.

Rep Rnds 4 through 7 two more times; rep Rnds 4 through 6 once more.

SKIRT

Rnd 1: Sl st in ch-2 sp, (sc, ch 3, sc) in same sp, skip next st, (sc, ch 3, sc) in each st up to last st, join with sl st in beg sc: 52 (60, 68) ch-3 sps.

Rnd 2: Sl st in ch-3 sp, ch 3, 2 dc in same sp, 3 dc in each ch-3 sp to end, join with sl st in top of beg ch.

Rnd 3: Sl st in next st, ch 5, dc in same st; *skip 2 sts, (dc, ch 2, dc) in next st; rep from * to end, join with sl st in 3rd ch of beg ch-5.

Rep Rnds 2 and 3 ten more times; rep Rnd 2 once more.

Last Rnd: Ch 1, sc in same sp as joining, ch 5; *skip next 3 sts, sc in sp before next 3 sts, ch 5; rep from * to end, join with sl st in beg sc. Finish off; weave in ends

BOTTOM TRIM

Hold piece with right side facing and last rnd at top.

Working in ch-5 sps of last rnd, join fur-type yarn with sc in any sp, 2 sc in same sp, sc around post of next st; *3 sc in next sp, sc around post of next st; rep from * to end, join with sl st in beg sc. Finish off; weave in ends.

STRAPS (make 2)

Leaving a long yarn end for sewing, with ribbon yarn make a sl knot on hook, ch 2.

Row 1: Sc in 2nd ch from hook, ch 1, turn.

Row 2: Sc in sc, ch 1, turn.

Rep Row 2 until strap measures 12" long, or desired length. Finish off, leaving a long yarn end for sewing. With tapestry needle, sew strap in place on front and back at top, placed about 3½" (4", 4") in from side.

FORM BUST

Hold garment with right side facing with Bodice to your left and skirt to your right.

Join fur-type yarn at center front of bodice in first ch-2 sp; sl st tightly in each ch 2 sp. Finish off; weave in ends.

FLORAL APPLIQUÉ VEST

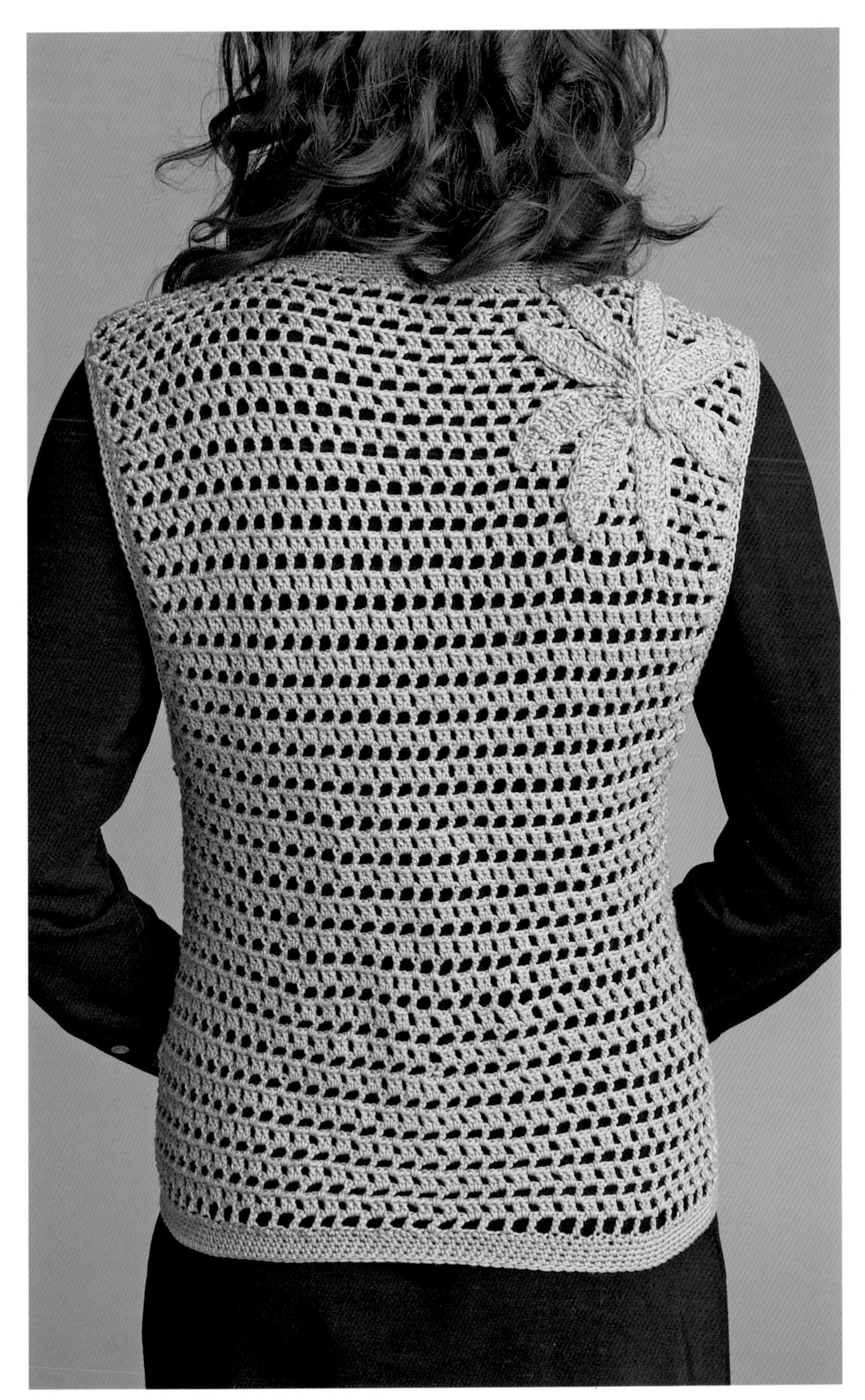

Designed by Margaret Hubert

A subtle tracery of flowers and leaves accents the openwork base of this go-everywhere vest. The flowers and leaves are worked separately, then appliquéd to the base. Dress it up or dress it down, the vest will become a wardrobe favorite.

FLORAL APPLIQUE VEST

SIZES	Small	Medium	Large	X-Large
Body Bust Measurements	32”	34”	36”	38”
Finished Bust Measurements	35”	37”	39”	41”

Note: *Instructions are written for size Small; changes for sizes Medium, Large and Extra Large are in parentheses.*

Materials

Cotton DK weight yarn,
14 (16, 20, 21) oz medium beige
Note: *Photographed model made with Patons® Grace #235 Champagne*
Six 3/8” diameter crystal shank buttons,
Tapestry needle
Size G (4mm) crochet hook (or size required for gauge)

Gauge

8 (2 dc, ch 1) groups = 4”
16 sc = 4”
11 rows = 4” in patt

Stitch Guide

Cluster: (2 dc, ch 1) in space indicated

Decreases on a space row: At end of row, ch 3, turn, skip one dc on following row.

Decreases on a cluster row: Work 1 dc instead of 2 in first and last cluster of row.

Note: *Vest is worked in one piece; flowers and leaves are worked separately and appliquéd to garment.*

INSTRUCTIONS

Starting at bottom edge, loosely ch 200 (212, 224, 236).

Foundation Row: Dc in 5th ch from hook; * ch 2, skip 2 chs, dc in next ch; rep from * to end: 66 (70, 74, 78) ch-2 sps; ch 3, turn.

Row 1 (cluster row): * (2 dc, ch 1) in next ch-2 sp, rep from * across, ending with dc in 3rd ch of beg ch-3; turn.

Row 2 (spaces row): Ch 5 (counts as a dc and ch-2 sp); * dc in next ch-1 space, ch 2; rep from * across, ending with dc in top of ch-3.

Rep Rows 1 and 2 until piece measures 9” (91/2”, 10”, 10”) from beg ch, or 1” less than desired finished length to underarm, ending by working a Row 1.

RIGHT FRONT

Starting with a spaces row, work 15 (16, 17, 18) sps, dc in next dc, ch 3, turn.

Working on these Right Front sts, continue in pattern as established, and dec 1 st at armhole edge every row 2 times: 14 (15, 16, 17) clusters rem. Work even in pattern until armhole measures 6 1/2” (7”, 7 1/2”, 81/2”), ending at front edge.

NECK SHAPING

Sl st over 6 (6, 7, 7) clusters, ch 3, working on rem 8 (9, 9, 10)clusters, dec 1 st at front edge every row twice. Work even on rem 6 (7, 7, 8) clusters until armhole measures 91/2” (10” , 101/2”, 111/2”). Finish off.

LEFT FRONT

Join yarn 15 (16, 17, 18) clusters in from left front edge, work to correspond to Right Front, reversing armhole and neck shaping.

BACK

Skip 3 (3, 4, 4) clusters after Right Front for underarm; join yarn in next dc, work across 30 (32, 32, 34) clusters, leaving 3 (3, 4, 4) clusters unworked for underarm. Working in pattern, dec 1 st each armhole edge 2 times then work even until piece measures same length as fronts to shoulder. Finish off; weave in ends.

FINISHING

Sew shoulder seams.

BORDERS

Note: *As you work borders, adjust sts as needed to keep work flat.*

Rnd 1: Hold piece with right side facing you and bottom edge at top; join yarn with sl st in 7th dc from right on Left Front, ch 1, sc in same st; sc across bottom edge, working 2 sc in each sp and sc in each dc, to right front corner; work 3 sc in corner, work sc in sides of rows up right front; 3 sc in first neck corner, continue around neck edge, 3 sc in 2nd neck corner; continue across rows of left front, 3 sc in bottom left corner, continue across bottom edge to beg sc, join with sl st, ch 1; do not turn, continue to work in rnds.

Rnd 2: Sc around, working 3 sc in center sc of each 3-sc corner group;

join in beg sc, ch 1, do not turn.

Place piece on a flat surface and measure for placement of buttons on Left Front Band. Place top button 6" down from Left Front top corner, and bottom button up 1" from beg of bottom. Evenly space rem four buttons between.

Rnd 3 (Buttonhole Rnd): Continue in sc, working corners as before, and working buttonholes on Right Front edge opposite markers on Left Front edge. To make a buttonhole, ch 2, skip 2 sc, continue in sc. At end of rnd, join, ch 1, do not turn.

Rnd 4: Continue in sc around, working corners as before, and working 2 sc in each ch-2 buttonhole space.

Rnd 5: Rep Rnd 2; finish off, weave in ends.

ARMHOLE BORDERS (make 2)

Rnd 1: Hold garment with right side facing; join yarn at underarm and work sc around, adjusting sts as needed to keep work flat; do not join, mark end of rnd.

Rnds 2 and 3: Sc in each sc around; at end of Rnd 3, join. Finish off; weave in ends.

FLOWERS AND LEAVES

Note: *Flowers are formed of individual petals arranged in a circle. Two flowers have 9 petals each; four flowers have 8 petals each.*

Petal (make 50)

Ch 20.

Rnd 1: Dc in 4th ch from hook and in next 12 chs; hdc in next 2 chs, sc in last 2 chs, ch 3, sc in same ch as last sc; now working in unused lps on opposite side of ch, sc in next lp, hdc in next 2 lps, dc in each rem lp, ch 2, sl st in same lp as last dc. Finish off; weave in ends.

Leaf (make 10)

Ch 12.

Rnd 1: 4 dc in 4th ch from hook, dc in each of next 3 chs, hdc in next 3 chs, sc in next 2 chs, ch 3, sc in last sc; working in unused lps on opposite side of ch, sc in first lp, hdc in 3 lps, dc in next 3 lps, 4 dc in next lp, ch 3, sl st in same lp. Finish off; weave in ends.

FORM FLOWERS

9-Petal Flower (make 2)

Thread an 18" piece of yarn into a tapestry needle, join 9 petals in a circle at one end by running yarn through the wide part of each petal pinching ends tog to form center of flower as you add petals. Secure tightly and use the same yarn to sew flower to vest, following placement as shown in photo. Place a 9-petal flower on the bottom edge of each front; be sure that one petal of the flower on the right front covers where the border rows are joined.

8-Petal Flower (make 4)

Using 8 petals, work as for 9-petal flower; sew to garment as shown in photo, one on Right Front, two on Left Front, and one on the Back at the right shoulder.

Sew leaves on Fronts, placed as shown in photo.

Sew buttons opposite buttonholes.

A TOUCH OF GLITTER

Designed by Tammy Hildebrand

There's glitter in the metallic yarn and glitter in the silver star buttons that decorate this halter. There's certainly to be just a touch of glitter in the eyes of the one who wears this fun garment.

A TOUCH OF GLITTER

SIZES	Small	Medium	Large
Body Bust Measurements	30"-32"	34"-36"	38"-40"
Finished Bust Measurements	29"	33"	37"

Note: *Instructions are written for size Small; changes for sizes Medium and Large are in parentheses.*

Materials

Worsted weight metallic yarn
1 3/4 (3 1/2, 3 1/2) oz gold

Note: *Photographed model made with Lion Brand® Glitterspun #170 Gold*

4 (6, 7) silver 1/2" diameter star shaped buttons

Size G (4mm) crochet hook (or size required for gauge)

Gauge

16 sc = 4"

Stitch Guide

Beg Cluster (begCl): Ch 3; YO hook and draw up a lp in same place; (YO and draw through 2 lps on hook) twice: begCl made.

Cluster (Cl): (YO hook, insert hook in specified st and draw up a lp, YO and draw through first 2 lps on hook) twice; YO and draw through all 3 lps on hook: Cl made.

V-Stitch (V-st): (Dc, ch 1, dc) in same st.

INSTRUCTIONS

BRA FIRST CUP

Ch 21 (29, 37).

Row 1: Sc 2nd ch from hook and each rem ch: 20 (28, 36) sc; ch 1, turn.

Rows 2 through 20: Skip first sc (dec made), sc across, ch 1, turn.

At end of Row 20, one sc rem. Do not finish off yarn, do not turn.

BORDER

Rnd 1: Sc in rows along side edge to beg ch; in unused lps of starting ch, (sc, ch 1, sc) in first lp, sc in each lp to last lp, (sc, ch 1, sc) in last lp; sc in each row end of opposite side, sc in rem one st of last row, join with sl st in beg sc. Do not turn or finish off: 63 (87, 111 sc).

Rnd 2: Work (begCl, ch 2, Cl) in same st; Cl in each st to next ch-1 sp, (sc, ch 1, sc) in ch-1 sp; sc in each st across to next ch-1 sp, (sc, ch 1, sc) in ch-1 sp; Cl in each st up to end, join with sl st in top of begCl; finish off; weave in ends.

BRA SECOND CUP

Work as for First Cup.

MIDRIFF

Rnd 1: Join yarn with sc in first ch-1 sp at bottom of first cup, sc in next 6 (8, 10) sts, hdc in next 6 (8, 10) sts; dc in next 6 (8, 10) sts, tr in next 6 (8, 10) sts, sc in next ch-1 sp; working across bottom of 2nd cup, sc in first ch-1 sp, tr in next 6 (8, 10) sts, dc in next 6 (8, 10) sts; hdc in next 6 (8, 10) sts, sc in next 6, (8, 10) sts, sc in last ch-1 sp; ch 60 (76, 92), join with sl st in beg sc.

Rnd 2: Ch 1, sc in each st up to last st of first cup, ch 1, skip first st on 2nd cup, sc in each st and ch to end, join with sl st in beg sc.

Rnd 3: Ch 1, sc to ch-1 sp, sc in ch-1 sp, sc in each st around, join with sl st in beg sc.

Rnds 4 through 6: Ch 1, sc in each st around, join with sl st in beg sc.

For size Small only

Rnd 7: Ch 1, sc in same st, sc in next 2 sts; [skip next 2 sts, (2 dc, ch 1, 2 dc) in next st, skip next 2 sts, sc in next st] 7 times, sc in each st to end, join with sl st in beg sc. Sl st to 3rd sc.

For size Medium only

Rnd 7: Ch 1, sc in same st, skip next st; [(2 dc, ch 1, 2 dc) in next st, skip next 2 sts, sc in next st, skip next 2 sts] 10 times; (2 dc, ch 1, 2 dc) in next st, skip next st, sc in each st around, join with sl st in beg sc.

For size Large only

Rnd 7: Ch 1, sc in same st, sc in next st; [skip next 2 sts, (2 dc, ch 1, 2 dc) in next st, skip next 2 sts, sc in next st] 13 times, sc in each st to end, join with sl st in beg sc. Sl st to 3rd sc.

For all sizes

Rnd 8: Ch 4, dc in same st; [(dc, ch 1, dc, ch 1, dc) in ch-1 sp; V-st in next sc] 7 times, skip next 2 sts, (dc, ch 1, dc, ch 1, dc) in next st; *skip next 2 sts, V-st in next sc, skip next 2 sts, (dc, ch 1, dc, ch 1, dc) in

next st rep from * around, join with sl st in 3rd ch of beg ch-4.

Rnd 9: Ch 3, (dc, ch 1, dc, ch 1, dc) in center st of next 3-dc group; [dc in next V-st, (dc, ch 1, dc, ch 1, dc) in center st of next 3-dc group] to end, join with sl st in top of beg ch.

Rnd 10: Ch 4, dc in same st; (dc, ch 1, dc, ch 1, dc) in center st of next 3-dc group, [V-st in next dc, (dc, ch 1, dc, ch 1, dc) in center st of next 3-dc group] to end, join with sl st in 3rd ch of beg ch-4.

Rnds 11 through 18 (22, 26): Rep Rnds 9 through 10, four, (six, eight) more times.

Rnd 19 (23, 27): Rep Rnd 9.

Rnd 20 (24, 28): Ch 1, sc in same st, 5 dc in center st of next 3-dc group, [sc in next dc, 5 dc in center st of next 3-dc group] to end, join with sl st in beg sc, finish off.

STRAP (make 2)

Row 1: Ch 46, sl st in 2nd ch from hook and each ch to end. Finish off, leaving a long yarn length for sewing. Sew one end of strap to ch-2 sp at top of one cup. Sew other end to back.

FINISHING

Sew one star button at front center where cups join; sew rem buttons evenly spaced across Rnd 2 of midriff on front.

SPUN SUGAR COCOON

Designed by
Vashti Braha

Wearing this cocoon is like slipping into a soft billowing cloud! Sweet as cotton candy, it's a perfect accent to top a slim dress for a wonderful evening.

SPUN SUGAR COCOON

Size

45" wide x 15" long

Materials

Bulky weight mohair blend yarn,
14 oz lt pink (A)
Super bulky weight fuzzy nylon yarn,
8¾ oz lt pink (B)

Note: *Photographed model made with Patons® Divine #06406 Chantilly Rose (A) and Patons® Allure #04415 Rose Quartz (B)*

One 2" diameter white plastic ring
Size K (6.5mm) crochet hook
Size Q (16mm) crochet hook (or size required for gauge)

Gauge

4 sc = 4"
1 row Pst and 1 row sc = 3¾"

Stitch Guide

Beginning Puff Stitch (begPst): YO, insert hook into specified st or ch and draw up a 3¾" lp; YO and draw through first 2 lps on hook (first leg of begPst made); YO, insert hook in next st or ch and draw up a 4" lp, YO and draw through first 2 lps on hook (2nd leg of begPst made); YO and draw through rem 3 lps on hook: begPst made.

Puff Stitch (Pst): YO, insert hook into specified st and draw up a 4" lp; YO and draw through first 2 lps on hook (first leg of Pst made); YO, insert hook in next st and draw up a 4" lp, YO and draw through first 2 lps on hook (2nd leg of Pst made); YO and draw through rem 3 lps on hook: Pst made. Next Pst starts in same st where previous Pst ended.

Joined sc: Insert hook from front to back under top 2 lps of previous st, then insert hook from back to front under top 2 lps of next st and draw up a lp; YO and draw through 2 lps on hook: joined sc made.

INSTRUCTIONS

Notes

- *Cocoon is worked with three strands together (two of A and one of B), from the top down in alternating rows of Pst and joined sc. Shaping is done in the single crochet rows by adding an additional stitch at shoulder points.*
- *Pst rows are supposed to curl. The back of the puffs is the right side of garment. Help puffs curl, cocoon-like, by fluffing the puffs so that the backs of the puffs curve outward.*

Working with 2 strands of A and 1 strand of B throughout pattern, with Q hook, ch 43.

Row 1: Work beg Pst starting in 4th ch from hook; starting first Pst in same chain as 2nd leg of the completed begPst; work Psts across to last st, dc in last st (where 2nd leg of last Pst was worked): 42 Psts, 1 dc; ch 1, turn.

Row 2 (right side): Sc in dc, insert hook from front to back under top 2 lps of same dc, then insert hook from back to front under top 2 lps of next Pst; YO and draw up a lp, YO and draw through 2 lps on hook: joined sc made; work joined sc around each of next 10 Pst; work 2 joined sc around next (12th) Pst: increase made; joined sc around each of next 16 sts, 2 joined sc increase around next Pst; work joined sc around each rem Pst, sc in top of turning ch: 43 sts; ch 3, turn.

Row 3: Work begPst, then work Pst across, at end of row, dc in last st (same place as the 2nd leg of Pst just completed.: 42 Psts and 1 dc; ch 1, turn.

Row 4: Sc in dc, joined sc around post of first Pst and each of next 11 Psts, 2 joined sc around 13th Pst; joined sc around each of next 17 Psts, 2 joined sc around next Pst, 2 joined sc around next Pst; joined sc around rem Psts, sc in top of ch-3: 46 sc; ch 3, turn.

Row 5: Rep Row 3 for a total of 45 Puff st plus 1 dc; ch 1, turn.

Row 6: Sc in dc; joined sc around next 13 Psts; 2 joined sc around next (14th) Pst; joined sc around next 18 Psts, 2 joined sc around next Pst; joined sc around each rem Pst, sc in top of turning ch-3: 49 sc; ch 3, turn.

Row 7: Rep Row 3: for 48 Psts and 1 dc; ch 1, turn.

Row 8: Sc in dc; joined sc around post of next 14 Psts; 2 joined sc around next Pst; joined sc around next 29 sts, 2 joined sc around next Pst; joined sc around rem Psts, sc in top of ch-3: 52 sc.

Do not turn and do not fasten off. Continue with Edging.

EDGING

With wrong side still facing, rotate work so that you can work around corner and down the nearest short side (do not chain to turn the corner).

Row 1: Hdc in side of Pst row just completed, *hdc in side of next sc row, hdc in side of next Pst row; rep from * across, end with sl st in edge of beg ch: 7 hdc; do not ch, turn.

Row 2: *Hdc in next hdc of a Pst row, skip a st, hdc in hdc of next Pst row; Rep from * across: 4 hdc; sl st in last st; do not ch, turn.

Row 3: (YO, insert hook in hdc one row below first hdc, pull up a 2" lp) 3 times, YO and draw through all lps on hook: edge Pst made; continuing across row, work a 2 1/2" edge Pst into each hdc of the row below: 4 edge Pst; sc in top of beg Psts of Row 1.

Row 4: Working around corner to to the next long side of cocoon, sl st in next 4 foundation chs; *skip next ch, sl st in next 5 chs; rep from * across, drawing in shoulder edge slightly.

Continue around corner, and work Rows 1, 2 and 3 into the next short side. Finish off; weave in ends.

FASTENING

Button

With smaller hook and one strand of A, work sc completely around plastic ring, sl st in first sc to join; ch 2 for shank. Finish off, leaving a 12" yarn end.

Feed the tail and 2 chains through the left short side of the cocoon, from front (Right Side) to back under 2 or 3 half-double crochets of Edging Row B, then feed the shank to the front again where it can be attached to the "button". With yarn needle, secure shank to button and the Cocoon.

Button Loop

With smaller hook and one strand of A, make a ch 5" long. Finish off.

Try on garment, wrap right side over left and position comfortably. Mark position for button and button lp.

Sew button on right side of left front; sew ends of button lp to wrong side of right front.

BARELY THERE BIKINI

Designed by Patons Design Department

Is there any doubt that all eyes will be on the lovely lady who dares to wear this oufit?

SIZES	Small	Medium	Large
Top Bra Cup Size	A	B	C
Bottom	One size with adjustable ties		

***Note:** Instructions for top are written for size Small; changes for sizes Medium and Large are in parentheses.*

Material

Sport weight yarn,
4 1/4 (4 1/2, 5) oz terracotta

***Note:** Photographed model made with Patons® Grace, #60604 Terracotta*

Size B (2.25 mm) crochet hook
(or size required for gauge)

Invisible elastic thread

Gauge

24 sc= 4"

28 sc rows = 4

Stitch Guide

Sc decrease (sc dec): (Insert hook in next st and draw up a lp) twice, YO and draw through all 3 lps on hook: sc dec made.

BARELY THERE BIKINI

INSTRUCTIONS

TOP

Cup (make 2)

Ch 15 (16, 20).

Row 1 (right side): Sc in 2nd ch from hook, sc in each ch across to last ch, 5 sc in last ch; place marker in center sc of 5 sc and move marker up in each row to indicate center sc of each row; working into unused lps on opposite side of ch, sc in each lp across: 31 (33, 41) sc; ch 1, turn.

Row 2: Sc in each sc around; ch 1, turn.

Row 3: Sc in each sc to center sc; work 5 (5, 3) sc in center sc; sc in each rem sc across: 35 (37, 43) sc; ch 1, turn.

Row 4: Rep Row 2.

Row 5: Sc in each sc to center sc; work 3 sc in center sc; sc in each rem sc across: 37 (39, 45) sc; ch 1, turn.

Rows 6 through 21 (25, 29): Rep Rows 2 through 5 four (five, six) times more: 61 (69, 69) sc.

Row 22 (26, 30): Sc in each of first 3 (4, 4) sc; *ch 1, skip next sc, sc in each of next 2 sc; rep from * to last 1 (2, 2) sc; sc in each of last 1 (2, 2) sc: 42 (48, 48) sc and 19 (21, 21) ch-1 sps; ch 1, turn.

Row 23 (27, 31): Sc in each of first 1 (2, 2) sc, (5 dc in next ch-1 sp, sc in next ch-1 sp) 9 (10, 10) times; 5 dc in next ch-1 sp, sc in each of last 1 (2, 2) sc: 11 (14, 14) sc and 50 (55, 55) dc. Finish off; weave in ends.

Join Cups and Make Ties

Ch 95.

Row 1: With wrong side facing, work 24 (28, 32) sc evenly spaced across bottom edge of first Cup, ch 4, work 24 (28, 32) sc evenly spaced across bottom edge of second Cup; ch 96, turn.

Row 2 (right side): Sl st in 2nd ch from hook, sl st in each of next 94 chs, sc in each of next 24 (28, 32) sc, sc in each of next 4 chs, sc in each of next 24 (28, 32) sc, sl st in each of next 95 chs. Finish off.

Neck Ties

With right side facing, join yarn with sl st in top center st on Row 23 (27, 31) of Cup, ch 106, sl st in 2nd ch from hook, sl st in each ch across, sl st in same st as joining. Finish off. Rep on other cup for second neck tie. Weave in all ends.

BOTTOM

Starting at Back, ch 63.

Row 1 (wrong side): Sc in 2nd ch from hook, sc in each ch across: 62 sc; ch 1, turn.

Row 2 (right side): Sc in each sc across; ch 1, turn.

Rows 3 through 9: Rep Row 2 seven times more.

Row 10: Sc dec in first 2 sc, sc in each sc to last 2 sc, sc dec in last 2 sc: 60 sc; ch 1, turn.

Row 11: Sc in first st, sc in each st across; ch 1, turn.

Rows 12 through 57: Rep Rows 10 and 11 twenty-three times more: 14 sc at end of Row 57.

Row 58: Sc in each sc across; ch 1, turn.

Rows 59 through 77: Rep Row 58 nineteen times more. Do not finish off.

FRONT

Row 78: 2 sc in first sc, sc in each sc to last sc, 2 sc in last sc: 16 sc; ch 1, turn.

Row 79: Sc in each sc across; ch 1, turn.

Row 80: Rep Row 79.

Rows 81 through 119: Rep Rows 78 through 80 thirteen times more: 42 sc at end of Row 119. Finish off.

Back Edging and Side Ties

Ch 55.

Row 1: With right side facing, sc in free lp of 62nd ch of foundation ch on Back, sc in free lp of each ch across top of Back: 62 sc; ch 56, turn.

Row 2: Sl st in 2nd ch from hook, sl st in each of next 54 chs, sc in each sc across Back, sl st in each of next 55 chs. Finish off.

Front Edging and Side Ties

Ch 55.

Row 1: With right side facing, sc in last sc on Row 119 on Front, sc in each sc across top of Front: 42 sc; ch 56, turn.

Row 2: Sl st in 2nd ch from hook, sl st in each of next 54 chs, sc in each sc across Front, sl st in each of next 55 chs. Finish off.

Leg Edging

Row 1: With right side facing, join with sl st in edge of Row 119 on Front below tie joining, ch 1, sc in same st as joining, work 1 row sc evenly along edge from Front to Back for leg opening, sl st in side tie; ch 1, turn.

Row 2: Sc in each sc across, sl st in side tie. Finish off.

Rep Rows 1 and 2 for second Leg Edging, joining with sl st in edge of Row 1 on Back below tie joining and work from Back to Front for Row 1 of leg opening.

Weave in all ends. Thread invisible elastic through Row 2 of Back, Front and Leg Edgings.

ACCENT ON BEADS

Designed by Pirkko Vega

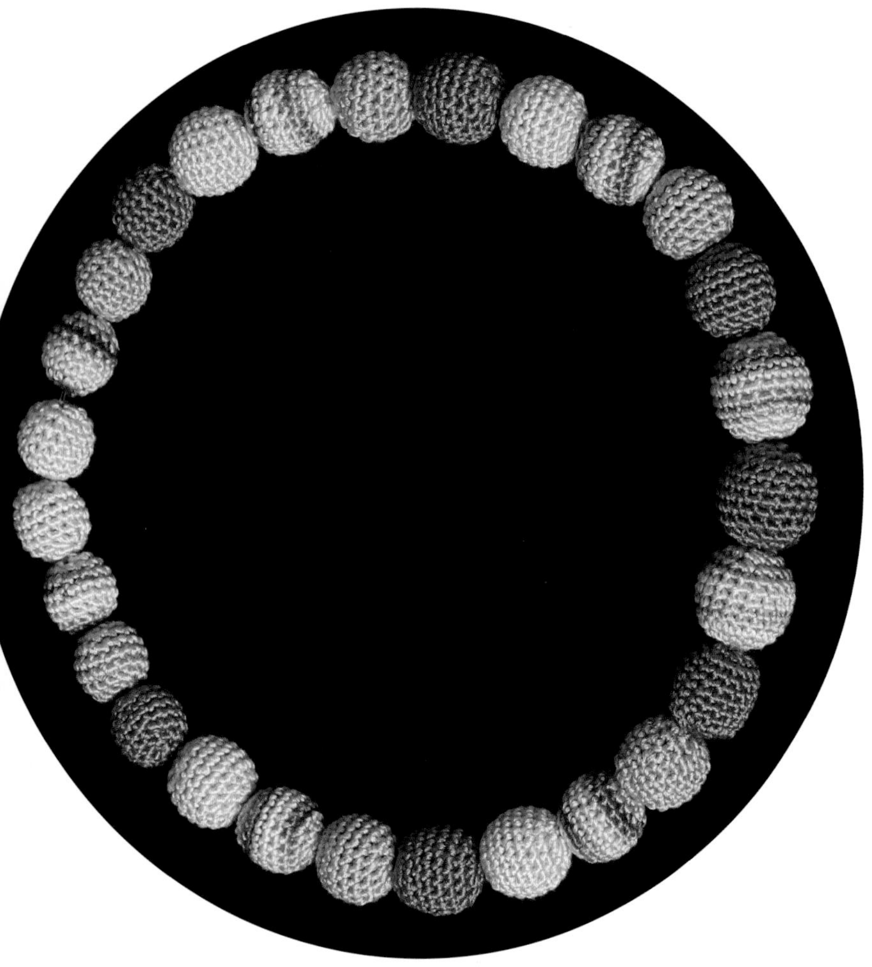

Bead necklaces are the key accessory seen on all the fashion runways. Now You can make your own bead necklace to wear with most any outfit.

Size

22" long

Materials

Round beads with center hole,
  Three 20 mm
  Eight 15 mm
  Sixteen 16 mm
6-strand embroidery floss,
  5 skeins medium green (A)
  6 skeins light green (B)
  6 skeins dark green (C)
  6 skeins variegated green (D)
1 yd stretchy clear plastic bead cord
Size 18 tapestry needle
Stitch marker or contrast thread
Size 5 (1.9 mm) steel crochet hook
  (or size required for gauge)

Gauge

4 sc = 1/2"
4 rows = 4"

Note: *Gauge is very important for this project.*

Stitch Guide

sc 2 tog decrease (sc 2 tog): Draw up a lp in each of next 2 sts, YO and draw through all 3 lps on hook: sc 2 tog made.

INSTRUCTIONS

20 mm BEADS (Make 1 with C and 2 with D):

Ch 2

Rnd 1: 7 sc in 2nd ch from hook; do not join, mark beg of rnds.

Rnd 2: 2 sc in each sc: 14 sc.

Rnd 3: (Sc in next 3 sc, 2 sc in next sc) 3 times, sc in last 2 sc: 17 sc.

Rnds 4 through 9: Sc in each sc.

Rnd 10: (Sc in next 3 sc, sc 2 tog) 3 times, sc in last 2 sc: 14 sc.

Insert bead in the crocheted cup, making sure the bead hole is facing up and down in the center of the crocheted cup.

Rnd 11: (Sc 2 tog) 7 times: 7 sc.

Finish off, leaving a long end. Thread end into tapestry needle and weave through rem 7 sc, pull up tightly to close opening and secure. Weave in ends.

16 mm BEADS (Make 4 with each color):

Ch 2

Rnd 1: 6 sc in the 2nd ch from hook; do not join, mark beg of rnds.

Rnd 2: 2 sc in each sc: 12 sc.

Rnd 3: (Sc in next 2 sc, 2 sc in next sc) 4 times: 16 sc.

Rnds 4 through 8: Sc in each sc.

Rnd 9: (Sc in each of next 2 sc, sc 2 tog) 4 times: 12 sc.

Insert bead in the crocheted cup, making sure the bead hole is facing up and down in center of bead.

Rnd 10: (Sc 2 tog) 6 times: 6 sc.

Finish off, leaving a long end. Thread end into tapestry needle and weave through rem 6 sc, draw up tightly to close opening and secure. Weave in ends.

15 mm BEAD (Make 2 with each color):

Ch 2.

Rnd 1: 6 sc in 2nd ch from hook; do not join, mark beg of rnds.

Rnd 2: 2 sc in each sc: 12 sc.

Rnd 3: (Sc in next 3 sc, 2 sc in next sc) 3 times: 15 sc.

Rnds 4 through 7: Sc in each sc.

Rnd 8: (Sc in next 3 sc, sc 2 tog) 3 times: 12 sc.

Insert bead in crochet cup, making sure bead hole is facing up and down in center of cup.

Rnd 9: (Sc 2 tog) 6 times: 6 sc. Finish off, leaving a long end.

Thread end into tapestry needle and weave through rem 6 sts; draw up tightly to close opening, fasten securely and weave in ends.

ASSEMBLY

Arrange beads in order they will be strung, starting at one end and finishing at opposite end.

Arrange as follows, from right to left:

15 mm B, 15 mm D, 15 mm A, 15 mm C; 16 mm B, 16 mm D, 16 mm A, 16 mm C, 16 mm B, 16 mm D, 16 mm A, 16 mm C; 20 mm D, 20 mm C, 20 mm D; 16 mm C, 16 mm A, 16 mm D, 16 mm B, 16 mm C, 16 mm A, 16 mm D, 16 mm B, 15 mm C, 15 mm A, 15 mm D, 15 mm B.

Thread stretch bead cord into tapestry needle and run through holes of beads, keeping to correct order. Knot cord securely and cut off excess.

CUTE CAPELET

Designed by Margaret Hubert

No matter where you choose to wear this fun fashion accessory, you will feel elegant!

CUTE CAPELET

Size

One size fits most; neckline is adjustable

Materials

Worsted weight metallic yarn, 805 yds black

Note: *Photographed model made with Lion Brand® Glitterspun #153 Onyx*

4 yards 1/2" wide black satin ribbon

Size I (5.5mm) crochet hook (or size required for gauge)

Gauge

6-tr shell = 1 1/2"

INSTRUCTIONS

Note: *Work in back lp of each st throughout pattern unless otherwise specified.*

Starting at neckline, ch 109

Row 1: Working in back lps, 6 tr in 6th ch from hook (shell made); *sk 2 chs, sc in next ch, skip 2 chs, 6 tr shell in next ch; rep from * 16 times more: 18 shells made; dc in last ch; ch 3 turn.

Row 2: *Sc in 3rd tr of first shell of prev row, 6-tr shell in next sc; rep from * across, ending with sc in 3rd tr of last shell, dc in top of turning ch: 17 shells made; ch 3. turn.

Row 3: * 6-tr shell in sc of prev row, sc in 3rd tr of next shell; rep from * across, ending with 6-tr shell in last sc of prev row, dc in top of turning ch.

Row 4 and 5: Rep Rows 2 and 3.

Rows 6 thru 11: Rep Rows 2 and 3, having 8 tr in each shell and making the sc in 4th tr of shell.

Rows 12 thru 15: Rep Rows 2 and 3, having 10 tr in each shell and making the sc in 5th tr of shell.

Rows 16 thru 19: Rep Rows 2 and 3, having 12 tr in each shell and making the sc in 6th tr of shell. At end of Row 19, ch 1, turn.

Row 20: Working in both lps of each st from here on, sc in each st across last row; do not cut yarn, do not turn.

FRONT AND NECK BORDER

Row 1: Sc up front edge, working 2 sc in each long sp and 1 sc in each short sp at row ends, adjusting sts as needed to keep work flat; at neckline corner work 5 sc. Working along neck edge, 2 sc in each skipped ch-2 space (skipping over the shell sts), 5 sc at next corner; sc down last front edge, again adjusting sts to keep work flat, ch 1, turn.

Row 2: Sc evenly around, working 3 sc in center sc at each corner, to bottom of second side, ch 1, turn (do not work across bottom sts).

Row 3: Sc up side edge to center of neck corner, ch 4 (counts as a tr and ch-1 sp), skip next st; *tr, ch 1, skip 1, rep from * to last 2 neckline sts, ch 4, skip 1, join with sl st to last st. Continue to work in sc down last side edge. Finish off.

FINISHING

Cut ribbon into two 2-yd lengths, hold tog and weave in and out of ch-1 sps of neckline. Tie bow to fasten.

HARLEQUIN VEST

Designed by Judith Solomon

For the advanced crocheter

Elegant and exciting, this beautiful long vest is made with a wide variety of gorgeous textured yarn. Flashes of metallics are seen when the vest swirls around the wearer as she moves. The garment is composed of modules which are started at the center, with subsequent rows building on the ones before, rather like building with blocks. This garment will have a starring role in your wardrobe.

HARLEQUIN VEST

SIZES	Small	Medium	Large
Body Bust Measurements	36”	40”	44”
Finished Bust Measurements	39”	43”	47”
Finished Hip Measurements	31”	32½”	34”

Note: Instructions are written for size Small; changes for sizes Medium and Large are in parentheses.

Materials

Worsted weight mohair,
 450 (630, 810) yds black (A)
DK weight metallic eyelash,
 5½ yds gold and white blend (B)
Worsted weight furry yarn,
 90 yds copper (C)
DK weight metallic slub yarn,
 50 g copper (D)
Eyelash yarn,
 60 yds copper (E)
Metallic ribbon yarn,
 115 yds bronze (F)
 115 yds gold (G)
 115 yds black (H)
Open weave ribbon yarn,
 115 yds champagne, (I)
Worsted weight slubbed metallic yarn,
 50 g beige blend (J)
 100 g black blend (K)
Eyelash yarn,
 20 g black and gold blend (L)
Worsted weight chenille,
 122 yds copper, (M)
Worsted weight nylon netting yarn,
 50 g black and gold mix, (N)
Eyelash yarn,
 82 yds bronze (O)

***Note:** Photographed model made with Classic Elite La Gran Mohair #6513 Black (A), Adriafil Gold 60 (B), Berroco® Furz #3814 Roan (C),Filatura di Crosa No Smoking #143 Copper (D), Lion Brand® Fun Fur #134 Copper (E), Lion Brand® Glitterspun #135 Bronze (F), Lion Brand® Glitterspun #170 Gold (G), Lion Brand® Glitterspun #153 Onyx (H), Lion Brand® Trellis #303 Champagne (I), Muench Cleo #124 beige and metallic (J), Muench Cleo #121 black and metallic (K), Muench New Marabu, #4212 black and gold (L), Muench Touch Me #3639 copper (M), Muench Verikeri #4104 black and gold (N), Trendsetter Vision #8092 Bronze (O)*

Size K (6.5 mm) crochet hook or size required for gauge
Tapestry needle
Safety pins

Gauge

One module before border = 10½” long x 3¾” wide
One module after border =
 14½” x 4¾” for size Small
 15¼” x 5¼” for size Medium
 16” x 6” for size Large
Module Section 1 worked in F, G or H = 3½” long

Stitch Guide

Dc decrease (dc dec): (YO, draw up a lp in next st and draw through first 2 lps on hook) twice; YO and draw through all 4 lps on hook: dc dec made.

Sc decrease (sc dec): Draw up a lp in each of next 2 sts, YO and draw through all 3 lps on hook: sc dec made.

Reverse sc: Ch 1; *working from left to right, sc in next st; rep from * for reverse sc.

INSTRUCTIONS

This vest is created by first working a series of modules in three different color combinations. Each module has eleven sections, and **Figure 1** shows how the modules are put together. *(**Note:** It is a good idea to make one module to be sure your gauge is accurate. For the following modules, you may want to crochet all of Section 1 in a color combination, then Section 2, and so on.)* The chart below shows which colors are used for each section of each Module Combination.

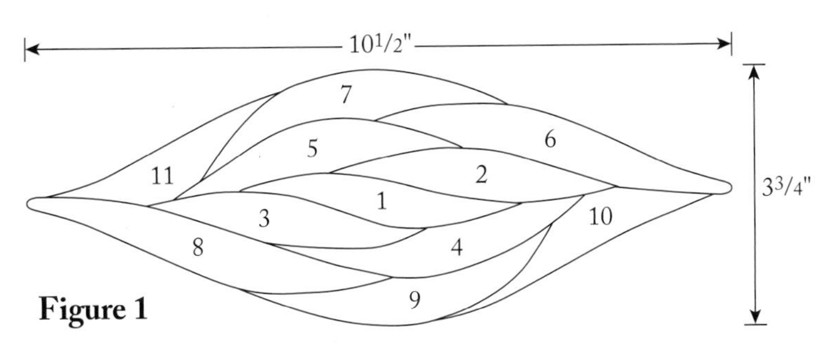

Figure 1

After the modules have been completed, a border is worked around the module following the border instructions below.

Before the modules are joined to create the jacket, four gussets must be created. They are also crocheted in sections in various color combinations. There is a chart which shows which colors are to be used.

Finally, the pieces are joined together according to **Figure 2** to create the vest.

MODULES (for all sizes)

Loosely ch 14.

Section 1: Working in back lp only of each ch, sl st in 2nd ch from hook, sc in 2 chs, hdc in 2 chs, dc in 3 chs, hdc in 2 chs, sc in 2 chs, sl st in last ch; finish off, do not turn. Place marker on back of piece to indicate right side of garment for use in assembling. Do not turn; all sections are worked on the wrong side unless otherwise specified. Work over yarn ends when possible to make finishing easier.

Section 2: Join yarn with sl st in turning ch at right edge of Section 1; *ch 5, sl st in 2nd ch from hook, working across rem ch and continuing along Section 1, work 2 sc, 2 hdc, 4 dc, hdc, 2 sc, sl st. Finish off.

Section 3: Turn piece upside down (do not turn to wrong side); join yarn at right-hand end of Section 1, rep Section 2 from *. Finish off.

Section 4: Count 6 sts from left to right of Section 3, join yarn in 6th st; * work sl st in next st, sc, hdc, dc, 2 dc in next st; dc, 2 hdc, 2 sc, sl st in next st. Finish off.

Section 5: Turn piece upside down; count 6 sts from left to right of Section 2, rep from * of Section 4.

Section 6: Join yarn in turning ch at end of Section 2; *ch 5, sl st in 2nd ch from hook, 2 sc, 3 hdc, dc; dc dec over next 2 sts, dc, 2 hdc, sc, sl st in next st. Finish off.

Section 7: Turn piece upside down; join yarn at the opposite end of module, rep from * of Section 6.

Section 8: Count 5 sts from left to right from end of Section 7; *join yarn in 4th st; sl st in next st, sc, 2 hdc, dc, 2 dc in next st; dc, 2 hdc, 2 sc, sl st in next st; finish off.

Section 9: Turn piece upside down; count 5 sts back from left end of Section 6, repeat from * of Section 8.

MODULE COMBINATIONS

	Module Combination I (make 9)	Module Combination II (make 8)	Module Combination III (make 7)
Section 1:	E	C	N and D
Section 2:	J	J	K
Section 3:	M	M	J
Section 4:	D and E	O	O
Section 5:	I and C	D	I and C
Section 6:	G and L	G and L	M
Section 7:	N and D	E	E
Section 8:	K	C and I	C and I
Section 9:	M	K	H and L
Section 10:	K	N and D	E and D
Section 11:	B	K	K

***Note:** Where two yarns are indicated, use them held together.*

Section 10: Count back 4 sts from left to right of Section 9, join yarn in 4th st; *sl st in next st, sc, hdc, 3 dc, hdc, 2 sc, sl st in next st. Finish off.

Section 11: Turn piece upside down; count back 4 sts from end of Section 8, rep Section 10 from *. Finish off.

BORDER FOR EACH MODULE

For size Small only:

Join A in center st of long side; * ch 1, sc in each st across to point, ch 5; sl st in 2nd and 3rd chs from hook, work 2 sc, sc along edge to center st, 2 sc in center st; rep from * once, sl st in first st. Finish off.

For size Medium only:

Join A in center st of long side; *ch 1; hdc to last st before point, sc in next st, ch 6; sl st in 2nd and 3rd chs from hook, work 2 sc, hdc, sc; hdc to center, 2 hdc in center st; rep from * once, sl st in first st. Finish off.

For size Large only:

Join A in center st of long side; *ch 2; dc in each st to last 2 sts before point, hdc, sc, ch 7; sl st in 2nd and 3rd chs from hook; work 2 sc, hdc, dc; along edge work sc, hdc; dc to center st, 2 dc in center st; rep from * once, in first st. Finish off.

GUSSETS

Section 1: Ch 9; dc in 4th ch from hook; working in chs, dc, 2 hdc, 2 sc, sl st in last ch, finish off; mark back of piece to indicate right side of garment.

Section 2: Join yarn in sl st end, ch 5; sl st in 2nd ch from hook, working in chs, 3 sc, 2 hdc, 3 dc, dc in top of ch-3 at beg of Section 1. Finish off.

Section 3: Turn piece upside down, join yarn in top of 3 skipped chs at beg of Section 1, ch 3, dc in same st, work 2 dc, 2 hdc, sc, sl st. Finish off.

Section 4: Join yarn in sl st-end of Section 2, ch 6, sl st in 2nd ch from hook; working in chs, 3 sc, 2 hdc, 3 dc, hdc, sc, sl st in next st. Finish off.

Section 5: Counting left to right, join yarn in 5th st from end of Section 4, sl st in next st, sc, hdc, dc across. Finish off.

Section 6: Join yarn in first dc of Section 3, ch 3, dc in same st; work dc, 3 hdc, sc, sl st. Finish off.

GUSSET COMBINATIONS

	Back Gusset Combination I (make 1)	Back Gusset Combination II (make 1)	Side Gusset Combination (make 2)
Section 1:	E	C	H
Section 2:	C and I	M	A
Section 3:	K	J	K
Section 4:	D and N	F	H
Section 5:	O	E and D	K
Section 6:	M	H and L	H
Section 7:	B	K	A

Note: *Where two yarns are indicated, use them held together.*

Section 7: Counting left to right, join yarn in 4th st from end of Section 6, sl st in next st, work sc, hdc, dc, 2 hdc, 2 sc, sl st. Finish off.

BORDER FOR EACH GUSSET

Holding gusset with point down, join A in upper right corner; ch 1, work 3 sc, 2 hdc, sc; in corner work (dc, hdc, 2 sc); work 7 sc , 3 sc 2 hdc; in corner work (2 sc, hdc, dc); work sc, hdc; dc, to point, 3 sc; in point work (3 hdc, 4 dc); work sc, hdc; dc to corner, sl st in beg sc. Finish off.

FINISHING VEST

Weave in all ends. Steam pieces lightly so that they don't curl, without touching the iron to the yarn. Allow to dry completely.

Lay pieces out according to **Figure 2**.

Turn some of the pieces in each colorway upside down. Pin together in small sections, with points touching, and sew pieces together.
Sew shoulders.

ARMHOLE EDGING (make 2)

Rnd 1: With right side of garment facing, join A in center of one side gusset. Sc to first corner, dec over 3 corner sts as follows: *draw up a lp in next st, YO, draw up a lp in next st, draw up a lp in next st; YO and draw through all 4 lps on hook: dec made*; work sc to top of armhole, s sc dec at angle of side and top, sc to center of top, 2 sc in next st, sc to angle of top and side, sc dec, sc to bottom corner, rep from * to * once, join with sl st, in beg sc. Finish off.

Rnd 2: Join H in last st; work reverse sc around, join. Finish off.

NECKLINE EDGING

Rnd 1: Join A in center of back; *ch 1, sc in next st, sc dec; rep from * to corner; in corner work decrease as for * to * in armhole edging; (sc to tip of next module, sc dec) twice; sc to first point, **3 sc in tip of point, sc to V between points, draw up a lp in last st, skip center st, draw up a lp in next st, YO and draw through all 4 lps on hook**; rep from ** to ** 8 times more; 3 sc in next point, sc along other front edge as before, work decrease as for * to * in armhole edging; rep from ** to ** to first st, join.

Rnd 2: Join H in left corner of back neck. Work reverse sc around, join with sl st . Finish off; weave in all ends.

Lay garment flat, and steam thoroughly without touching the iron to the garment. Smooth garment into shape if necessary, shaping and aligning the points. Allow to dry thoroughly.

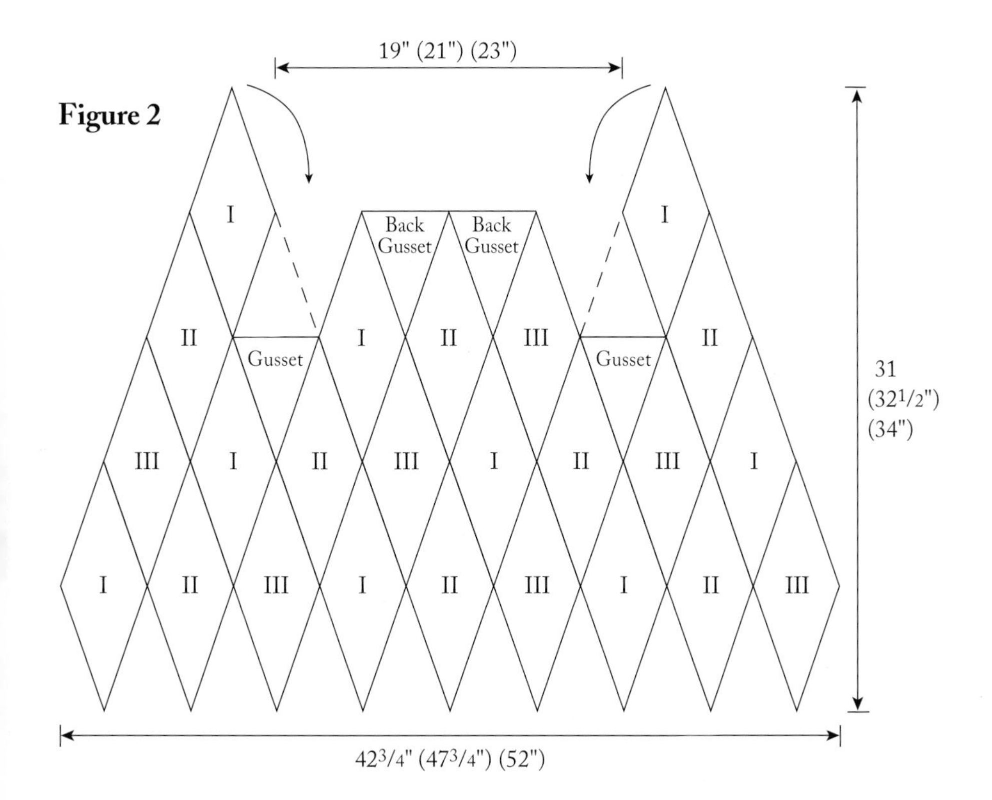

MEXICAN HERITAGE

Designed by Nancy Nehring for DMC

Mix and match four different pieces: a short sleeved top, crop pants, a calf-length skirt and a rebozo or shawl, and you can create many different outfits. The edging of circular sun motifs and rainbow bars reflects the Mexican influence common in the Southwest.

MEXICAN HERITAGE

Note: Instructions are written for size Small; changes for sizes Medium and Large are in parentheses.

Materials (for 4-piece outfit)

Size 8 pearl cotton (88 yd balls),
- 177 (195, 212) balls terra cotta
- 10 balls yellow
- 8 balls gold
- 8 balls coral
- 8 balls green
- 8 balls purple
- 8 balls blue
- 9 balls brown

***Note:** Photographed models made with DMC Pearl Cotton #8, #356 Med. Terra Cotta, #742 Lt. Tangerine, #782 Dk. Topaz, #892 Med. Carnation, #367 Dk. Pistachio Green, #552 Med. Violet, #825 Dk. Blue and #938 Ultra Dk. Coffee Brown.*

Size 5 (1.9 mm) steel crochet hook (or size required for gauge)

Size 6 (1.8 mm) steel crochet hooks (or size required for gauge)

Size 11 (1.1 mm) steel crochet hook

Gauge

Gauge is specified with each individual pattern.

Pattern Stitches

Long single crochet (long sc): Insert hook in specified st one rnd below, YO and draw up a lp to height of current rnd, YO and draw through 2 lps on hook: long sc made.

Long double crochet (long dc): YO, insert hook in specified st one rnd below, YO and draw up a lp to height of current rnd, (YO and draw through 2 lps on hook) twice: long dc made.

Sc decrease (sc dec): (Insert hook in next st and draw up a lp) twice; YO and draw through all 3 lps on hook: sc dec made.

To change color: Work st until 2 lps rem on hook, drop old color, pick up new color and draw through both lps on hook. Do not cut dropped color.

GENERAL INSTRUCTIONS

***Note:** Use size 6 (1.8 mm) hook and 2 strands of pearl cotton held together throughout, except where noted. Whenever possible, work over thread ends as you go.*

CIRCLE TRIM BAND

Drop Stitch Circle

With green, ch 4; join with sl st to form a ring.

Rnd 1 (right side): Ch 3 (counts as first dc now and throughout), 11 dc in ring; join with sl st in 3rd ch of beg ch-3: 12 dc. Finish off.

Rnd 2: Join yellow with sl st in 3rd ch of beg ch-3, ch 3, dc in same ch, 2 dc in next dc and in each dc around; join as before: 24 dc. Finish off.

Rnd 3: Join green with sl st in 3rd ch of beg ch-3, ch 1, sc in same ch as joining and in next dc, long sc in next dc on Rnd 1; *sc in next 2 dc, long sc in next dc on Rnd 1; rep from * around; join with sl st in first sc: 36 sts. Finish off.

Rnd 4: Join gold with sl st in first sc, ch 1, sc in first sc and in each st around; join as before: 36 sc. Finish off.

***Note:** Work Rnd 5 only with size 5 (1.9mm) hook*

Rnd 5: Join blue with sl st in first sc, ch 1, sc in first sc and in each st around; join. Finish off.

Rnd 6: Join coral with sl st in first sc, ch 3; *2 dc in next st, dc in next 2 sts; rep from * around to last 2 sts; 2 dc in next st, dc in last st; join with sl st in 3rd ch of beg ch-3: 48 dc. Finish off.

Rnd 7: Join purple with sl st in 3rd ch of beg ch-3, ch 3, dc in next 3 dc, long dc in 4th sc on Rnd 5; *dc in next 4 dc, skip 2 sc on Rnd 5, long dc in next sc on Rnd 5; rep from * around; join as before: 60 sts. Finish off, leaving 6" thread end. Weave in all rem ends.

Double Drop Stitch Circle

Rnds 1 through 6: Rep Rnds 1 through 6 of Drop Stitch Circle using blue for Rnd 1, coral for Rnd 2, blue for Rnd 3, yellow for Rnd 4, green for Rnd 5 and purple for Rnd 6.

Rnd 7: Join gold with sl st in 3rd ch of beg ch-3, ch 3, dc in next 2 dc, 2 long dc in 4th sc on Rnd 5, skip next dc; *dc in next 3 dc, skip 2 sc on Rnd 5, 2 long dc in next sc on Rnd 5, skip next dc; rep from * around; join as before: 60 sts. Finish off, leaving 6" thread end.

V-Stitch Circle

Rnds 1 through 6: Rep Rnds 1 through 6 of Drop Stitch Circle using yellow for Rnd 1, purple for Rnd 2, yellow for Rnd 3, green for Rnd 4, coral for Rnd 5 and gold for Rnd 6.

Rnd 7: Join blue with sl st in first dc, ch 3, dc in next dc, long dc in 3rd sc on Rnd 5, skip next dc, dc in next dc, long dc in same sc on Rnd 5; *dc in next 2 dc, skip 2 sc on Rnd 5, long dc in next sc on Rnd 5, skip next dc, dc in next dc, long dc in same sc on Rnd 5; rep from * around; join as before: 60 sts. Finish off, leaving 6" end.

With right sides facing, using 6" ends, alternating circle colors, sew circles together into a band as follows: sew 6 sts of adjacent circles together on sides, leaving 24 unjoined sts at top and bottom of circles between joinings.

Yellow Triangles

Fill in triangular spaces between circles at top and bottom of circles as follows:

With wrong side facing, join yellow with sl st in first unjoined st on both circles after circle joining; ch 1, turn.

Row 1 (right side): Drop lp from hook, insert hook from front to back in next st on right circle, draw dropped lp through st, sc in turning ch-1 sp, sc in beg sl st, drop lp from hook, insert hook from back to front in next st on left circle, draw dropped lp through st: 2 sc; ch 1, turn.

Note: *Right circle becomes left circle and left circle becomes right circle on wrong side.*

Row 2 (wrong side): Drop lp from hook, insert hook from front to back in next st on right circle, draw dropped lp through st, sc in turning ch-1 sp, sc in next 2 sc, drop lp from hook, insert hook from back to front in next st on left circle, draw dropped lp through st: 3 sc; ch 1, turn.

Row 3: Drop lp from hook, insert hook from front to back in next st on right circle, draw dropped lp through st, 2 sc in turning ch-1 sp, sc in next 2 sc, 2 sc in last sc, drop lp from hook, insert hook from back to front in next st on left circle, draw dropped lp through st: 6 sc; ch 1, turn.

Row 4: Drop lp from hook, insert hook from front to back in next st on right circle, draw dropped lp through st, sc in turning ch-1 sp, sc in next **6** sc, drop lp from hook, insert hook from back to front in next st on left circle, draw dropped lp through st: 7 sc; ch 1, turn.

Rows 5 and 6: Rep Row 4 increasing bold number by one more in each row than in previous row: one more sc in each row than in previous row. At end of Row 6: 9 sc; ch 1, turn.

Row 7: Drop lp from hook, insert hook from front to back in next st on right circle, draw dropped lp through st, 2 sc in turning ch-1 sp, sc in next 8 sc, 2 sc in last sc, drop lp from hook, insert hook from back to front in next st on left circle, draw dropped lp through st: 12 sc; ch 1, turn.

Row 8: Drop lp from hook, insert hook from front to back in next st on right circle, draw dropped lp through st, sc in turning ch-1 sp, sc in next 12 sc, drop lp from hook, insert hook from front to back in next st on left circle, draw dropped lp through st: 13 sc; ch 1, turn.

Note: *There should be 6 unused sts at top and bottom of each circle between Row 8 of triangles.*

EDGING

Rnd 1: With right side facing and size 5 (1.9 mm) hook, join brown with sl st in first unused st on Rnd 7 of center back circle of band, ch 1, sc in same st and in next 5 unused sts of same circle, sc in ending sl st on Row 8 of next yellow triangle, sc in each of next 13 sc on same triangle; *sc in each of next 6 unused sts on next circle, sc in ending sl st on Row 8 of next yellow triangle, sc in each of next 13 sc on same triangle; rep from * around; join with sl st in beg sc: 20 sc times number of circles; ch 1, turn. Work 2 stitches in one space or skip a space if needed to get the right number of single crochets over each unit.

Rnd 2: Sc in first sc and in each sc around; join with sl st in first sc. Finish off; weave in ends.

Rnd 3: With right side facing and size 5 hook, using 40" lengths of thread, work in color sequence as follows: yellow, coral, gold, green, purple, blue. Join yellow with sl st in first sc on Rnd 2, ch 1, sc in same sc as joining, sc in next 9 sc, changing to coral in last sc, dropping old color; *sc in next 10 sc, changing to next color in last sc; rep from * around; join with sl st in first sc; ch 1, turn to work back and for next 2 rnds. ***Note:*** *Adjust colors at end as necessary so colors are not too close to each other.*

Rnd 4: Sc over carried thread in next to last sc and in last sc on Rnd 3, sc in next 8 sc, changing to next dropped color from Rnd 3 in last sc, drop last color to front of work; *sc over carried thread in next 2 sc, sc in next 8 sc, changing to next dropped color from Rnd 3 in last sc, drop last color to front of work; rep from * around; join with sl st in first sc; ch 1, turn.

Rnd 5: Skip first 2 sc; *sc in next 8 sc, sc over next dropped color in next 2 sc, changing to next dropped color from Rnd 4 in last sc; rep from * around; join with sl st in last sc. Finish off; weave in ends.

Rnd 6: With wrong side facing and size 5 hook, join brown in last sc on Rnd 5, ch 1, sc in same sc as joining and in each sc around; join with sl st in first sc; ch 1, turn.

Rnd 7: Sc in first sc and in each sc around; join with sl st in first sc. Finish off; weave in ends.

Rep edging on opposite edge of band.

TWISTED CORD DRAWSTRING

Cut 26 pieces of terra cotta thread 60" long each (uses one ball of thread). Lay pieces together and tie a knot in each end. Slip one end over a chair, door knob, etc. Slip a pencil or crochet hook into other end and pull taunt. Twist clockwise until thread begins to kink. Bring two ends of twisted thread together and allow middle of thread to hang. Thread will twist back on itself. Tie an overhand knot about 2 1/2" from each end. Trim ends to 2" long. Shorten drawstring as needed.

TOP

SIZES	Small	Medium	Large
Body Bust Measurements	32"-34"	36"-38"	40"-42"
Finished Bust Measurements	39"	42"	45"

Note: *Instructions are written for size Small; changes for sizes Medium and Large are in parentheses.*

Materials

Size 8 pearl cotton (88 yd balls),
38 (42, 45) balls terra cotta
2 balls yellow
2 balls gold
2 balls coral
2 balls green
2 balls purple
2 balls blue
2 balls brown

Gauge

20 sc = 3" with size 5 steel hook
circle = 3" diameter with size 6 steel hook

INSTRUCTIONS

***Note:** Use size 6 hook and 2 strands of pearl cotton held together throughout, except where noted.*

CIRCLE TRIM

Make circle trim band following General Instructions with 13 (14, 15) circles. Work yellow triangles and edging following General Instructions.

Position circle trim band with edge of two joined circles at side seam for an even number of circles or center of one circle at side seam for an odd number of circles.

BOTTOM EDGE

Rnd 1: With wrong side facing and size 5 hook, join terra cotta with sl st in first sc after side seam, ch 1, sc in same sc as joining and in each sc around: 260 (280, 300) sc; join with sl st in first sc; ch 1, turn.

Rnds 2 through 8: Sc in first sc and in each sc around; join as before; ch 1, turn. At end of Rnd 8, do not ch 1. Finish off; weave in ends.

TOP BODY

Rnd 1: With wrong side facing and size 5 hook, join terra cotta with sl st in first sc after side seam on opposite edge of circle trim band. Ch 1, sc in same sc as joining and in each sc around: 260 (280, 300) sc; join sl st in first sc; ch 1, turn.

Rnd 2: Sc in first sc and in each sc around; join as before; ch 1, turn.

Rep Rnd 2 until top measures 8" to 9" long, or to desired length, ending by working a right side row. Finish off; weave in ends.

FRONT ARMHOLE SHAPING

Row 1: With wrong side facing and size 5 hook, join terra cotta with sl st in 10th (11th, 12th) sc, ch 1, sc in same sc as joining and in next 111 (119, 127) sc, leaving last 9 (10, 11) sc of front unworked: 112 (120, 128) sc; ch 1, turn.

Row 2: Sc in first sc and in each sc across; ch 1, turn.

Rep Row 2 until armhole measures 9½" (10", 10½"), ending by working a wrong-side row.

RIGHT NECK AND SHOULDER SHAPING

Row 1 (right side): Sc in first 19 sc, sc dec in next 2 sc: 20 sc; ch 1, turn.

Row 2: Sc dec in first 2 sc, sc in each rem sc across: 19 sc; ch 1, turn.

Row 3: Sc in each sc across to last 2 sc, sc dec in last 2 sc: 18 sc; ch 1, turn.

Rows 4 through 7: Rep Rows 2 and 3 two times more. At end of Row 7: 14 sc. Finish off; weave in ends.

LEFT NECK AND SHOULDER SHAPING

Row 1: Hold front with right side facing and last row worked at top, skip next 70 (78, 86) sc from right neck and shoulder shaping, with size 5 hook, join terra cotta with sl st in next sc, ch 1, sc dec in same sc and in next sc, sc in next 19 sc: 20 sc; ch 1, turn.

Row 2: Rep Row 3 of right neck and shoulder shaping: 18 sc; ch 1, turn.

Rows 3 through 7: Rep Rows 2 and 3 of right neck and shoulder shaping two times more, then Row 2 of right neck and shoulder shaping once. At end of Row 7: 14 sc. Finish off; weave in ends.

BACK ARMHOLE SHAPING

Row 1: Holding piece with wrong side facing and last row worked on top body at top, skip next 18 (20, 22) sc on last row of top body, with size 5 hook and terra cotta, join with sl st in next sc, ch 1, sc in same sc as joining and in next 111 (119, 127) sc, leaving rem 9 (10, 11) sc of back unworked: 112 (120, 128) sc; ch 1, turn.

Row 2: Sc in first sc and in each sc across; ch 1, turn.

Rep Row 2 until arm measures 9½" (10", 10½"), ending by working a wrong side row. Work Row 2 two more times.

LEFT NECK AND SHOULDER SHAPING

Row 1 (right side): Sc in first 17 sc, sc dec in next 2 sc: 18 sc; ch 1, turn.

Row 2: Sc dec in first 2 sc, sc in each rem sc across: 17 sc; ch 1, turn.

Row 3: Sc in each sc across to last 2 sc, sc dec in last 2 sc: 16 sc; ch 1, turn.

Rows 4 and 5: Rep Rows 2 and 3. At end of Row 5: 14 sc. Finish off; weave in ends.

RIGHT NECK AND SHOULDER SHAPING

Row 1: Hold back with right side facing and last row worked at top, skip next 74 (82, 90) sc from left neck and shoulder shaping, with size 5 hook, join terra cotta with sl st in next sc, ch 1, sc dec in same sc and in next sc, sc in next 17 sc: 18 sc; ch 1, turn.

Row 2: Rep Row 3 of right neck and shoulder shaping: 17 sc; ch 1, turn.

Rows 3 through 5: Rep Rows 2 and 3 of left neck and shoulder shaping once, then Row 2 of left neck and shoulder shaping once. At end of Row 5: 14 sc. Finish off; weave in ends

SLEEVES (make 2)

With size 5 hook and terra cotta, ch 175 (185, 195).

Row 1: Sc in 2nd ch from hook and in each sc across: 174 (184, 194) sc; ch 1, turn.

Row 2: Sc in first sc and in each sc across to last 2 sc, sc dec in last 2 sc: 173 (183, 193) sc; ch 1, turn.

Rep Row 2 fifty one times more. At end of last row: 122 (132, 142) sc. Finish off; weave in ends.

Sew underarm seam with terra cotta. 2 sc will be lost in seaming, leaving 120 (130, 140) sc.

BORDER

Rnd 1: With right side facing and size 5 hook, join brown with sl st in first sc on last row next to underarm seam, ch 1, sc in same sc as joining and in each sc around: 120 (130, 140) sc; join with sl st in first sc; ch 1, turn.

Rnd 2: Sc in first sc and in each sc around; join as before. Finish off; weave in ends.

Rnds 3 through 7: Work same as Rnds 3 through 7 on circle trim edging in General Instructions.

Rnd 8: With wrong side facing and size 5 hook, join terra cotta with sl st in first sc, ch 1, sc in same sc as joining, sc in next sc and in each sc across: 120 (130, 140) sc; join; ch 1, turn.

Rnds 9 through 15: Rep Rnd 2 seven times more. At end of Row 15, do not ch 1. Finish off; weave in ends.

Sew shoulder seams and sew in sleeves.

SKIRT

Materials

Size 8 pearl cotton, in 88 yd balls
- 51 (55, 59) balls terra cotta
- 3 balls yellow
- 2 balls gold
- 2 balls coral
- 2 balls green
- 2 balls purple
- 2 balls blue
- 2 balls brown

Gauge

20 sc = 3" with size 5 steel hook
circle = 3" diameter with size 6 steel hook

SIZES	Small	Medium	Large
Body Hip Measurements	32"-34"	36"-38"	40"-42"
Finished Hip Measurements	42"	45"	48"

Note: *Instructions are written for size Small; changes for sizes Medium and Large are in parentheses.*

INSTRUCTIONS

Note: Use size 6 hook and 2 strands of pearl cotton held together throughout, except where noted.

CIRCLE TRIM

Make circle trim band following General Instructions with 14 (15, 16) circles. Work yellow triangles and edging following General Instructions.

BOTTOM EDGE

Rnd 1: With wrong side facing and size 5 hook, join terra cotta with sl st in 13th sc on Rnd 7 of edging (center back), ch 1, sc in same sc as joining, sc in each sc around: 280 (300, 320) sc; join with sl st in first sc; ch 1, turn.

Rnds 2 through 8: Sc in first sc and in each sc around; join as before; ch 1, turn. At end of Rnd 8, do not ch 1. Finish off; weave in ends.

SKIRT BODY

Rnd 1: With wrong side facing and size 5 hook, join terra cotta with sl st in 13th sc on Rnd 7 of edging (center back) on opposite edge of circle trim band, ch 1, sc in same sc as joining, sc in each sc around: 280 (300, 320) sc; join with sl st in first sc; ch 1, turn.

Rnd 2: Sc in first sc and in each sc around; join as before; ch 1, turn.

Rep Rnd 2 until skirt measures 24" to 28" long from Rnd 8 of skirt bottom to last rnd on skirt body, or to desired length, ending by working a wrong side row. At end of last rnd, finish off; weave in ends.

WAISTBAND

Rnd 1: With right side facing, size with 11 hook and 1 strand of terra cotta, join with sl st in front lp of 4th st after center front in last rnd of skirt body, ch 1, 2 sc in front lp of same st, 2 sc in front lp of each sc around: 560 (600, 640) sc; join with sl st in first sc; ch 2 (counts as turning ch and ch-1 sp), turn.

Rnd 2: Skip first sc, sc in next sc; *ch 1, skip next sc, sc in next sc; rep from * around: 280 (300, 320) sc and 280 (300, 320) ch-1 sps; join with sl st in 2nd ch of turning ch-2; ch 1, turn.

Rnd 3: Sc in first sc, *ch 1, skip next ch-1 sp, sc in next sc; rep from * around to last 11 sts, leaving last 11 sts unworked: 275 (295, 315) sc and 274 (294, 314) ch-1 sps; ch 1, turn.

Rnds 4 through 6: Sc in first sc; *ch 1, skip next ch-1 sp, sc in next sc; rep from * around; ch 1, turn. At end of Rnd 6, do not ch 1. Finish off; weave in ends.

EYELETS

Row 3: With right side facing, size 11 hook and 1 strand of terra cotta, skip 3 sts (ch, sc, ch) of 11 unworked sts at center front, join with sl st in next sc, ch 1, sc in same sc as joining; *ch 1, skip next ch-1 sp, sc in next sc; rep from * once: 3 sc and 2 ch-1 sps; ch 1, turn.

Rows 4 through 6: Sc in first sc, *ch 1, skip next ch-1 sp, sc in next sc; rep from * once; ch 1, turn. At end of Row 6, do not ch 1. Finish off; weave in ends.

Rnd 7: With right side facing, size 11 hook and 1 strand of terra cotta, join with sl st in last sc on Rnd 6, ch 1, sc in same sc as joining; *ch 1, skip next ch-1 sp, sc in next sc; rep from * around to middle 11 sts, ch 3, sc in next sc on Row 6; **ch 1, skip next ch-1 sp, sc in next sc; rep from ** once; ch 3: 278 (298, 318) sc, 276 (296, 316) ch-1 sps and 6 chs; join with sl st in first sc; ch 2, turn.

Rnd 8: Skip first ch, sc in next ch, ch 1, skip next ch, sc in next sc; *ch 1, skip next ch-1 sp, sc in next sc; rep from * once; ch 1, skip next ch, sc in next ch, ch 1, skip next ch, sc in next sc; **ch 1, skip next ch-1 sp, sc in next sc; rep from ** around: 280 (300, 320) sc and 280 (300, 320) ch-1 sps; join with sl st in 2nd ch of turning ch-2; ch 1, turn.

Rnd 9: Sc in first sc; ch 1, skip next ch, sc in next sc; rep from * around to last st; ch 1, skip next ch; join with sl st in first sc; ch 2, turn.

Rnd 10: Skip first ch-1 sp, sc in next sc; *ch 1, skip next ch-1 sp, sc in next sc; rep from * around; join with sl st in 2nd ch of turning ch-2; ch 1, turn.

Rnds 11 through 13: Rep Rows 9 and 10 once, then rep Row 9 once more. At end of Row 13, ch 1, do not turn.

WAISTBAND JOINING

Rnd 14: With right side facing and size 11 hook, sc in next sc on Rnd 13 of waistband and in back lp of next sc on last rnd of skirt body, sc in next sc on Rnd 13 of waistband and in back lp of same sc on last rnd of skirt body; rep from * around: 560 (600, 640) sc; join with sl st in first sc. Finish off; weave in ends.

EYELET REINFORCEMENT

With right side facing, size 11 hook and 1 strand of terra cotta, sc in each st and in edge of each row around each eyelet.

Make drawstring following General Instructions. Thread drawstring into one eyelet, around waistband and out other eyelet.

CROP PANTS

SIZES	Small	Medium	Large
Body Hip Measurements	32"-34"	36"-38"	40"-42"
Finished Hip Measurements	39"	43½"	48"

Note: *Instructions are written for size Small; changes for sizes Medium and Large are in parentheses.*

Materials

Size 8 pearl cotton (88 yd balls)
- 61 (68, 75) balls terra cotta
- 3 balls yellow
- 2 balls gold
- 2 balls coral
- 2 balls green
- 2 balls purple
- 2 balls blue
- 3 balls brown

Gauge

20 sc = 3" with size 5 steel hook
circle = 3" diameter with size 6 steel hook

INSTRUCTIONS

Note: *Use size 6 hook and 2 strands of pearl cotton held together throughout, except where noted.*

CIRCLE TRIM

Make two circle trim bands following General Instructions with 9 (10, 11) circles in each, one for each leg.

Work yellow triangles and edging following General Instructions.

BOTTOM EDGE

Rnd 1: With wrong side facing and size 5 hook, join terra cotta with sl st in 13th sc on Rnd 7 of edging (inseam), ch 1, sc in same st as joining, sc in each sc around: 180 (200, 220) sc; join with sl st in first sc; ch 1, turn.

Rnds 2 through 8: Sc in first sc and in each sc around; join as before; ch 1, turn. At end of Rnd 8, do not ch 1. Finish off; weave in ends.

Rep bottom edge on other circle trim band.

PANT LEG

Rnd 1: With wrong side facing and size 5 hook, join terra cotta with sl st in 13th sc on Rnd 7 of edging (inseam) on opposite edge of circle trim band, ch 1, sc in same sc as joining, sc in each sc around: 180 (200, 220) sc; join with sl st in first sc; ch 1, turn.

Rnd 2: Sc in first sc and in each sc around; join as before; ch 1, turn.

Rep Row 2 until pant inseam measures 20" to 22" long, or to desired length. At end of last row, turn; do not ch 1. Do not finish off.

PANT BODY

First Leg

Row 1: Sl st in first sc, ch 1, sc in next sc and in each sc across to last 5 (6, 7) sc, leaving last 5 (6, 7) sc unworked: 174 (193, 212) sc; turn.

Row 2: Sl st in first 5 (6, 7) sc, ch 1, sc in next sc and in each sc across to last sc, leaving last sc unworked: 168 (186, 204) sc; turn.

Rows 3 and 4: Rep Rows 1 and 2. At end of Row 4: 156 (172, 188) sc.

Row 5: Sl st in first sc, ch 1, sc in next sc and in each sc across to last 2 (3, 3) sc, leaving last 2 (3, 3) sc unworked: 153 (168, 184) sc; turn.

Row 6: Sl st in first 2 (2, 3) sc, ch 1, sc in next sc and in each sc across to last sc, leaving last sc unworked: 150 (165, 180) sc; turn.

Row 7: Sl st in first sc, ch 1, sc in next sc and in each sc across to last 2 sc, leaving last 2 sc unworked: 147 (162, 177) sc; turn.

Row 8: Sl st in first sc, ch 1, sc in next sc and in each sc across to last sc, leaving last sc unworked: 145 (160, 175) sc; turn.

Row 9: Rep Row 8: 143 (158, 173) sc; turn.

Row 10: Sl st in first sc, ch 1, sc in next sc and in each sc across: 142 (157, 172) sc; turn.

Row 11: Rep Row 8: 140 (155, 170) sc; turn.

Row 12: Rep Row 10: 139 (154, 169) sc; ch 1, turn.

Row 13: Sc in first sc and in each sc across to last sc, leaving last sc unworked: 138 (153, 168) sc; turn.

Row 14: Sl st in first sc, ch 1, sc in next sc and in each sc across: 137 (152, 167) sc; ch 1, turn.

Rows 15 through 20: Rep Rows 13 and 14 three times more. At end of Row 20: 131 (146, 161) sc; ch 1, turn.

Row 21: Sc in first sc and in each sc across; ch 1, turn.

Rep Row 21 until crotch is 10" to 12" long.

Rep Pant Leg on other circle trim band. Do not finish off.

SECOND LEG

Row 1: Rep Row 1 of first leg: 174 (193, 212) sc; turn.

Row 2: Rep Row 2 of first leg.

Rows 3 through 4: Rep Rows 1 and 2 of first leg. At end of Row 4: 156 (172, 188) sc.

Row 5: Sl st in first 2 (3, 3) sc, ch 1, sc in next sc and in each sc across to last sc, leaving last sc unworked: 153 (168, 184) sc; turn.

Row 6: Sl st in first sc, ch 1, sc in next sc and in each sc across to last 2 (2, 3) sc, leaving last 2 (2, 3) sc unworked: 150 (165, 180) sc; turn.

Row 7: Sl st in first 2 sc, ch 1, sc in next sc and in each sc across to last sc, leaving last sc unworked: 147 (162, 177) sc; turn.

Rows 8 and 9: Rep Row 8 of first leg two times more. At end of Row 9: 143 (158, 173) sc; ch 1, turn.

Row 10: Rep Row 13 of first leg: 142 (157, 172) sc.

Row 11: Rep Row 8 of first leg: 140 (155, 170) sc.

Rows 12 through 20: Rep Rows 13 and 14 of first leg 4 times more, then Row 13 of first leg once. At end of Row 20: 131 (146, 161) sc; ch 1, turn.

Row 21: Rep Row 21 of first leg.

Rep Row 21 until crotch is 10" to 12" long.

Sew crotch seam together with mattress stitch.

WAISTBAND

Work waistband and waistband joining same as skirt. At end of Rnd 1: 516 (576, 636) sc. At end of Rnd 2: 258 (288, 318) sc and 258 (288, 318) ch-1 sps. At end of Rnd 3: 253 (283, 313) sc and 252 (282, 312) ch-1 sps. At end of Rnd 7: 256 (286, 316) sc, 254 (284, 314) ch-1 sps and 6 chs. At end of Rnd 8: 258 (288, 318) sc and 258 (288, 318) ch-1 sps. At end of Rnd 14: 516 (576, 636) sc. Work eyelet reinforcement same as skirt.

Make drawstring following General Instructions. Thread drawstring into one eyelet, around waistband and out other eyelet.

REBOZO (Shawl)

Size

18" wide x 56" (62", 68") long

Materials

Size 8 pearl cotton (88 yd balls)
- 27 (30, 33) balls terra cotta
- 2 balls yellow
- 2 balls gold
- 2 balls coral
- 2 balls green
- 2 balls purple
- 2 balls blue
- 2 balls brown

Gauge

20 sc = 3"; 35 sc rows = 4" with size 5 steel hook

circle = 3" diameter with size 6 steel hook

INSTRUCTIONS

***Note:** Use size 6 hook and 2 strands of pearl cotton held together throughout, except where noted.*

CIRCLE TRIM

Make two circle trim bands following General Instructions with 6 circles in each, leaving bands flat. Work yellow triangles between circles following General Instructions.

YELLOW HALF TRIANGLES

At both ends of each circle trim band, fill in with half triangles as follows, leaving 6 center sts on end of beg circle and end circle on band unworked:

TOP OF RIGHT CIRCLE

With right side facing, join yellow with sl st in st after 6 sts that will be left unworked (15th st before next yellow circle); ch 1; do not turn.

Row 1 (right side): Drop lp from hook, insert hook from back to front in next st on circle, draw dropped lp through st; ch 1, turn.

Row 2: Drop lp from hook, insert hook from front to back in next st on circle, draw dropped lp through st, sc in turning ch-1 sp, sc in turning ch-1 on Row 1: 2 sc; ch 1, turn.

Row 3: Sc in next 2 sc, drop lp from hook, insert hook from back to front in next st on circle, draw dropped lp through st; ch 1, turn.

Row 4: Drop lp from hook, insert hook from front to back in next st on circle, draw dropped lp through st, sc in turning ch-1 sp, sc in next 2 sc: 3 sc; ch 1, turn.

Row 5: Sc in next 3 sc, drop lp from hook, insert hook from back to front in next st on circle, draw dropped lp through st; ch 1, turn.

Row 6: Drop lp from hook, insert hook from front to back in next st on circle, draw dropped lp through st, 2 sc in turning ch-1 sp, sc in next 3 sc: 5 sc; ch 1, turn.

Row 7: Sc in next 5 sc, drop lp from hook, insert hook from back to front in next st on circle, draw dropped lp through st; ch 1, turn.

Row 8: Drop lp from hook, insert hook from front to back in next st on circle, draw dropped lp through st, sc in turning ch-1 sp, sc in next 5 sc: 6 sc. Finish off; weave in ends.

TOP OF LEFT CIRCLE

With right side facing, join yellow with sl st in stitch before 6 sts that will left unworked; ch 1, do not turn.

Row 1 (right side): Drop lp from hook, insert hook from front to back in next st on circle, draw dropped lp through st; ch 1, do not turn.

Row 2 (right side): Drop lp from hook, insert hook from front to back in next st on circle, draw dropped lp through st, sc in turning ch-1 sp, sc in turning ch-1 sp on Row 1: 2 sc; ch 1, turn.

Row 3 (wrong side): Sc in next 2 sc, drop lp from hook, insert hook from back to front in next st on circle, draw dropped lp through st; ch 1, turn.

Row 4: Drop lp from hook, insert hook from front to back in next st on circle, draw dropped lp through st, sc in turning ch-1 sp, sc in next 2 sc: 3 sc; ch 1, turn.

Row 5: Sc in next 3 sc, drop lp from hook, insert hook from back to front in next st on circle, draw dropped lp through st; ch 1, turn.

Row 6: Drop lp from hook, insert hook from front to back in next st on circle, draw dropped lp through st, 2 sc in turning ch-1 sp, sc in next 3 sc: 5 sc; ch 1, turn.

Row 7: Sc in next 5 sc, drop lp from hook, insert hook from back to front in next st on circle, draw dropped lp through st; ch 1, turn.

Row 8: Drop lp from hook, insert hook from front to back in next st on circle, draw dropped lp through st, sc in turning ch-1 sp, sc in next 5 sc: 6 sc; join with sl st in next st on circle. Finish off; weave in ends.

EDGING

Row 1: With right side facing and size 5 hook, join brown with sl st in last sc on Row 8 on yellow half triangle on top of right circle, ch 1, sc in same sc as joining, sc in next 6 sc on yellow half triangle, sc in next 6 unused sts on first circle; *sc in beg sl st on Row 8 of next yellow triangle, sc in each of next 13 sc on same triangle, sc in next 6 unused sts on next circle; rep from * across; sc in next 5 sc on last half triangle, 2 sc in last sc on same half triangle: 120 sc; ch 1, turn.

Row 2: Sc in first sc and in each sc across. Finish off; weave in ends.

Row 3: With right side facing and size 5 hook, using 40" lengths of thread, work in color sequence as follows: green, gold, coral, yellow, blue, purple. Join green with sl st in last sc on Row 2, ch 1, sc in same sc as joining, sc in next 9 sc, changing to gold in last sc; *sc in next 10 sc, changing to next color in last sc; rep from * across: 120 sc; ch 1, turn.

Row 4: Sc in first 8 sc, changing to next dropped color from Rnd 3 in last sc, drop last color to front of work (wrong side); *sc over new thread color in next 2 sc, sc in next 8 sc, changing to next dropped color from Rnd 3 in last sc, drop last color to front of work (wrong side); rep from * across, changing to 12" length of purple in last sc of last group of 8 sc, sc in last 2 sc; ch 1, turn.

Row 5: Sc in first 2 sc, sc over end of next dropped color in next 2 sc, changing to next dropped color from Rnd 4 in last sc; *sc in next 8 sc, sc over end of next dropped color in next 2 sc, changing to next dropped color from Rnd 4 in last sc; rep from * across, ending with sc in last 6 sc. Finish off; weave in ends.

Row 6: With wrong side facing and size 5 hook, join brown with sl st in last sc on Row 5, ch 1, sc in same sc as joining and in each sc across; ch 1, turn.

Row 7: Sc in first sc and in each sc across. Finish off; weave in ends.

Rep edging on other edge of same circle trim band. Rep on both edges of other circle trim band.

REBOZO ENDS

Row 1: With wrong side of band facing and size 5 hook, join terra cotta with sl st in last sc on Row 7 of edging, sc in same sc as joining, sc in each sc across: 120 sc; ch 1, turn.

Rows 2 through 8: Sc in first sc and in each sc across; ch 1, turn. At end of Row 8, do not ch 1. Finish off; weave in ends.

Rep on one edge of other circle trim band.

REBOZO BODY

Row 1: Working on opposite edge of circle trim band, with wrong side facing and size 5 hook, join terra cotta with sl st in last sc on Row 7 of edging, sc in same sc as joining, sc in each sc across: 120 sc; ch 1, turn.

Rows 2 through 37: Sc in first sc and in each sc across; ch 1, turn. At end of Row 37, do not ch 1. Finish off; weave in ends.

Row 38: With right side facing and size 5 hook, join brown with sl st in last sc on Row 37, ch 1, sc in same sc as joining, sc in each sc across; ch 1, turn.

Row 39 through 44: Rep Rows 2 through 7 on edging, changing starting color.

Row 45: With wrong side facing and size 5 hook, join terra cotta with sl st in last sc on Row 7 of edging, ch 1, sc in same sc as joining, sc in each sc across: 120 sc; ch 1, turn.

Rows 46 through 88: Rep Rows 2 through 44.

Rep Rows 45 through 88 once, then rep Rows 45 through 87. Finish off; weave in ends.

On unworked edge of other circle trim band, rep Rows 1 through 44. Rep Rows 45 through 88 three (four, five) times more, then rep Rows 45 through 82. Finish off; weave in ends.

With right sides facing and brown, whip stitch two halves together.

TERRIFIC TANK TOP

Designed by Tammy Hildebrand

Long and lean, this fur-trimmed tank pleases the eye. Wear it with jeans for an informal look, or dress it up with jewels and a slinky long skirt for a formal occasion. Either way, you'll be in style.

SIZES	X-Small	Small	Medium	Large
Body Bust Measurements	28"-30"	32"-34"	36"-38"	40"-42"
Finished Bust Measurements	30"	34"	38"	42"

***Note:** Instructions are written for size Extra Small; changes for sizes Small, Medium, and Large are in parentheses.*

Materials

Worsted weight yarn,
6 1/4 (7, 7 3/4, 8 1/4) oz red

Eyelash yarn,
1 oz red

***Note:** Photographed model was made with Lion Brand® Glitterspun #113 Ruby and Lion Brand® Fun Fur #113 Red*

3 craft rings, 2" diameter

Size I (5.50 mm) crochet hook (or size required for gauge)

Gauge

15 sc = 4"

Pattern Stitches

Sc decrease (sc dec): (Insert hook in next st and draw up a lp) twice; YO and draw through all 3 lps on hook; sc dec made.

Beg cluster (beg Cl): Ch 3; (YO, insert hook in specified st, YO and draw up a lp) twice; YO and draw through all 5 lps on hook: beg cl made.

Cluster (Cl): (YO, insert hook in specified st, YO and draw up a lp) 3 times times; YO and draw through all 7 lps on hook: Cl made.

Picot: Ch 3, sc in 3rd ch from hook: picot made.

INSTRUCTIONS

Note: *Use worsted yarn unless otherwise stated.*

FRONT AND BACK

Top ring

Rnd 1: Work 42 sc over one craft ring; join in first sc: 42 sc.

Rnd 2: Ch 1, sc in same sc as joining, ch 3, skip next 2 sc; *sc in next sc, ch 3, skip next 2 sc; rep from * around; join as before: 14 ch-3 sps and 14 sc. Finish off; weave in ends.

Middle Ring

Rnd 1: On second ring, rep Rnd 1 on top ring.

Rnd 2: Ch 1, sc in same sc as joining; *ch 1, drop lp from hook, insert hook in center ch of any ch-3 sp on top ring, pick up dropped lp and pull through ch; ch 1, skip next 2 sc, sc in next sc; rep from * 2 times more; ch 3, skip next 2 sc; **sc in next sc, ch 3, skip next 2 sc; rep from ** around; join: 3 joined ch sps, 11 ch-3 sps and 14 sc. Finish off; weave in ends.

Bottom Ring

Rnd 1: On third ring rep Rnd 1 on top ring.

Rnd 2: Ch 1, sc in same sc as joining, skip next 6 ch-3 sps on middle ring; *ch 1, drop lp from hook, insert hook in center ch of next ch-3 sp on middle ring, pick up dropped lp and pull through ch; ch 1, skip next 2 sc, sc in next sc; rep from * 2 times more; ch 3, skip next 2 sc; **sc in next sc, ch 3, skip next 2 sc; rep from ** around; join: 3 joined ch sps, 11 ch-3 sps and 14 sc. Finish off; weave in ends.

LEFT HALF

Row 1 (right side): Join yarn with sl st in 4th ch-3 sp on bottom ring before joined ch sps, ch 3 (counts as dc), 2 dc in same sp; *3 dc in next ch-3 sp on same ring; rep from * 2 times more; tr around first ch sp joining on same ring, 3 dc in next ch-3 sp on next ring; rep from * once; 3 dc in each of next 3 ch-3 sps on same ring: 36 dc and 2 tr; ch 1, turn.

Row 2: Sc in first 9 dc; *hdc in next 3 dc, dc in next tr, hdc in next 3 dc, sc in next 6 dc; rep from * once; sc in last 3 dc: 24 sc, 12 hdc and 2 dc; ch 1, turn.

Row 3: Sc in first 11 sts; *skip next st, 3 dc in next st, skip next st, sc in next 10 sts; rep from * once; sc in last st: 32 sc and 6 dc; ch 1, turn.

Row 4: Sc in each st across: 38 sc; ch 1, turn.

Rep Row 4 until piece measures about 13½" (15½", 17½", 19½") from Row 1 to end, having an odd number of rows. At end of last row, finish off; weave in ends.

RIGHT HALF

Row 1 (right side): Join yarn with sl st in 4th ch-3 sp on top ring before joined ch sps, ch 3 (counts as dc), 2 dc in same sp; *3 dc in next ch-3 sp on same ring; rep from * 2 times more; tr around 3rd ch sp joining on next ring, 3 dc in next ch-3 sp on next ring; rep from * once; 3 dc in each of next 3 ch-3 sps on same ring: 36 dc and 2 tr; ch 1, turn.

Rows 2 through 4: Rep Rows 2 through 4 on Left Side.

Rep Row 4 until piece measures about 13½" (15½", 17½", 19½") from Row 1 to end, making sure number of rows is same as on Left Half. At end of last row, finish off; weave in ends.

Sew back seam.

TOP EDGING

With right side facing, join with sc in second unworked ch-3 sp on top ring, 2 sc in next unworked ch-3 sp, 2 sc around beg ch-3 on Row 1 on Right Half, sc in edge of each row to last row before center front, 2 sc around post of last dc on Row 1 on Left Half, 2 sc in first unworked ch-3 sp on top ring, sc in same ch-3 sp as first sc; join with sl st in beg sc. Finish off; weave in ends.

RIGHT SHOULDER STRAP

Row 1: With right side facing, measure 3" (3¾", 4½", 5¼") to left of first sc on Top Edging, join with sc in next st, sc in next 14 sts: 15 sc; ch 1, turn, leaving rem sts unworked.

Rows 2 through 4: Skip first st, sc in next st and in each st across to last st, leaving last st unworked: 2 sts fewer in each row than in previous row; ch 1, turn. At end of Row 4: 9 sc.

Row 5: Sc in each st across: 9 sc; ch 1, turn.

Rep Row 5 until strap measures about 14" long, or desired length to top edge of back, having an even number of rows. At end of last row, finish off, leaving a long length for sewing.

LEFT SHOULDER STRAP

Row 1: With right side facing, measure 3" (3¾", 4½", 5¼") to right of last sc on Top Edging, join with sc 15th st to right of measurement, sc in next 14 sts: 15 sc; ch 1, turn, leaving rem sts unworked.

Note: Make sure there is an even number of sts between shoulder straps on Front.

Rows 2 through 5: Rep Rows 2 through 5 on Right Shoulder Strap.

Rep Row 5 until strap measures about 14" long, or desired length to top edge of back, making sure number of rows is same as on Right Shoulder Strap. At end of last row, finish off, leaving long length for sewing.

Sew end of straps to top edge of back, leaving 2" (2½", 3", 3½") between front and back of each strap along Top Edging for armhole openings and 3" (3¾", 4½", 5¼") from center of back to edge of straps, or as desired.

Note: Make sure number of sts on Back between shoulder straps is evenly divisible by 4 and number of sts for each armhole opening is the same.

NECK

Rnd 1: With right side facing and working around neck opening, join with sc in neck edge of last row of Left Shoulder Strap on back, sc in edge of each row on Left Shoulder Strap, sc in each st across front between straps, sc in edge of each row on Right Shoulder Strap; *sc dec in next 2 sts on back; rep from * across back between straps; join with sl st in beg sc. Finish off; weave in ends.

Rnd 2: With right side facing, join eyelash yarn with sc in first sc on Rnd 1, ch 1, skip next st; *sc in next st, ch 1, skip next st: rep from * around; join with sl st in beg sc.

Rnd 3: Sl st in next ch-1 sp, work beg cl in same ch-1 sp; *ch 2, work cl in next ch-1 sp; rep from * around; ch 2; join with sl st in top of beg cl. Finish off; weave in ends.

ARMHOLES

Rnd 1: With right side facing, join with sc in first unworked st of armhole opening on Top Edging, sc in next st and in each st of armhole opening, sc in edge of each row on strap; join with sl st in beg sc.

Rnd 2: Ch 1, skip next st; *sl st in next st, ch 1, skip next st; rep from * around; join with sl st in joining sl st. Finish off; weave in ends.

Rep Rnds 1 and 2 on second armhole.

BOTTOM EDGING

Rnd 1: With right side facing, join with sc in first unworked ch-3 sp on bottom ring, (3 dc, picot, 3 dc) in next ch-3 sp, sc in next ch-3 sp, sc in edge of each row around; join with sl st in beg sc.

Rnd 2: Sl st in next dc, ch 1, sc in same st, picot, skip next st, sc in next st, (sc, picot, sc) in ch-3 sp on next picot; *sc in next st, picot, skip next st; rep from * around to center back; sc in next st, picot; **sc in next st, picot, skip next st; rep from ** around to beg; join with sl st in beg sc. Finish off; weave in ends.

LITTLE JEWEL OF A VEST

Designed by Margaret Hubert

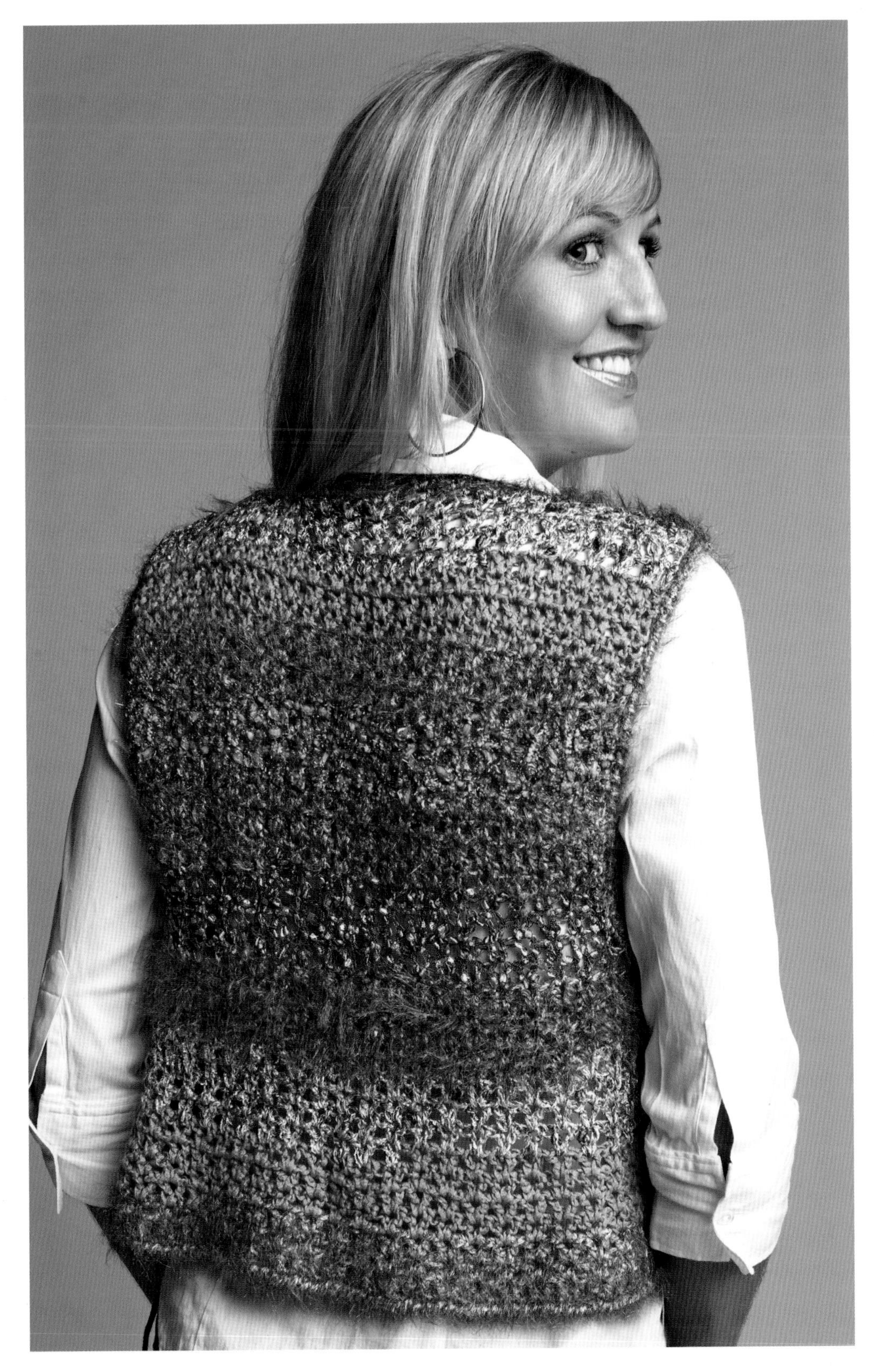

The glittering metallic yarns used in this vest make it shimmer like a jewel when it is worn! It's so versatile it can dress up a pair of jeans, or spark an evening out when worn with a skirt or dress.

LITTLE JEWEL OF A VEST

SIZES	Small	Medium	Large
Body Bust Measurements	32"	36"	40"
Finished Bust Measurements	34"	38"	42"

Note: *Instructions are written for size Small; changes for sizes Medium and Large are in parentheses.*

Materials

Worsted weight yarn,
- 3½ oz rayon ribbon yarn, med rust (A)
- 3½ oz nylon yarn, metallic copper (B)
- 1¾ oz nylon yarn, metallic bronze (C)
- 1¾ oz metallic rayon component yarn, copper (D)
- 1¾ oz bumpy component yarn, copper (E)

1 oz metallic railroad ribbon yarn, copper/black (F)

Note: *Photographed model made with Berroco® Glace™ #2591 Tumeric (A), Quest™ #9812 Polished Copper (B), Quest™ #9811 Bronze (C), Jewel FX™ #6912 Montmartre (D), Opulent FX™ #7812 Polished Copper (E) Mosaic FX™ #4602 Armani Mix(F)*

Marking tags

Size G (4 mm) crochet hook for size Small (or size required for gauge)

Size 7 (4.5 mm) crochet hook for size Medium (or size required for gauge)

Size H (5 mm) crochet hook for size Large (or size required for gauge).

Gauge

For Small: 6 V-sts = 4" with G hook

For Medium: 5½ V-sts = 4" with 7 hook

For Large: 5 V-sts = 4" with H hook

Stitch Guide

V-stitch (V-st): (dc, ch 1, dc) in ch or st specified: V-st made.

V-st in V-st: V-st in ch-1 sp of V-st in row below.

Front Post tr (Fptr): YO twice; insert hook from front to back to front around post (vertical bar) of specified st and draw up a lp; (YO and draw through first 2 lps on hook) 3 times: Fptr made.

Single crochet decrease: (sc dec): Draw up a lp in each of next 2 sts, YO and draw through all 3 lps on hook: sc dec made.

Reverse single crochet (reverse sc): Ch 1; *working from left to right, sc in next st; rep from * for reverse sc.

INSTRUCTIONS

FRONTS

The fronts are made of separate motifs that are sewn together, much like creating a crazy quilt. As you complete each motif, tag it with its number to aid in assembly later. When changing yarns, work over ends whenever possible; weave in other ends as you go to save time in finishing.

Work all motifs with appropriate size hook.

MOTIF 1

Make 1 motif with B as Color 1 and A as Color 2.

Make 1 motif with A as Color 1 and B as Color 2

With Color 1, ch 6, join with sl st to form a ring.

Rnd 1: Ch 1, (3 sc in ring, ch 5) 4 times; join with sl st in beg ch-1: 4 ch-5 lps.

Rnd 2: Ch 1; * sc in next 3 sc; holding ch-5 lp to front, sl st under the ch-5 (between the sc sts), ch 12, sl st in same place; rep from * 3 times more; finish off: 4 ch-12 lps.

Rnd 3: Hold any ch-12 lp to front, bring ch-5 lp from front to back through ch-12 lp; join Color 2 with sl st in same ch-5 lp; ch 3 (counts as a dc), (dc, ch 2, 2 dc) all in same ch-5 lp; dc in each of next 3 sc; *bring next ch-5 lp through ch-12 lp, (2 dc, ch 2, 2 dc) in same ch-5 lp, dc in each of next 3 sc; rep from * twice more, join with sl st in top of beg ch-3.

Rnd 4: Ch 3, dc in next dc; * 2 dc in next ch-2 space, dc in ch-12 lp, ch 8, sl st in top of last dc made; 2 dc under same ch-2 sp, dc in each of next 2 dc; ch 3, skip 3 dc, dc in each of next 2 dc; rep from * 3 times more, ending last rep, ch 3, join with sl st in top of beg ch-3. Draw Color 1 through lp on hook. Finish off Color 2.

Rnd 5: With Color 1, ch 3, dc in each of next 3 dc; *holding ch-8 lp to front, in dc where ch-8 was started, work (2 dc, ch 1, 2 dc); dc in each of next 4 dc, Fptr around post of each of next 3 dc of Rnd 3, dc in each of next 4 dc; rep from * around, end last rep with 3 Fptr, join with slip st in beg ch-3.

Rnd 6: Ch 1; * sc in each st to corner; in corner ch-1 sp work (sc, sc through ch-8 and corner sp); rep from * around, end last rep sl st in beg ch-1. Finish off; weave in ends.

MOTIF 2:

Make 2 in each color except F.

Make 2 using E and B held together.

Ch 11.

Row 1: Sc in 2nd ch from hook and in each rem ch: 10 sc; ch 1 turn.

Row 2: Sc across, ch 1, turn.

Rows 3 through 10: Rep Row 2; at end of last row, do not ch. Finish off; weave in ends.

MOTIF 3

Make 2

With A, ch 21.

Row 1: Sc in 2nd ch from hook and in each rem ch: 20 sc; ch 1, turn.

Row 2: Sc in each sc; draw B lp through, ch 3 with B, turn. Finish off A.

Row 3: *Hdc in next st, ch 2; working over post (vertical bar) of hdc just made, (YO and draw up a long lp) 3 times, YO and draw through all 7 lps on hook: wrap st made; ch 1, skip next st; rep from * across, end hdc in last st: 9 wrap sts made; ch 1, turn.

Row 4: Sc in hdc; 2 sc in each ch-1 space, sc in top of beg ch-3: 20 sc; draw A through lp on hook, ch 1 with A, turn. Finish off B.

Row 5: With A, sc in each sc across, ch 1, turn.

Row 6: Sc in each sc; draw up a lp with B, ch 3 with B, turn. Finish off A.

Rows 7 and 8: With B, rep Rows 3 and 4.

Rows 9 and 10: With B, rep Rows 5 and 6. Finish off; weave in ends.

MOTIF 4

Make 2

With A, ch 18.

Row 1: In 6th ch from hook, work shell of (hdc, ch 1, hdc) skip next ch; * (hdc, ch 1, hdc) in next ch, skip next ch; rep from * across, end hdc in last ch: 6 shells made; ch 3 (counts as hdc here and throughout), turn.

Row 2: * In next ch-1 sp work shell of (hdc, ch 1, hdc); rep from * across, end hdc in top of turning ch-3; ch 3, turn.

Rows 3 through 7: Rep Row 2. Finish off.

MOTIF 5

Make 2

With B, ch 3, join with sl st to form a ring.

Rnd 1 (right side): Ch 3 (counts as a dc), work 15 more dc in ring, join with sl st in top of beg ch-3: 16 dc; join A and ch 3, turn. Finish off B.

Rnd 2: Working in back lps only, (2 dc in next st, dc in next st) 8 times: 24 dc; join with sl st in top of ch-3; ch 1 (counts as sc), turn.

Note: From here on, work in rows instead of rnds.

Row 3: (2 sc in next st, sc in next st) twice: 7 sc (counting ch-1 as a st); ch 1, turn.

Row 4: Sc dec over first 2 sts, sc in next 3 sts, sc dec over last 2 sts; ch 1, turn.

Row 5: Sc dec over first 2 sts, sc in next st, sc dec over last 2 sts: 3 sc; ch 1, turn.

Row 6: Draw up a lp in each of next 3 sts, YO and draw through all 4 lps on hook. Finish off, do not turn.

Row 7: Join B in last st, ch 1, 3 sc in same st for point; sc in end of each sc row, working across sts of original circle in back lps only, sc in 5 sc, (hdc, ch 1, hdc) in next st for corner; sc in 5 sc, (hdc, ch 1, hdc) in next st for corner; sc in next 6 sts, sc in sides of last 5 sc rows, join in beg sc. Finish off.

Row 8: Join F in center sc of point, 3 sc in same sc; sc in each st around, working 3 sc in ch-1 sp of both corners; join in beg sc. Finish off; weave in ends.

MOTIF 6

Make 2

With B, ch 26.

Row 1: Sc in 2nd ch from hook; * skip 3 chs, 7 dc next ch, skip 3 chs, sc in next ch; rep from * two times more; draw up D and ch 3, turn; do not finish off B.

Row 2: (YO, draw up a lp in next dc, YO, draw through first 2 lps on hook) 3 times, YO and draw through 4 lps on hook; ch 1 (eye) (1/2 shell); * ch 3, sc in next dc, ch 3; (YO, draw up a lp in next st, YO and draw through 2 lps) 7 times; YO and draw through through 8 lps on hook; ch 1 (eye) (shell); rep from * once, ch 3, sc next dc, ch 3, (YO, draw up a lp , YO and draw through 2 lps on hook), 4 times, YO and draw through 5 lps; ch 1 (eye), ch 3, turn.

Row 3: 3 dc in eye of next shell; *sc next sc, 7 dc next eye; rep from * across, end last rep with 4 dc in last eye of last 1/2 shell.

Row 4: Pick up B and ch 3; *(YO, draw up a lp in next st, YO and draw through 2 lps) on hook 7 times, YO and draw through 8 lps, ch 1 (eye); ch 3, sc in next st, ch 3; rep from * across, end last rep ch 3, sc in top of ch-3, ch 1 turn.

Row 5: Sc in first sc; * 7 dc in eye of next shell, sc in next sc; rep from * across, end last rep with sc in top of ch-3, drop B and pick up D, ch 3 with D, turn.

Row 6: Rep Row 2.

Row 7: Rep Row 3.

Row 8: Rep Row 4. Finish off.

MOTIF 7

Make 2 with B

Note: This little motif is used as a filler as needed when joining motifs for fronts. In the pictured garment, we have used one at the lower armhole on each side. Make as many as needed when joining is being done.

Ch 11.

Row 1: Sc in 2nd ch from hook and in each rem ch: 10 sc; ch 1, turn.

Rows 2 and 3: Sc in each sc, ch 1, turn.

Row 4: Sc in each sc, finish off.

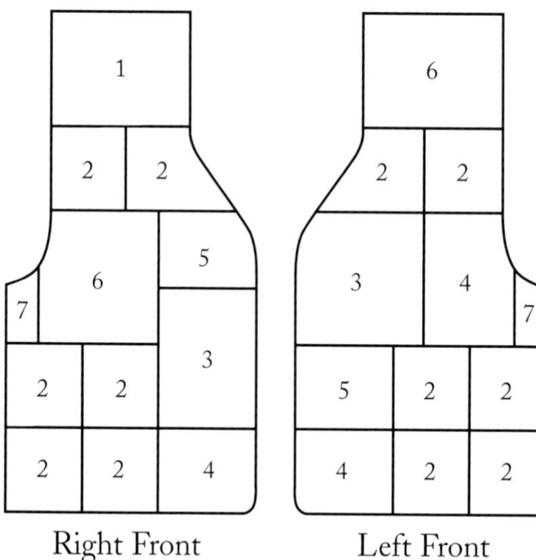

ASSEMBLY

Following charts for Right Front and Left Front, lay motifs out in order on a flat surface. Make as many of Motif 7 as needed to fill in gaps. Sew motifs tog with matching yarn.

BACK

Back is made with all of the yarns, worked in a staggered striping patt-tern. Begin new colors in the middle of rows, rather than at the end. This gives a more interesting design.

With B, ch 80.

Row 1: In 4th ch from hook work (dc, ch 1, dc): V-st made; * skip 2 chs, V-st in next ch; rep from * across, end dc in last st: 26 V-sts; ch 3 (counts as a dc on following rows), turn.

Row 2: * V-st in V-st; rep from * across, end dc in top of ch-3.

Rep Row 2 for patttern.

Row 3: Work in patt to last 8 V-sts, join A and complete row. Finish off B.

Rows 4 through 6: Work in patt with A.

Row 7: Work with A to last 16 sts; join D and complete row; finish off A.

Rows 8 through 10: Work in patt with D.

Row 11: Work first 4 V-sts with D, change to C and complete row. Finish off D.

Rows 12 through 14: Work in patt with C.

Row 15: Work with C to last 8 V-sts; change to F and complete row. Finish off C.

Row 16: Work in patt with F.

SHAPE UNDERARM

Row 17: With F, sl st over first 2 V-sts; ch 3, beginning in 3rd V-st work in patt to last 2 V-sts, dc in first dc of next V-st, ch 3, turn: 2 V-sts decreased on each side.

Row 18: With F and C, rep Row 3.

Rows 19 through 21: Work in patt with C.

Row 22: Work in patt with C for first 6 V-sts, change to E and com-plete row.

Rows 23 through 25: Work in patt with E.

Keeping patt as established on 22 V-sts, work color sequence starting again with Row 1, until back is same length as fronts to shoulder. Finish off; weave in ends.

FINISHING

Sew shoulder and side seams with matching yarns.

OUTER EDGING

With right side of garment facing, join B at bottom of right front side seam; ch 1, work sc around entire outer edge of garment, working 3 sc in each bottom corner; join with sl st in beg sc. Do not turn. Ch 1, work reverse sc around to beg, join with sl st. Finish off; weave in ends.

ARMHOLE EDGINGS

With right side of garment facing, join B at side seam of one armhole; ch 1, sc around entire armhole open-ing, adjusting sts as needed to keep work flat; join in beg sc. Do not turn. Ch 1, work reverse sc around to beg, join with sl st. Finish off; weave in ends. Rep on opposite armhole.

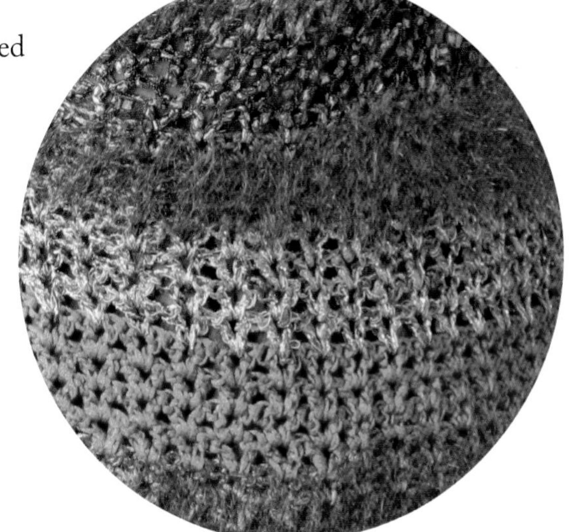

OOH-LA-LA TOPPER

Designed by Belinda "Bendy" Carter for Berroco®

The look of Paris chic, crafted in a suede-type yarn, this coat is certain to be a "show stopper." Worn with jeans, it adds a touch of glamour to an informal occasion. Button the coat, add the belt, and wear it over a long dress, and you are sure to be the belle of the ball.

OOH-LA-LA TOPPER

SIZES	Small	Medium	Large
Body Bust Measurements	30"-34"	36"-40"	42"-46"
Finished Bust Measurements	38"	44"	50"
Length	52"	54"	54"

Note: *Instructions are written for size Small; changes for sizes Medium and Large are in parentheses.*

Note: *Garment is stretchy lengthwise*

Materials

Worsted weight suede-type yarn, 17½ (21, 22¾) oz bright pink

Note: *Photographed model made with Berroco® Suede™ #3754 Annie Oakley*

7 bone rings, 1" diameter

Size H (5mm) crochet hook

Size K (6.5mm) crochet hook (or size required for gauge)

Gauge

7 sc = 2" with larger hook

Stitch Guide

V-st = (Dc, ch 3, dc) in indicated st or ch.

Shell = 5 dc in indicated st or ch.

Decreases:

Dec 1: Work (dc, ch 1, dc) in 2nd ch of V-st: 2-st dec made

Dec 2: Work dc in ch-1 of Dec 1: 2-st dec made

Dec 3: Skip dc worked in Dec 2: 1-st dec made

Increases:

Inc 1: Work extra dc in first and/or last st: 1-st inc made

Inc 2: Work (dc, ch 1, dc) in extra dc of Inc 1: 2-st inc made

Inc 3: Work V-st in ch 1 of Inc 2: 2-st inc made

INSTRUCTIONS

BACK

Starting at bottom edge with larger hook, ch 96 (106, 116).

Row 1: V-st in 6th ch from hook, (skip 4 chs, V-st in next ch) 4 (5, 6) times; * ch 2, skip 3 chs, sc in next ch, skip 2 chs, shell in next ch; skip 2 chs, sc in next ch, ch 2, skip 3 chs; * (V-st in next ch, skip 4 chs) 4 times, V-st in next ch; rep from * to * once more, (V-st in next ch, skip next 4 chs) 4 (5, 6) times, V-st in next ch, skip 2 chs, dc in last ch; turn.

Row 2: Ch 3; *(V-st in 2nd ch of next V-st) 5 (6, 7) times *; ch 2, V-st in 3rd dc of shell, ch 2, (V-st in 2nd ch of V-st) 5 times; ch 2, V-st in 3rd dc of shell, ch 2; rep from * to * once, dc in top of ch; turn: 95 (105, 115) sts.

Row 3: Ch 3; *(V-st in 2nd ch of V-st) 5 (6, 7) times *; ch 2, sc in ch-2 sp, shell in 2nd ch of V-st, sc in ch-2 sp, ch 2, (V-st in 2nd ch of V-st) 5 times; ch 2, sc in ch-2 sp, shell in 2nd ch of V-st, sc in ch-2 sp, ch 2, rep from * to * once, dc in top of ch; turn.

Rep Rows 2 and 3 until piece measures 7" from beg ch.

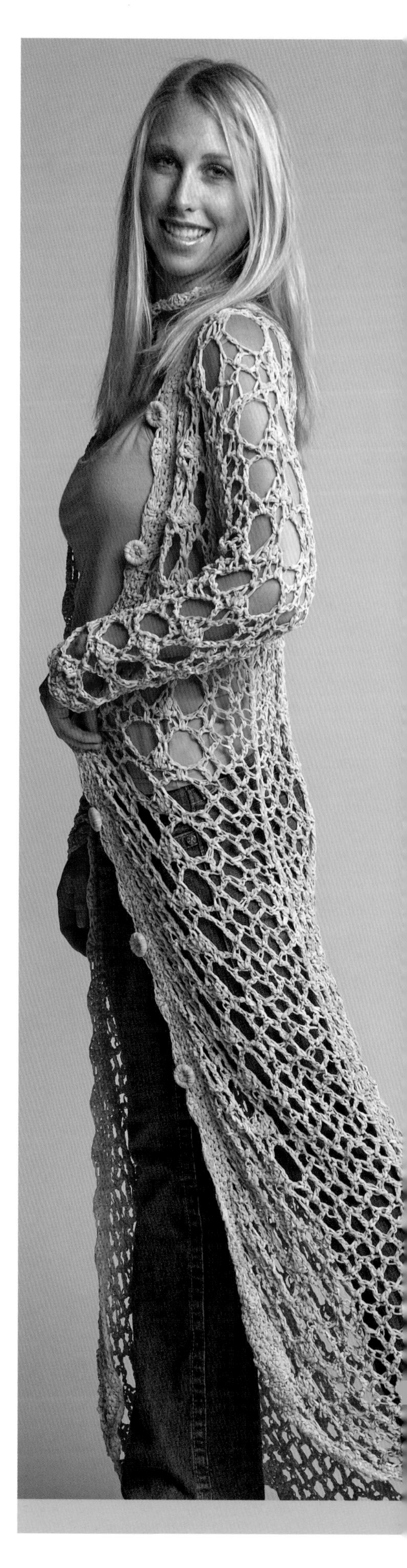

SIDE SHAPING

Row 1: Work in patt as established, working Dec 1(see Stitch Guide) at beg and end of row

Row 2: Work even in patt.

Row 3: Work in patt, working Dec 2 at beg and end of row.

Row 4: Work even in patt.

Row 5: Work in patt, working Dec 3 at beg and end of row.

Rows 6 through 8: Work even in patt.

Rep Rows 1 through 8 two times more. Then work even until piece measures 30", or desired length to underarm.

SHAPE ARMHOLE

Row 1: Sl st to 2nd ch in first (2nd, 2nd) V-st, work in est patt across until 1 (2, 2) V-st rem, dc in 2nd ch of next V-st; turn.

Work even in patt until piece measures 7 1/2" (9 1/4", 9 1/4") from start of armhole, ending by working a Row 3 of Back.

SHAPE NECK

Row 1: Ch 3; *(V-st in 2nd ch of V-st) 1 (1, 2) times *; ch 2, V-st in 3rd dc of shell, ch 2, dc in 2nd ch of next V-st. Finish off.

Skip next 3 V-sts, join yarn in 2nd ch of next V-st, ch 5, V-st in 3rd dc of shell, ch 2, rep from * to * once more, dc in last st. Finish off.

LEFT FRONT

With larger hook, ch 48 (53, 58).

Row 1 (right side): V-st in 6th ch from hook; (skip 4 chs, V-st in next ch) 4 (5, 6) times; ch 2, skip 3 chs, sc in next ch, skip 2 chs, shell in next ch; skip 2 chs, sc in next ch, ch 2, skip 3 chs, V-st in next ch; skip 4 chs, V-st in next ch, skip 2 chs, dc in last ch; turn.

Row 2: Ch 3; (V-st in 2nd ch of V-st) 2 times, ch 2, V-st in 3rd dc of shell, ch 2; (V-st in 2nd ch of V-st) 5 (6, 7) times, dc in top of ch; turn: 46 (51, 56) sts.

Row 3: Ch 3; (V-st in 2nd ch of V-st) 5 (6, 7) times, ch 2, sc in ch-2 sp, shell in 2nd ch of V-st, sc in ch-2 sp, ch 2; (V-st in 2nd ch of V-st) 2 times, dc in top of ch; turn.

Rep Rows 2 and 3 until piece measures 7" from beg ch.

SIDE SHAPING

Row 1: Work in patt as established, working Dec 1 at arm edge (edge furthest from shell st).

Row 2: Work even in patt.

Row 3: Work even in patt, working Dec 2 at arm edge.

Row 4: Work even in patt.

Row 5: Work in patt, working Dec 3 at arm edge.

Rows 6 through 8: Work even in patt.

Rep Rows 1 through 8 two times more. Then work even until piece measures 30", or desired length to underarm, ending at arm edge.

SHAPE ARMHOLE

Row 1: Sl st to 2nd ch in first (2nd, 2nd) V-st, work in patt across; turn.

Work even in patt until Front measures 3 rows shorter than Back, ending at arm edge.

SHAPE NECK

Row 1: Ch 3; (V-st in 2nd ch of V-st) 1 (1, 2) times; ch 2, V-st in 3rd dc of shell, ch 2; V-st in 2nd ch of V-st, dc in 2nd ch of next V-st; turn.

Row 2: Sl st to 2nd ch in first V-st, ch 5, sc in ch-2 sp, shell in 2nd ch of V-st; sc in ch-2 sp, ch 2, (V-st in 2nd ch of V-st) 1 (1, 2) times, dc in top of ch; turn.

Row 3: Ch 3; (V-st in 2nd ch of V-st) 1 (1, 2) times, ch 2, V-st in 3rd dc of shell, ch 2, dc in 3rd ch of ch-5. Finish off.

RIGHT FRONT

With larger hook, ch 48 (53, 58).

Row 1 (right side): V-st in 6th ch from hook, skip 4 chs, V-st in next ch, ch 2, skip next 3 chs, sc in next ch; skip 2 chs, shell in next ch, skip 2 chs, sc in next ch; ch 2, skip 3 chs, V-st in next ch, (skip 4 chs, V-st in next ch) 4 (5, 6) times, sk 2 ch, dc in last ch; turn.

Row 2: Ch 3; (V-st in 2nd ch of V-st) 5 (6, 7) times, ch 2; V-st in 3rd dc of shell, ch 2, (V-st in 2nd ch of V-st) 2 times, dc in last st; turn: 46 (51, 56) sts.

Row 3: Ch 3; (V-st in 2nd ch of V-st) 2 times, ch 2, sc in ch-2 sp; shell in 2nd ch of V-st, sc in ch-2 sp, ch 2, (V-st in 2nd ch of V-st) 5 (6, 7) times, dc in last st; turn.

Rep Rows 2 and 3 until piece measures 7" from beg ch.

SIDE SHAPING

Finish same as Left Front.

SLEEVE (make 2):

With larger hook, ch 33 (43, 43).

Row 1: V-st in 6th ch from hook; (skip 4 chs, V-st) 1 (2, 2) times; ch 2, skip 3 chs, sc in next ch, skip 2 chs, shell in next ch; skip 2 chs, sc in next ch, ch 2, skip 3 chs; (V-st, in next ch, skip 4 chs) 1 (2, 2) times, V-st in next ch, skip 2 chs, dc in last ch; turn.

Row 2: Ch 3; (V-st in 2nd ch of V-st) 2 (3, 3) times, ch 2; V-st in 3rd dc of shell, ch 2, (V-st in 2nd ch of V-st) 2 (3, 3) times, dc in top of ch; turn: 31 (41, 41) sts.

Row 3: Ch 3; (V-st in 2nd ch of V-st) 2 (3, 3) times, ch 2; sc in ch-2 sp, shell in 2nd ch of V-st, sc in ch-2 sp, ch 2; (V-st in 2nd ch of V-st) 2 (3, 3) times, dc in last st; turn.

Row 4: Work in patt, working Inc 1 at beg and end of row: 2 sts increased.

Row 5: Work in patt, working Inc 2 at beg and end of row: 4 sts increased.

Row 6: Work in patt, working Inc 3 at beg and end of row: 4 sts increased.

Rep Rows 4 through 6 until there are 67 (71, 71) sts. Finish off; weave in all ends.

ASSEMBLY

Sew shoulder seams; sew sleeves into armholes; sew side and sleeve seams.

FINISHING

Sleeve Edging

Hold one sleeve with right side facing and beg ch at top; with smaller hook, join yarn with sl st at seam.

Rnd 1: Ch 1; working in unused lps of ch, sc around, having a st number divisible by 6; join with sl st in beg sc.

Rnd 2: Ch 1; * sc in same st, skip 2 sts, shell in next st, skip 2 sts; rep from * around, join in beg sc. Finish off.

Rep for second sleeve.

Garment Edging

Hold garment with right side facing and right front edge at top; with smaller hook, join yarn at bottom of front.

Rnd 1: Ch 1, 3 sc in joining; sc evenly up right front, around neck, and down left front, and across entire bottom of garment, working 3 sc in each corner; join, do not turn.

On left front edging, mark positions for 6 buttons, placing first button 1" down from top corner and last button 15" up from bottom.

Rnd 2 (buttonhole rnd): Ch 1, work in sc, working 3 sc in corners, working buttonholes on right front opposite button markers. To make buttonhole, ch 2, skip 2 sc; continue in sc around; join.

Row 3: Rep Rnd 2 of Sleeve edging, working into buttonhole chs. Finish off.

BUTTONS (make 7)

With smaller hook, join yarn with sl st to bone ring, ch 1, work 20 sc in ring, join in beg sc. Fasten off leaving a long yarn tail. Weave tail in and out of each st. Pull tight to close. Back side of work is front of button.

Sew 6 buttons on left front opposite buttonholes.

BELT

With smaller hook, ch 149 (161, 173).

Rnd 1: Dc in 8th ch from hook; * ch 2, skip 2 chs, dc in next ch; rep from * across.

Rnd 2: Ch 1, (sc, shell, sc) in side of end dc; working across bottom, * skip 2 chs, shell in next dc, sk 2-chs, sc in next dc; rep from * across; (shell, sc) in side of end dc; working across top, * skip 2 chs, shell in next dc, skip 2 chs, sc in next dc; rep from * across omitting last sc on last rep, join in beg st. Finish off. Sew button on one end.

FANCY FANS

designed by Doris Chan

Crisp white lace fans adorn this lovely top and are continued in the magnificent shawl addition. Wear either piece alone, or combine them both for a truly lovely outfit.

FANCY FANS

TOP SIZES	Small	Medium	Large	X-Large
Body Bust Measurements	34"	38"	42"	46"
Finished Bust Measurements	36"	40"	44"	48"

Note: *Instructions are written for size Small; changes for sizes Medium, Large and Extra Large are in parentheses.*

SHAWL SIZE

66" wide x 27" long at center back

Materials

For top: Fingering weight yarn, 7 (7, 9, 9) oz white

For shawl: Fingering weight yarn, 9 oz white

Note: *Photographed model made with Brown Sheep Cotton Fine #CW100 Cotton Ball*

4 st markers or small safety pins

Size D (3.25mm) crochet hook (or size required for gauge) for top

Size J (6mm) crochet hook (or size required for gauge) for shawl

Gauge

With one strand of yarn, two pattern reps (fan, sc) and 8 rows = 4" (for top)

With two strands held tog, one pattern rep (fan, sc) and 4 rows = 3" (for shawl)

Stitch Guide

V-st: (tr, ch 4, tr) all in same st or sp

Scallop: (sl st, ch 3, dc) all in next st or sp

Open Fan Pattern Stitches

Beg Fan: Ch 6; [tr, (ch 2, tr) 3 times] all in first ch-sp.

Fan: [tr, (ch 2, tr) 4 times] all in same st or sp.

End Fan: (tr, ch 2) 4 times in turning ch sp, tr in 4th ch of turning ch.

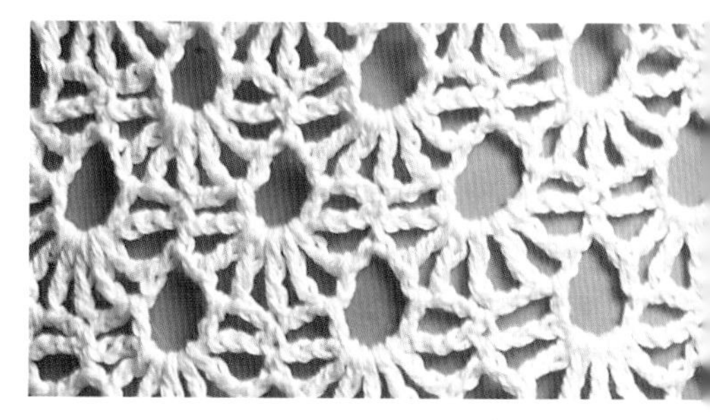

TOP

INSTRUCTIONS

YOKE

Starting at neckline with smaller hook, loosely ch 100 (100, 100, 112); join with sl st in beg ch to form a ring, being careful not to twist sts.

Rnd 1: Ch 1, sc in each ch around, sl st in beg sc, turn: 100 (100, 100, 112) sc.

For sizes Small, Medium and Large only:

Rnd 2: Ch 1; [sc in first sc, ch 1, skip next 4 sc, work fan in next sc, ch 1, skip next 4 sc] 10 times, join in beg sc, turn: 10 fans made.

For size X-Large only:

Rnd 2: Ch 1; *sc in next sc, ch 1, sk next 4 sc, work fan in next sc, ch 1, skip next 4 sc*; [sc in next sc, ch 1, sk next 3 sc, fan in next sc, ch 1, sk next 3 sc] twice; rep from * to * 4 times more; rep from [to] twice more; rep from * to * around, join in beg sc, turn: 12 fans made.

For all sizes:

Rnd 3: Ch 6 (counts as tr, ch 2), sk next tr; *dc in next ch-2 sp, ch 3, sk next tr, sc in next tr, ch 3, sk next tr, dc in next ch-2 sp, ch 2*; rep from * to * once, 2 V-st in next sc, ch 2; rep from * to * 3 (3, 3, 4) times, V-st in next sc, ch 2; rep from * to * 2 times, V-st in next sc, ch 2; rep between * to * 3 (3, 3, 4) times, tr in same sc as beg, ch 2, hdc in 4th ch of beg ch (beg V-st completed), turn; mark the 4 V-sts for corners. ***Note:** V-sts form basis for fan increases on following rnds.*

Rnd 4: Ch 1, sc in ch sp of beg V-st, ch 1, work fan in next ch-2 sp; [ch 1, sc in next sc, ch 1, fan in next ch-2 sp] 3 (3, 3, 4) times to marked corner V-st, ch 1 sc in ch-4 sp of V-st, ch 1, fan in next ch-2 sp; rep from [to] 2 times to next marked corner V-st, ch 1, sc in ch-4 sp of V-st, ch 1, work fan in next ch-2 sp. Rep from [to] 4 (4, 4, 5) times to next marked corner V-st, ch 1, sc in ch-4 sp of V-st, ch 1; work fan in next ch-2 sp; rep from [to] 2 times, ch 1, sl st in beg sc, turn: 14 (14, 14, 16) fans made.

Rnd 5: Ch 6, sk next tr, [dc in next ch-2 sp, ch 3, sk next tr, sc in next tr, ch 3, sk next tr, dc in next ch-2 sp, ch 2] 3 times, V-st in corner sc, ch 2; rep from [to] 4 (4, 4, 5) times, V-st in corner sc, ch 2; rep from [to] 3 times, V-st in corner sc, ch 2; rep from [to] 4 (4, 4, 5) times; tr in same sc as beg, ch 2, hdc in 4th ch of beg ch, turn.

Rnds 6 through 12 (14, 16, 16): Work Rnds 4 through 5, 3 (4, 5, 5) more times, then Rnd 4 once more, increasing in patt as established: 30 (34, 38, 40) fans made.

Rnds 13 (15, 17, 17): Sl st in next ch-1 sp, next tr and next ch-2 sp; ch 6 (counts as dc, ch 3), skip next tr, sc in next tr, ch 3, sk next tr, dc in next ch-2 sp; [ch 2, dc in next ch-2 sp, ch 3, skip next tr, sc in next tr, ch 3, skip next tr, dc in next ch-2 sp] 29 (33, 37, 39) times around, ch 1, sc in 3rd ch of beg ch, turn. Cont to mark corners.

Rnd 14 (16, 18, 18): Ch 6, (tr, ch 2, tr) in beg ch-sp, ch 1, sc in next sc, ch 1; [fan in next ch-2 sp, ch 1, sc in next sc, ch 1] 29 (33, 37, 39) times around; (tr, ch 1) 2 times in same ch-sp as beg, sl st in 4th ch of beg ch, turn: 30 (34, 38, 40) fans.

UNDERARMS (for all sizes):

Ch 1, sc in same st; *ch 9 loosely for underarm, skip sts of sleeve, sc in marked center tr of next corner fan; [ch 3, skip next tr, dc in next ch-2 sp, ch 2, dc in next ch-2 sp, ch 3, skip next tr, sc in next tr] across*, placing sc in marked center tr of next corner fan; rep from * to *, except omit last sc, instead sl st in beg sc, turn.

***Note:** Keep markers in center trs at corners, now located on either side of two underarms.*

BODY

Rnd 1: Ch 1, sc in same sc; *[ch 1, fan in next ch-2 sp, ch 1, sc in next sc] across to underarm ch, ch 1, skip 4 chs, fan in next ch, ch 1, skip 4 chs, sc in next sc; rep from *, except omit last sc, instead sl st in beg sc, turn: 18 (20, 22, 24) fans.

Rnd 2: Sl st in beg ch-1 sp, next tr and next ch-2 sp; ch 6, sk next tr, sc in next tr, ch 3, sk next tr, dc in next ch-2 sp; rep [ch 2, dc in next ch-2 sp, ch 3, skip next tr, sc in next tr, ch 3, skip next tr, dc in next ch-2 sp] around, ch 1, sc in 3rd ch of beg ch, turn.

Rnd 3: Ch 6, (tr, ch 2, tr) in beg ch-sp, ch 1, sc in next sc, ch 1; rep [fan in next ch-2 sp, ch 1, sc in next sc, ch 1] around, ending (tr, ch 2) twice in same sp as beg, sl st in 4th ch of beg ch, turn.

Rnd 4: Ch 1, sc in same st; [ch 3, skip next tr, dc in next ch-2 sp, ch 2, dc in next ch-2 sp, ch 3, skip next tr, sc in next tr] around, except omit last sc, instead sl st in beg sc, turn.

Rnd 5: Ch 1, sc in same st; [ch 1, fan in next ch-2 sp, ch 1, sc in next sc] around, except omit last sc, instead sl st in beg sc, turn.

Rnds 6 through 23: Repeat Rnds 2 through 5, four times, then Rnds 2 and 3 once more; at end of last rnd, do not turn.

Edging Rnd: Work (scallop in next ch-2 sp of fan) 2 times; * scallop in next sc, (scallop in next ch-2 sp of fan) 4 times; rep from * 16 (18, 20, 22) times around, scallop in last sc, scallop in next 2 ch-2 sps, sl st in same ch-sp as beg. Finish off; weave in ends.

SLEEVE (make 2)

With wrong side facing, join yarn with sl st in marked corner tr on left-hand side of underarm ch.

Rnd 1 (wrong side): Ch 1, sc in same st; [ch 3, skip next tr, dc in next ch-2 sp, ch 2, dc in next ch-2 sp, ch 3, skip next tr, sc in next tr] 7 (8, 9, 9) times around, placing last sc in marked tr at other side of underarm ch, leave underarm chs unworked, turn.

Rnd 2: Ch 1, sc in same st, ch 1; [fan in next ch-2 sp, ch 1, sc in next sc, ch 1] to underarm ch, sk 4 chs of underarm, fan in unused lp of ch worked for body, ch 1, sl st in beg sc, turn: 8 (9, 10, 10) fans.

Rnds 3 through 20: Work same as Body Rnds 2 through 5, four times; then work Body Rnds 2 through 3 . once; do not turn.

Work Edging same as for body, adjusting for the fewer sts. Weave in ends.

SHAWL

INSTRUCTIONS

Note: Shawl is crocheted from the neck down.

With larger hook and 2 strands of yarn held tog throughout, ch 37.

Row 1 (right side): Tr in 7th ch from hook, (ch 2, tr) 3 times in same ch (beg fan made); *ch 1, sk next 4 chs, sc in next ch; ch 1, sk next 4 chs, work fan in next ch; rep from * 2 times more, turn: 4 fans made.

Row 2: Ch 6 (counts as tr, ch 2); *dc in next ch-2 sp, ch 3, sk next tr, sc in next tr, ch 3, sk next tr, dc in next ch-2 sp, ch 2, V-st in next sc, ch 2, sk next tr; rep from * twice more; dc in next ch-2 sp, ch 3, skip next tr, sc in next tr; ch 3, sk next tr, dc in turning ch sp, ch 2, tr in 4th ch of turning ch, turn.

Row 3: Work beg fan, ch 1, sc in next sc, ch 1; *fan in next ch-2 sp, ch 1, sc in ch-4 sp of V-st, ch 1; fan in next ch-2 sp, ch 1, sc in next sc, ch 1; rep from * 2 times more, work end fan, turn: 8 fans made.

Row 4: Ch 6; *[dc in next ch-2 sp, ch 3, skip next tr, sc in next tr; ch 3, skip next tr, dc in next ch-2 sp, ch 2], skip next tr, rep between brackets once, V-st in next sc, ch 2; rep from * twice, rep between brackets once, skip next tr, dc in next ch-2 sp, ch 3, skip next tr, sc in next tr, ch 3, dc in 6th ch of turning ch, ch 2, tr in 4th ch of turning ch, turn.

Row 5: Work beg fan; *[ch 1, sc in next sc, ch 1, fan in next ch-2 sp] 2 times; ch 1, sc in next ch-4 sp of V-st, ch 1, fan in next ch-2 sp; rep from * twice, rep between brackets twice, ch 1, sc in next sc, ch 1, work end fan, turn: 12 fans made.

Place a marker at center back sc; move marker up as you work.

Row 6: Ch 6; *dc in next ch-2 sp, ch 3, skip next tr, sc in next tr; ch 3, skip next tr, dc in next ch-2 sp, ch 2;* rep from * to * across to marked center back sc, V-st in center back sc, ch 2; rep from * to * across, end tr in 4th ch of turning ch; turn.

Row 7: Work beg fan; *ch 1, sc in next sc, ch 1, fan in next ch-2 sp;* rep from * to * across to center back V-st, ch 1, sc in ch-4 sp of V-st; **ch 1, fan in next ch-2 sp, ch 1, sc in next sc**; rep from ** to ** across, end, ch 1, work end fan, turn: 14 fans made.

Rows 8 through 21: Work Rows 6 and 7, seven more times, increasing in pattern as established: at end of Row 21: 28 fans.

Row 22: Ch 6; *dc in next ch-2 sp, ch 3, skip next tr, sc in next tr; ch 3, sk next tr, dc in next ch-2 sp, ch 2; rep from * across, end tr in 4th ch of turning ch, turn.

Row 23 (right side): Work beg fan, ch 1, sc in next sc, ch 1; *fan in next ch-2 sp, ch 1, sc in next sc, ch 1; rep from * across, work end fan: 29 fans; do not turn.

FINISHING

Working across top edge, ch 1, then work 3 sc over each ch-4 or tr post at ends of rows along edge to neck area at center; work 3 sc in each ch-4 sp of skipped foundation chs and 1 sc in ch at base of each fan on center neck area; work rem top edge as before (3 sc over each ch-4 or tr post) to bottom corner.

Continuing across bottom edge, work scallops (see Stitch Guide) as follows: ch 3, dc in turning ch sp, (scallop in next ch-2 sp of fan) 3 times; *scallop in next sc, (scallop in next ch-2 sp of fan) 4 times; rep from * 27 times to end, sl st in top of last tr, join in beg sc. Finish off; weave in ends.

RED HOT!

Designed by Angela Best

A flippy skirt and a backless top add up to one hot look! Make it in red for even more sizzle and wear it with attitude!

RED HOT!

SIZES	Small	Medium	Large
TOP:			
Body Bust Measurements	32"-34"	36"-38"	40"-42"
Finished Bust Measurements (adjustable)	33"	37"	42"
SKIRT:			
Body Waist Measurements	24"-25"	26"-28"	30"-32"
Finished Waist Measurements (streches to fit)	24"	26"	30"
Body Waist Measurements	32"-34"	36"-38"	40"-42"
Finished Hip Measurements (streches to fit)	33"	37"	41"

***Note:** Instructions are written for size Small; changes for sizes Medium and Large are in parentheses.*

Materials:

DK weight yarn,
4 (5, 6) oz red
Size E (3.5mm) crochet hook
(or size required for gauge)
2 shank buttons, 3/4" diameter
(for skirt)
24" (26", 30") round covered elastic
(optional)

Gauge

16 sts = 4" in sc
16 rows = 4" in sc

Stitch Guide

Shell: (3 dc, ch 1, 3dc) all in same st or sp

Shell in Shell: Work shell in ch-1 sp of shell in row or rnd below

V-st: (dc, ch 1, dc) all in same st or sp

V-st in V-st: Work V-st in ch-1 sp of V-st in row or rnd below

Double Triple Crochet (dtr): YO 3 times; insert hook in specified sp and draw up a lp; (YO and draw through 2 lps on hook) 4 times: dtr made.

SKIRT

INSTRUCTIONS

***Note:** The top part of the skirt is worked sideways; shaping is done with short rows.*

BODY

Ch 31.

Row 1: Sc in 2nd ch from hook and in each rem ch: 30 sc.

Rows 2 through 8: Sc in 30 sc, ch 1, turn.

Row 9: Sc in next 18 sc, ch 1, turn, leaving rem sts unworked.

Row 10: Sc in 18 sc, ch 1, turn.

Row 11: Sc in next 13 sc, ch 1 turn, leaving rem sts unworked.

Row 12: Sc in 13 sc, ch 1 turn.

Row 13: Sc in next 8 sc, ch 1 turn.

Row 14: Sc in 8 sc, ch 1 turn.

Row 15: Sc in 30 sc, ch 1, turn.

Rep Rows 2 through 15, 6 (7, 8) times; at end of last row, finish off.

Fold piece with short ends tog, and sew front seam, leaving 3" open at waist (narrow) edge. Finish off; weave in ends.

SKIRT TRIM

Rnd 1: Hold piece with right side facing and with long edge at top; join yarn with sl st at seam; ch 1, sc in joining; working across ends of rows, work 162 (180, 198) sc evenly spaced; join in beg sc, ch 1; do not turn; work trim in rnds.

Rnd 2: Sc in same st as joining, skip 2 sc; *shell in next sc, skip 2 sc, sc in next sc, skip 2 sc; rep from * around, ending shell in next sc, skip 2 sc, join to first sc.

Rnd 3: Ch 4 (counts as a dc and ch-1 sp), dc in same st (beg V-st made); shell in shell, V-st in next sc; rep from * around, ending with shell in last shell, join in 3rd ch of beg V-st.

Rnds 4 through 7: Rep Rnd 3. At end of last rnd, finish off, weave in ends.

BUTTON AND BUTTONHOLE BANDS

Hold garment with right side facing and untrimmed short side to the right.

Button Band:

Row 1: Join yarn with sl st at top of front opening on right side; ch 1, sc in same st and in rem open sts, ch 1, turn.

Row 2: Sc in each sc, finish off. Mark for two buttons, one placed at top and the other about 3 sc below.

Buttonhole Band

Row 1: Join yarn at bottom of front opening on opposite side, ch 1, sc in same st and in rem open sts; ch 1, turn.

Row 2: Sc in each sc, working (ch 2, skip 2 sc) opposite button markers; ch 1, turn.

Row 3: Sc in each sc, working 2 sc in each ch-2 sp; finish off, weave in ends.

WAISTBAND

Row 1: Hold skirt with waist at top and right side facing ; join yarn with sl st at top of buttonhole band; working along sides of rows sc in each row around, ch 1, turn.

Row 2: Sc in each sc, ch 1, turn.

Row 3: If you are using elastic, sc in each sc, working over elastic; otherwise, sc in each sc. Finish off; weave in ends.

Sew buttons on button band.

TOP

INSTRUCTIONS

FIRST CUP

Ch 21 (25, 29).

Row 1: Sc in 2nd ch from hook and in each rem ch: 20 (24, 28) sc; ch 1, turn.

Rows 2 through 10 (12, 14): Sc in each sc, ch 1, turn.

Row 11 (13, 15): Sc in 10 (12, 14) sc, ch 1, turn, leaving rem sts unworked.

Rows 12 (14, 16) through Rows 20 (22, 24): Sc in each sc, ch 1, turn. At end of last row, do not ch 1, finish off.

EDGING

Piece will be an "L" shape. Sew inner edges tog to form cup. Hold cup with right side facing and join and long edge at top. Join yarn with sl st in upper right corner.

Rnd 1: Ch 1, 3 sc in same st; sc around, working 3 sc in each outer corner, join in beg sc.

Rnds 2 and 3: Work Rnds 2 and 3 of Skirt Trim, adjusting st placement as needed to have a shell in each corner. Finish off.

SECOND CUP:

Work same as First Cup through Rows 10 (12, 14).

Row 11 (13, 15): Sl st across first 10 (12, 14) sc; ch 1, sc across rem 10 (12, 14) sc.

Rows 12 (14, 16) through Rows 20 (22, 14): Sc in each sc, ch 1, turn. At end of last row, do not ch 1; finish off.

Fold and sew as for First Cup, reversing placement of seam.

EDGING

Work same as First Cup, but on 3rd row of edging, join to First Cup by working the 2 corner center bust shells together as follows: When you have reached the corner center shell, work 3 dc, sc in corner ch 1 sp of first cup's center bust corner shell, then 3 dc back in sp where the first 3 dc was worked; complete rnd, finish off.

MIDRIFF

Hold piece with bottom of cups at top and right side of work facing.

Row 1: Join yarn with sl st in ch-1 sp of first shell at right; ch 3, (2 dc, ch 1, 3 dc) in same sp; work shell in shell, V-st in V-st to where the cups meet, 3 dc in corner center shell of one cup, ch 1, 3dc in corner center shell of second cup, finish row in established pattern; ch 5 turn.

Row 2: Work in pattern across, ending with a dtr (see Stitch Guide), (3 loop around hook) in last st of previous row's shell, ch 5, turn.

Rows 3 through 8: Rep Row 2. At end of last row, do not ch 5. Finish off; weave in all ends.

NECK TIES

With right side facing, join yarn in ch-1 sp of top shell at outer coner of one cup; ch 150; sl st in each ch and in ch-1 sp. Finish off.

Repeat on opposite side.

MIDRIFF TIES (optional)

Work as for Neck Ties, placing one tie in ch-1 sp of a V-st at each side of midriff.

VESTED INTEREST

Designed by Marty Miller

Faux suede and faux shearling combine to create this fashion look of the year. Wear it for fun, knowing that almost everyone who sees it will never believe that it's created with a crochet hook.

VESTED INTEREST

SIZES	Small	Medium	Large	X-Large
Body Bust Measurements	32"-34"	36"-38"	40"-42"	44"-46"
Finished Bust Measurements	35"	39"	43"	47"

Note: *Instructions are written for size Small; changes for sizes Medium, Large and Extra Large are in parentheses.*

Materials

Worsted weight suede-type yarn, 8 3/4 (10 1/2, 12 1/4, 14) oz beige

Bulky boucle yarn, 5 1/4 (7, 8 3/4, 8 3/4) oz white

Note: *Photographed model made with Berroco® Suede™ #3714 Hopalong Cassidy and Berroco® Softy™ #2901 Snow Bunny*

Size K (6.50 mm) crochet hook (or size required for gauge)

Gauge

10 sts in (sc, dc) patt = 4" with suede-type yarn

INSTRUCTIONS

BLOCK A (make 20)

With suede yarn ch 13 (15, 17, 19)

Row 1: Sc in 2nd ch from hook, dc in next ch; *sc in next ch, dc in next ch; rep from * across: 6 (7, 8, 9) sc, 6 (7, 8, 9) dc; ch 1, turn.

Row 2 (right side): Sc in first st, dc in next st; *sc in next st, dc in next st; rep from * across; ch 1, turn.

Rows 3 through 12 (12, 14, 14): Rep Row 2. Finish off; weave in ends.

BLOCK B1 (make 2)

With suede yarn, ch 9 (11, 13, 15).

Row 1: Sc in 2nd ch from hook, dc in next ch; *sc in next ch, dc in next ch; rep from * across: 4 (5, 6, 7) sc, 4 (5, 6, 7) dc; ch 1, turn

Row 2 (right side): Sc in first st, dc in next st; *sc in next st, dc in next st; rep from * 1 (2, 3, 4) more times, sc in next st: 4 (5, 6, 7) sc, 3 (4, 5, 6) dc; ch 1, turn.

Row 3: Skip first st; *sc in next st, dc in next st; rep from * across: 3 (4, 5, 6) sc, 3 (4, 5, 6) dc; ch 1, turn.

Rows 4 through 12 (12, 14, 14): Sc in first st, dc in next st; *sc in next st, dc in next st; rep from * across, ch 1, turn.

At the end of last row, do not ch-1. Finish off; weave in ends.

BLOCK B2 (make 2)

With suede yarn, ch 9 (11, 13, 15).

Row 1: Sc in 2nd ch from hook, dc in next ch; *sc in next ch, dc in next ch; rep from * across: 4 (5, 6, 7) sc, 4 (5, 6, 7) dc; ch 1, turn

Row 2 (right side): Skip first st, dc in next st; *sc in next st, dc in next st; rep from * across: 3 (4, 5, 6) sc, 4 (5, 6, 7) dc; ch 1, turn.

Row 3: Sc in first st, dc in next st; *sc in next st, dc in next st; rep from *1 (2, 3, 4) more times, sl st in next st: 3 (4, 5, 6) sc, 3 (4, 5, 6) dc; ch 1, turn.

Row 4: Skip sl st; *sc in next st, dc in next st; rep from * across; ch 1, turn.

Rows 5 through 12 (12, 14, 14): Sc in first st, dc in next st; *sc in next st, dc in next st; rep from * across; ch 1, turn.

At the end of last row, do not ch 1. Finish off; weave in ends.

BLOCK C (make 4)

Ch 7 (9, 11, 13)

Row 1 (wrong side): Sc in 2nd ch from hook, dc in next ch; *sc in next ch, dc in next ch; rep from * across: 3 (4, 5, 6) sc, 3 (4, 5, 6) dc; ch 1, turn.

Rows 2 through 12 (12, 14, 14): Sc in first st, dc in next st; *sc in next st, dc in next st; rep from * across, ch 1, turn.

At end of last row, do not ch 1. Finish off; weave in ends.

BLOCK D1 (make 2)

Ch 13 (15, 17, 19).

Row 1: Sc in 2nd ch from hook, dc in next ch; *sc in next ch, dc in next ch; rep from * across: 6 (7, 8, 9) sc, 6 (7, 8, 9) dc; ch 1, turn.

Row 2 (right side): Sc in first st, dc in next st; *sc in next st, dc in next st; rep from * across; ch 1, turn.

Rows 3 through 10 (10, 12, 12): Rep Row 2.

Row 11 (11, 13, 13): Sc in first st, dc in next st; *sc in next st, dc in next st; rep from * 0 (1, 2, 3) times; sc in next st, sl st in next st: 3 (4, 5, 6) sc, 2 (3, 4, 5) dc; ch 1, turn.

Row 12 (12, 14, 14): Sl st in first sc; *sc in next st, dc in next st; rep from * 1 (2, 3, 4) times: 2 (3, 4, 5) sc, 2 (3, 4, 5) dc.

At end of last row, do not ch 1. Finish off; weave in ends.

BLOCK D2 (make 2)

Ch 13 (15, 17, 19).

Row 1: Sc in 2nd ch from hook, dc in next ch; *sc in next ch, dc in next ch; rep from * across: 6 (7, 8, 9) sc, 6 (7, 8, 9) dc; ch 1, turn.

Row 2 (right side): Sc in first st, dc in next st; *sc in next st, dc in next st; rep from * across; ch 1, turn.

Rows 3 through 10 (10, 12, 12): Rep Row 2.

Row 11 (11, 13, 13): Sl st across 7 st, sc in next st; *sc in next st, dc in next st; rep from * across: 3 (4, 5, 6) sc, 2 (3, 4, 5) dc; ch 1, turn.

Row 12 (12, 14. 14): Sc in first st, dc in next st; *sc in next st, dc in next st; rep from * 0 (1, 2, 3) more times, sl 1 st in last st: 2 (3, 4, 5) sc, 2 (3, 4, 5) dc. Finish off; weave in ends.

FINISHING

Follow diagrams to join Right Front, Left Front and Back. Hold blocks with wrong sides tog and join with 2 strands of bulky yarn, working through both layers. Then join blocks in rows.

In same manner, sc the back to fronts at shoulders.

OUTER EDGING

Rnd 1: Hold vest with right side facing; join 2 strands of bulky yarn at bottom back. Sc evenly around the vest, placing 3 sc in each bottom corner. At the neck edge, dec in the corners as follows: sc to one st before corner; (insert hook in next st and draw up a lp) 3 times; YO and draw through all 4 lps on hook: dec made; at end of rnd, join with sl st, ch 1, do not turn.

Rnd 2: Sc in each sc, adjusting sts to keep edge flat.

ARMHOLE EDGINGS

With right side facing, join 2 strands of bulky yarn at underarm. Work Rnds 1 and 2 of Outer Edging, adjusting sts to keep work flat.

Right front

C	D1
B1	A
A	A
A	A

Left front

D2	C
A	B2
A	A
A	A

Back

C	D1	D2	C
B1	A	A	B2
A	A	A	A
A	A	A	A

FOR A SPECIAL EVENING

A hint of skin showing through the mesh panel adds to the glamour of this lovely blouse. A wonderful addition to any wardrobe!

Materials

Fingering weight yarn,
150 (200, 200, 250) grams black

Note: *Photographed model made with Twilleys Silky, Black*

Size 1.75 mm steel crochet hook

Size 2 mm steel crochet hook (or size required for gauge)

Gauge

30 dc = 4” with larger hook

Stitch Guide

2sctog: Draw up a lp in each of next 2 sts, YO and draw through all 3 lps on hook: 2sctog made.

2dctog: (YO, insert hook in next st and draw up a lp, YO and draw through first 2 lps on hook) twice, YO and draw through all 3 lps on hook: 2dctog made.

3dctog: (YO, insert hook in next st and draw up a lp; YO and draw through first 2 lps on hook) 3 times; YO and draw through rem 4 lps: 3dctog made.

SIZES	Small	Medium	Large	X-Large
Body Bust Measurements	32"	34"	36"	38"
Finished Bust Measurements	32"	34"	35"	36"

***Note:** Instructions are written for size Small; changes for sizes Medium, Large and Extra Large are in parentheses.*

***Note:** Garment hugs body and stretches to fit.*

BACK

Beginning at bustline with larger hook, loosely ch 111 (119, 123, 131).

Foundation Row (right side): Dc in 4th ch from hook, dc in each rem ch: 109 (117, 121, 129) sts, counting first 3 skipped chs as a dc; ch 3, turn.

Row 1: Dc in each dc across, ending dc in top of beg ch-3; ch 3, turn.

Row 2: Dc to last 2 sts, 2 dc in next st, dc in last st: 110 (118, 122, 130) sts; ch 3, turn.

Rows 3 through 14: Rep Row 2; 121 (129, 133, 141) sts at end of Row 14.

Rep Row 1, for 2 (2, 4, 4) times more; at end of last row, turn, do not ch.

SHAPE ARMHOLES

Row 1: Sl st across first 8 dc, ch 2, 2dctog; dc in each dc to last 10 sts, 3dctog, leaving rem sts unworked: 103 (111, 115, 123) dc; ch 2, turn.

Row 2: Skip 3dctog of previous row; 2dctog over next 2 dc, dc in each dc to last 3 sts, 3dctog over last 2 dc and over the 2dctog of previous row: 99 (107, 111, 119) sts.

Rows 3 through 11 (12, 12, 13): Rep Row 2; at end of last row, finish off.

MESH PANEL

Hold piece with right side facing and beg ch at top; with larger hook, join yarn in first ch at right.

Row 1: Ch 1, sc in same ch; *ch 5, skip 3 chs, sc in next ch; rep from * across: 27 (29, 30, 32) ch-5 lps; turn.

Row 2: * Ch 5, sc in next ch-5 lp; rep from * across, ending sc in last ch-5 lp, ch 2, dc in last sc; turn.

Row 3: Ch 1, sc in first dc; *ch 5, sc in next ch-5 lp; rep from * across, ending ch 5, sc in 3rd ch of ch-5 lp at beg of prev row, turn.

Rows 4 through 19: Change to smaller hook and rep Rows 2 and 3, eight more times.

Change to larger hook. Rep Rows 1 and 2 until piece measures 12¼" (12¼", 13", 13") from beg of armhole shaping, ending by working a Row 3. Finish off.

FRONT

Work same as back.

ASSEMBLY

Hold Front and Back with right sides tog and sew side seams, carefully matching rows.

BOTTOM BORDER

Hold vest with right side facing and bottom edge at top; join yarn with smaller hook in side seam at right.

Rnd 1: Ch 1, sc in joining; *6 dc in next ch-5 lp, sl st in next sc; rep from * around, join with sl st in beg sc. Finish off.

LEFT ARMHOLE BORDER AND STRAP

With right side of work facing, with smaller hook join yarn in top right corner of Front.

Rnd 1: Ch 62 (68, 68, 74) for strap; sc in dc at top left corner of Back; work sc evenly around armhole edge, adjusting sts as needed to keep work flat; join in first ch of strap.

Rnd 2: Ch 1, sc in each ch of strap and in each sc around armhole, join in beg sc; finish off.

RIGHT ARMHOLE BORDER AND STRAP

With right side of work facing, with smaller hook join yarn in top right corner of Back.

Complete as for Left Armhole Border and Strap.

NECK BORDER

With right side of Front facing, join yarn in 2nd dc at top right of neckline.

Rnd 1: Ch 1, sc in each dc along center top edge of Front, 2sc tog at corner, sc in base of each ch along strap, 2sctog at corner; sc in each dc along center top edge of Back, 2sctog at corner, sc in base of each ch along strap, 2sctog at corner, join in beg sc. Finish off; weave in all ends.

PERFECTLY PINK CORSET

Designed by Dora Ohrenstein

Wear this provocative top under a shrug or sweater, or – if you dare – by itself. If you want to make a strong impact for a special occasion, crochet it in bright red and lace it with black satin ribbon! The fit is adjusted by tightening or loosening the ribbon lacing.

PERFECTLY PINK CORSET

Size

One size fits 32" to 38" bust

Materials

Sport or DK weight cotton yarn, 8¾ oz pink

Note: *Photographed model made with Patons® Grace # 60416 Blush*

1" wide hot pink satin ribbon, 2 yds

Size C (2.75mm) crochet hook (or size required for gauge)

Gauge

4 (2 dc, ch 1, 2 dc) shells plus 4 post sts = 4½"

Stitch Guide

Front Post dc: With right side of garment facing, YO, insert hook from front to back to front around post (vertical bar) of specified st and draw up a lp; (YO and draw through 2 lps on hook) twice: FPdc made.

Back Post dc: With wrong side of garment facing, YO, insert hook from back to front to back around post (vertical bar) of specified st and draw up a lp; (YO and draw through 2 lps on hook) twice: BPdc made.

Shell: (2 dc, ch 1, 2 dc) in same st or sp: shell made

Shell in Shell: (2 dc, ch 1, 2 dc) in ch-1 sp of shell.

INSTRUCTIONS

Starting at bottom of midriff, ch 146.

Row 1 (wrong side): In 5th ch from hook, work (3 dc, ch 1, 3 dc); skip 2 chs, dc in next ch; *skip 2 chs, (3 dc, ch-1, 3 dc) in next ch; skip 2 chs, dc in next ch; rep from * across: 24 (3 dc, ch 1, 3 dc) groups; ch 3, turn.

Row 2 (right side): *(3 dc, ch 1, 3 dc) in ch-1 sp of next group, FPdc around next dc; rep from * across, ending last rep with dc in 3rd ch of turning ch; ch 3, turn.

Note: *You now have 24 sections separated by post sts.*

Row 3 (begin decreases): * Shell of 2 dc, ch 1, 2 dc) in ch-1 sp of next section, BPdc around post of next FPdc; [(3 dc, ch 1, 3 dc) in next ch-1 sp, BPdc in next FPdc] twice; rep from * across, ending dc in top of turning ch; ch 3, turn.

Row 4: *[Shell of (2 dc, ch 1, 2 dc) in next ch-1 sp, FPdc around next BPdc] twice; (3 dc, ch 1, 3 dc) in next ch-1 sp, FPdc around next BPdc; rep from * across, dc in turning ch; ch 3, turn.

Row 5: *(2 dc, ch 1, 2 dc) in next ch-1 sp, BPdc around next FPdc; rep from * across, ending last rep, dc in turning ch; ch 3, turn.

Row 6: Rep Row 5, working FPdc around each BPdc.

Note: *From here on, post sts will not be mentioned; remember to work FP dc sts around BPdc sts, and BP sts around FP sts on every row until Bra begins. On all following rows, when working a (2 dc, ch 1, 2-dc) shell into a 3-dc group, work shell into center dc of 3-dc group.*

Row 7: Shell in first 3 sections, 3 dc in next section; shell in 2 sections, 3 dc in next section; shell in 2 sections, 3 dc in next section; shell in 3 sections, 3 dc in next section; shell in 2 sections, 3 dc in next section, shell in 2 sections; 3 dc in 2 sections, shell in last 3 sections, dc in last st, ch 3, turn.

Row 8: Shell in first 2 sections, 3 dc in 2 sections; shell in next section; 3 dc in 2 sections, shell in 2 sections, 3 dc in next section; shell in 3 sections, 3 dc in next section, shell in 2 sections; 3 dc in next section; shell in 2 sections, 3 dc in 2 sections, shell in last 3 sections; dc in last st, ch 3, turn.

Rows 9 through 15: Shell in two sections, 3 dc in 5 sections, shell in next section; 3 dc in 3 sections, shell in 2 sections, 3 dc in 3 sections; shell in next section, 3 dc in 5 sections, shell in last 2 sections; ch 3, turn.

Rows 16 and 17: Shell in 3 sections; 3 dc in next section, shell in next section, 3 dc in 2 sections, shell in 2 sections; 3 dc in next section, shell in 4 sections, 3 dc in next section, shell in 2 sections; 3 dc in 2 sections, shell in next section; 3 dc in next section, shell in last 3 sections; ch 3, turn.

Rows 18 and 19: Shell in 3 sections, 3 dc in next section; shell in 2 sections, 3 dc in next section; shell in 2 sections, 3 dc in next section; shell in 4 sections, 3 dc in next section; shell in 2 sections, 3 dc in next section; shell in 2 sections, 3 dc in next section; shell in last 3 sections, dc in last st; ch 3, turn.

Row 20: Rep Row 5.

BEGIN BRA SHAPING

Note: *Maintain FPdc and BPdc as established throughout pattern.*

Row 1: Shell in first 3 sections,

dc; [dc in next 5 dc, (2 dc in next dc) twice , dc in next 5 dc: 14 dc made]; (dc in next 5 dc) 3 times; (shell in shell) 12 times; (dc in next 5 dc) 3 times; [dc in next 5 dc, (2 dc in next dc) twice, dc in next 5 dc: 14 dc made]; dc in next 5 dc, shell in shell, dc in last st; ch 3, turn.

Row 5: Shell in shell; dc in next 5 dc; dc in next 14 dc; (dc in next 5 dc) 3 times; shell in shell 12 times; (dc in next 5 dc) 3 times; dc in next 14 dc; dc in next 5 dc, shell in shell, dc in last st; ch 3 turn.

Row 6 (right half): Shell in shell; dc in next 5 dc; [skip next dc, dc in next 12 dc, skip next dc: 12 dc]; (dc in next 5 dc) twice, FPdc around next BPdc; skip next 2 dc, dc in next dc; finish off, leaving rem sts unworked.

Row 7: Rejoin yarn in first st at right edge, ch 3; (shell in shell) twice; FPdc around FPdc; *skip next 3 dc, (3 dc, ch 1, 3 dc) in next dc; rep from * once, FPdc around FPdc, skip 2 dc, shell in next dc, FPdc around FPdc, skip 2 dc, shell in next dc, ch 3, turn.

6 dc in ch-1 sp of next shell; shell in shell across to last 3 shells; 6 dc in ch-1 sp of next shell, (shell in shell) twice, dc in last st; ch 3, turn.

Row 2: Shell in shell; dc in each dc and ch-1 sp of next shell; dc in first 3 dc of next shell, (2 dc in next dc of same shell) twice, dc in last 3 dc of same shell: 10 dc; (dc in each dc and ch-1 sp of next shell) 3 times; (shell in shell) 12 times; (dc in each dc and ch-1 sp of next shell) 3 times; [dc in first 3 dc of next shell, (2 dc in next 2 dc of same shell) twice, dc in last 3 dc of same shell: 10 dc made]; dc in each dc and ch-1 sp of next shell, shell in shell, dc in last st; ch 3, turn.

Row 3: Shell in shell; dc in next 5 dc; [dc in next 4 dc, (2 dc in next dc) twice, dc in next 4 dc:12 dc made]; (dc in next 5 dc) 3 times; (shell in shell) 12 times; (dc in next 5 dc) 3 times; [dc in next 4 dc, (2 dc in next dc) twice, dc in next 4 dc : 12 dc made]; dc in next 5 dc, shell in shell, dc in last st; ch 3, turn.

Row 4: Shell in shell; dc in next 5

Row 8: (Shell in next ch-1 sp) 5 times, dc in last st; ch 3, turn.

Row 9: Shell in shell; (3 dc in ch-1 sp of next shell) 4 times, work post st, dc in last st. Finish off.

COMPLETE OPPOSITE SIDE:

Row 6 (left half): With right side facing, rejoin yarn in 3rd dc to right of 4th post st from left edge; ch 3, maintaining post sts as established, (dc in each of next 5 dc) twice, [skip next dc, dc in next 12 dc, skip next

PERFECTLY PINK CORSET

dc]; dc in next 5 dc, shell in shell, dc in last st; ch 3, turn.

Row 7: 6: Shell in shell, skip next 2 dc, shell in next dc, skip next 2 dc; post st around post st; *skip next 3 dc, (3 dc, ch 1, 3 dc in next dc); rep from * once, skip 3 dc; skip 3 dc, shell in next dc, skip 3 dc, shell in next dc; post st around post st, ch 3, turn.

Rows 8 and 9: Rep Rows 8 and 9 of right half. Finish off; weave in all ends.

FINISHING

Edging

Rnd 1: With right side facing and last row at top, join yarn with sc in first st on right front; sc across last row to 4th post st; ch 87 for strap; sc in 2nd ch from hook and in each rem ch, sc in same sc where ch was started; continue in sc across row to 6th post st; *sc in post st, sc in next 2 sts, (sc, ch 3, sc) in ch-1 sp, sc in next 2 sts;* rep from * across to 4th post st from other end, work 2nd strap same as first; sc in rem sts; do not finish off.

Working along left front side edge, 3 sc in edge of first row for corner; *ch 3, (2 sc in next row edge) 3 times; rep from * to bottom edge, 4 sc in ch sp for corner; **(sc in base of next shell, ch 3, sc into base of same shell, sc in next 5 sts; rep from ** across bottom edge; 4 sc in ch sp for corner; 2 sc in bottom row of right front edge; [ch 3, 2sc in next row edge 3 times)] to top edge, ending 2 sc in edge of last row, sl st in top of sc worked for border of top, ch 1 turn.

Rnd 2: Sc in first 2 sc; *[2 sc in lp, (2 sc in edge of next row) 3 times]* along front edge, sc in each st at corner; working along bottom edge, *skip sc next to lp, 3 sc in loop, skip next sc, sc in next 5 sc; rep from * around, ending with 5 sc around corner; work up left edge front same as opposite side, sl st in sc at top edge. Finish off; weave in all ends.

FINISHING

Thread ribbon through lps at center edge as follows: Weave ribbon from back to front through bottom lp on each side and centering length of ribbon; run each side of ribbon across and up to the next lp, inserting from front to back each time. At top lp, insert ribbon back to front so that bow is made in front.

ABBREVIATIONS AND SYMBOLS

Crochet patterns are written in a special shorthand which is used so that instructions don't take up too much space. They sometimes seem confusing, but once you learn them, you'll have no trouble following them.

These are Abbreviations

BB . . . . bobble
Beg. . . . . beginning
BL. back loop
Blsc. . . . . . . back loops single crochet
BPdc. . . . . . back post double crochet
BPsc. . . . . . . back post single crochet
CL(s) . . . . cluster(s)
Ch(s) . . . . chain(s)
Cont . . . . continue
Crst. . . . . cross stitch
Dc. . . . . double crochet
Dec . . . . decrease
Ds . . . . diagonal stitch
Dtr . . . . double triple crochet
Fig. . . . . figure
Fbsc. . . . . front bar single crochet
FL . . . . front loop
FPdc . . . . . front post double crochet
FPtr . . . . front post triple crochet
G. . . . . grams
Hdc . . . . half double crochet
Inc . . . . Increase(ing)
Lp(s) . . . . loop(s)
Long dc . . . . long double crochet
Long sc . . . . long single crochet
Oz . . . . ounces
Patt . . . . pattern
Prev. previous
Pst . . . . puff stitch
Rem . . . . remaining
Rep . . . . repeat(ing)
Rev sc. . . . . reverse single crochet
Rnd(s). . . . . round(s)
Sc . . . . single crochet
Sl st. slip stitch
Sp(s). space(s)
St(s) . . . . stitch(es)
Tog . . . . together
Tr . . . . triple crochet
V-st . . . . V-stitch
YO . . . . yarn over hook

These are Standard Symbols

* An asterisk (or double asterisks **) in a pattern row, indicates a portion of instructions to be used more than once. For instance, "rep from * three times" means that after working the instructions once, you must work them again three times for a total of 4 times in all.

† A dagger (or double daggers ††) indicates that those instructions will be repeated again later in the same row or round.

: The number of stitches after a colon tells you the number of stitches you will have when you have completed the row or round.

( ) Parentheses enclose instructions which are to be worked the number of times following the parentheses. For instance, "(ch 1, sc, ch1) 3 times" means that you will chain one, work one sc, and then chain again three times for a total of six chains and three sc's.

Parentheses often set off or clarify a group of stitches to be worked into the same space of stitch. For instance, "dc, ch2, dc) in corner sp".

[ ] Brackets and **( )** parentheses are also used to give you additional information.

Terms

Front Loop – This is he loop toward you at the top of the crochet stitch.

Back Loop – This is he loop away from you at the top of the crochet stitch.

Post – This is the vertical part of the crochet stitch

Join – This means to join with a sl st unless another stitch is specified.

Finish Off – This means to end your piece by pulling the cut yarn end through the last loop remaining on the hook. This will prevent the work from unraveling.

Continue in Pattern as Established – This means to follow the pattern stitch as it has been set up, working any increases or decreases in such a way that the pattern remains the same as it was established.

Work even – This means that the work is continued in the pattern as established without increasing or decreasing.

Right Side – This means the side of the garment that will be seen.

Wrong Side – This means the side of the garment that is inside when the garment is worn.

Leftt hand side – This means the side of the garment that is near the right hand when worn.

Right hand side – This means the side of the garment that is near the left hand when worn.

ABBREVIATIONS AND SYMBOLS

Gauge

This is probably the most important aspect of crocheting!

GAUGE simply means the number of stitches per inch, and the numbers of rows per inch that result from a specified yarn worked with a hook in a specified size. But since everyone knits or crochets differently—some loosely, some tightly, some in between—the measurements of individual work can vary greatly, even when the crocheters or knitters use the same pattern and the same size yarn and hook.

If you don't work to the gauge specified in the pattern, your garment will never be the correct size, and you may not have enough yarn to finish your project. The hook size given in the instructions is merely a guide and should never be used without a gauge swatch.

To make a gauge swatch, crochet a swatch that is about 4" square, using the suggested hook and the number of stitches given in the pattern. Measure your swatch. If the number of stitches is fewer than those listed in the pattern, try making another swatch with a smaller hook. If the number of stitches is more than is called for in the pattern, try making another swatch with a larger hook. It is your responsibility to make sure you achieve the gauge specified in the pattern.

Fringe

Cut a piece of cardboard about 6" wide and half as long as specified in the instructions for strands, plus 1/2" for trimming allowance. Wind the yarn loosely and evenly lengthwise around the cardboard. When the card is filled, cut the yarn across one end. Do this several times; then begin fringing. You can wind additional strands as you need them.

Hold the specified number of strands for one knot of fringe together, and then fold in half.

Hold the project with the right side facing you. Using a crochet hook, draw the folded ends through the space of stitch from right to wrong side.

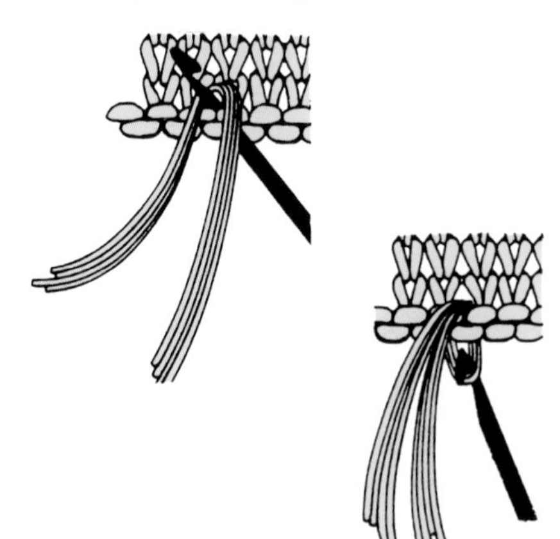

Pull the loose ends through the folded section.

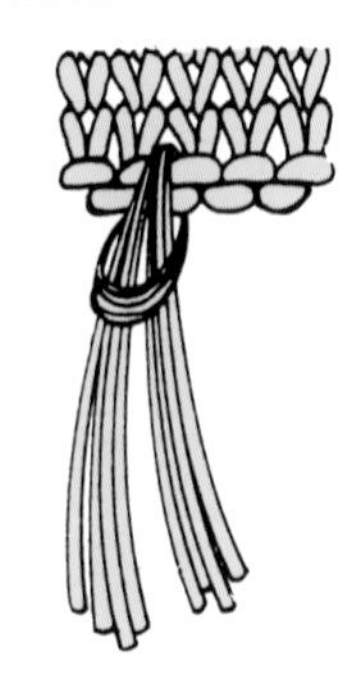

Draw the knot up firmly. Space the knots evenly and trim the ends of the fringe.

The patterns in this book have been written using the crochet terminology that is used in the United States. Terms which may have different equivalents in other parts of the world are listed below.

United States	International
Double crochet (dc)	treble crochet (tr)
Gauge	tension
Half double crochet (hdc)	half treble crochet (htr)
Single crochet	double crochet
Skip	miss
Slip stitch	single crochet
Triple crochet (tr)	double treble crochet (dtr)
Yarn over (YO)	yarn forward (yfwd)
Yarn over (YO)	Yarn around needle (yrn)

ACKNOWLEDGEMENTS

The authors extend their thanks and appreciation to these contributing designers

Angela Best, Toronto, Canada

Vashti Braha, Longboat Keys, Florida

Belinda "Bendy" Carter, Marionville, Missouri

Doris Chan, Boothwyn, Pennsylvania

Tammy Hildebrand, Kernersville, North Carolina

Margaret Hubert, Pawling, New York

Jenny King, Australia

Marty Miller, Greensboro, North Carolina

Nancy Nehring, Sunnyvale, California

Dora Ohrenstein, New York, New York

Penny O'Neill, Australia

Judith Solomon, Rolling Hills Estates, California

Pirkko Vega, Toronto, Canada

Whenever we have used a special yarn we have given the brand name. If you are unable to find these yarns locally, write to the following manufacturers who will be able to tell you where to purchase their products, or consult their internet sites. We also wish to thank these companies for supplying yarn for this book.

Bernat Yarns
320 Livingston Avenue South
Listowel, Ontario
Canada N4W 3H3
www.bernat.com

Berroco, Inc.
14 Elmdale Road
Uxbridge, Massachusetts 01569
www.berroco.com

Brown Sheep
10062 Country Road 16
Mitchell, Nebraska 69357
www.brownsheep.com

Cleckheaton Yarn
Australian Country Spinners PTY, LtD
314 Albert Street
Brunswick, Victoria 3056
Australia
www.cleckheaton.biz

DMC Corporation
S. Hackensack Avenue
Port Kearny Bldg #10F
South Kearny, New Jersey 07032
www.dmc-usa.com

J&P Coats
Coats and Clark
Consumer Services
P.O. Box 12229
Greenville, South Carolina 29612-0229
www.coatsandclark.com

Lion Brand Yarn
34 West 15th Street
New York, New York 10011
www. lionbrand.com

Moda Dea Fashion Yarns
Coats and Clark
Consumer Services
P.O. Box 12229
Greenville, South Carolina 29612-0229
www.coatsandclark.com

Muench Yarns, Inc.
1323 Scott Street
Petaluma, California 94953
www.muenchyarns.com

Patons Yarns
2700 Dufferin Street
Toronto, Ontario
Canada M6B 4J3
www. patonsyarns.com

Plymouth Yarn Co., Inc
(distributors in the U.S. of Cleckheaton Yarn)
500 Lafayette Street
P.O. Box 28
Bristol, Pennsylvania 19007-0028
www.plymouthyarn.com

TLC Yarns
Coats and Clark
Consumer Services
P. O. Box 12229
Greenville, South Carolina 29612-0229
www.coatsandclark.com

Twilleys of Stamford
S. R. Kertzer Limited
50 Trowers Rd
Woodbridge Ontario L4L 7K6
Canada
www.kertzer.com

INDEX